Slugs of Brita... & Ireland

Identification, understanding and control

Ben Rowson, James Turner,
Roy Anderson & Bill Symondson

First edition

ISBN: 978 1 908819 13 0
OP160

First Published 2014

FSC Publications
Unit 1
Stafford Park 15
Telford
TF3 3BB

www.field-studies-council.org

ISBN: 978 1 908819 13 0
OP160

Printed by: Henry Ling Ltd, The Dorset Press, Dorchester DT1 1HD

Contents

Acknowledgements

This guide and the supporting research were made possible by Amgueddfa Cymru – National Museum Wales and a grant from the Leverhulme Trust (Research Project Grant RPG-068, 2011).

Many people tested and provided feedback on earlier versions of the keys. We would like to thank them all, and for their particular help with fieldwork and other matters, Chris du Feu, Adrian Norris, Simon Allen, Adrian Sumner, Christian Owen, and Ron Carr. We are also grateful to the following for providing specimens or other assistance: Sam Aberdeen, Jon Ablett, Roy Baker, Chris Barron, Jane Bonney, Ron Boyce, Robert Cameron, Ron Carr, Michael Cawley, June Chatfield, Richard Chilcott, Alison Cotton, Terry Crawford, M. Davies, Rebecca Farley-Brown, Garth Foster, Tim Frayling, Jen Gallichan, Jasmin Glossop, S. Green, Rosemary Hill, R. Harding, V. Haynes, Derek Howlett, Andy Karran, Brian Levey, Jan Light, David Lindley, Matthew Law, Graham Long, Mike Lush, Eoghain Maclean, J. Moore, Brian Nelson, Graham Oliver, Alan Orange, Megan Paustian, Richard Preece, Vicky Purewal, Tim Rich, Hywel Roberts, Rhian & Llinos Rowson, M. Sheen, Chris Sinclair, Tony Smith, Deb Spillards, Peter & Cathy Tattersfield, Sandra Turner, Gavin Tyte, Tony Wardhaugh, J. Whyte, Rosemary Winnall, Paul Williams, Martin Willing, Karen & Andy Wilkinson, Mike Wilson, Harry Wood.

Reference specimens

Nearly all of the photographs in this guide are of slugs collected across Britain and Ireland especially for the project in 2011-2012. These reference specimens were photographed alive under identical conditions, were DNA-barcoded to help confirm their identity, and are preserved at the National Museum of Wales, Cardiff, UK. The small grey numbers on the species plates refer to the specimen / DNA sequence codes in the appendix, and in a paper discussing the findings (Rowson *et al.*, 2014).

Nomenclatural disclaimer

This publication includes a few species that appear not to have yet been formally named or described. The informal names used here [*Arion* (*A.*) sp. "Davies" and *Testacella* (*T.*) sp. "*tenuipenis*"] are disclaimed for nomenclatural purposes, following the International Code on Zoological Nomenclature (Article 8.2, 8.3, as amended 2012).

Introduction

Slugs are part of everyday life, rural and urban, in Britain and Ireland. They are – literally – wildlife on our doorsteps. This is not the case in all parts of the world. Our climate and landscape are in many ways ideal for these animals. Our native fauna derives from Europe, which has a diversity of slugs to rival that of any continent. And our human history of trade, invasion and being invaded continues to introduce exotic slug species to our fauna. Many of our native slugs likewise cause problems overseas.

Until the twentieth century, slugs held a place in British folk life as "cures" for consumption and sore throats (when swallowed) or warts (when rubbed on the skin). In Lincolnshire and in France they were regarded as barometers, their emergence or the stickiness of their mucus being considered a sign of approaching rain (Taylor, 1902-7). In Scandinavia they were once thrown in to lubricate windmill machinery or used for axle grease for carts (Svanberg, 2006). They have probably been widely eaten only during the hardest of times, although there are reports of them being salted or pickled in southwest England (Marren & Mabey, 2010). They were no doubt used as poultry feed, but there are good reasons, apart from gastronomic ones, not to eat slugs (see Slugs and parasites, p. 8). Slugs have otherwise mainly been noticed as plant pests, as in the eighteenth century by Thomas Pennant and by Gilbert White, who recorded the "amazing havoc" they caused (Ellis, 1969). Among the many practical measures developed, prayers and exorcisms were sometimes employed against slug plagues (Taylor, 1902-7).

Slugs are still widely detested, even by those otherwise indifferent to the natural world and by many of those who appreciate it. Children become fond of garden snails (*Cornu aspersum* and *Cepaea* spp., themselves both serious pests) but learn to persecute slugs. This disgust is a mark of slugs' success as pests and detritivores and at repelling potential predators, humans included. This success is all the more remarkable given the apparent design flaws in these naked, limbless animals that shed water, protein and energy when they move. Many think the only good slug is a dead one, and newcomers to limacology (the study of slugs) invariably claim that all slugs look the same. This guide shows that neither is the case, although the differences can be challenging to define or recognise. For example, the large *Arion* species (p. 30-59) are some of the most variable in colour of all British animals. The guide also aims to show that these differences are important as well as interesting in their own right. Each species has its own biology, ecology and geographical history and, as a result, a different impact on human lives. If those that are pests are to be controlled, a variety of approaches may be needed.

What is a slug?

"The quintessence of slugdom": the Large Black Slug *Arion* (*Arion*) *ater* from the Scottish highlands. Quote from Herbert & Kilburn (2004).

Slugs are highly specialised snails. Both slugs and snails are air-breathing molluscs belonging to the Class Gastropoda, a very large animal group which includes many marine and freshwater species. Superficially slug-like animals include leeches, flatworms and the larvae of some insects including the "Pear Slug" sawfly *Caliroa*, chrysomelid beetles, limacodid moths and some flies. However none is related to true slugs, which are not larvae and have no larval stage. Our many "sea slugs" and the seashore air-breathing slug *Onchidella* are also gastropods, but are only distantly related to the slugs in this guide.

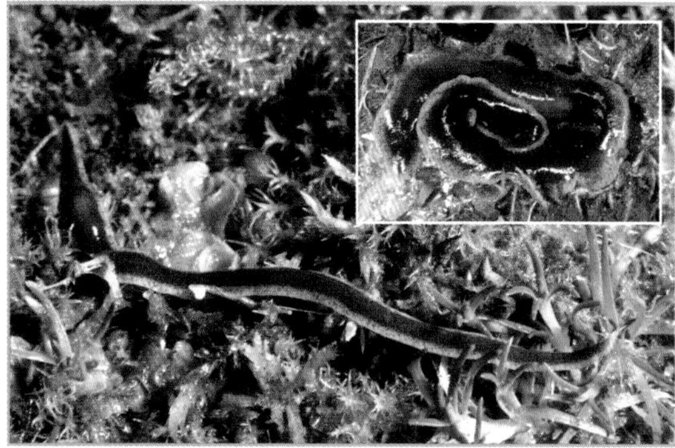

Not a slug, but a slug predator: the New Zealand Flatworm *Arthurdendyus triangulatus*, common in Scotland and Northern Ireland.

Terrestrial slugs evolved from terrestrial snails, shrinking and simplifying their coiled shell in the process. The remnants of the shell are found under the skin of the back or near the tail (p. 124). Though uncoiled, slugs retain the "right-handed" asymmetrical body of their snail ancestors ("left-handed" mutants are extremely rare). This same evolutionary process has occurred on many separate occasions, producing slugs in many different families. It appears that at least four such events, from perhaps as long ago as the Mesozoic, produced the slug families represented in Britain and Ireland (Wade *et al.*, 2006). This guide treats the families in four groups, or sections, which largely reflect their origins. The groups are the Round-backed Slugs (Family Arionidae, p. 30-62); Short-Keeled Slugs (Limacidae and Agriolimacidae, p. 80-89); Long-keeled Slugs (Boettgerillidae and Milacidae, p. 90-99); and Worm-killing Slugs (Testacellidae and Trigonochlamydidae, p. 100-107). We also have three "semi-slug" species in the family Vitrinidae (p. 108). Each seems to be at a different stage in their own ongoing process of becoming a slug. Slugs and semi-slugs make up around a third of the terrestrial mollusc species in Britain and Ireland, the others being snails.

The Greater Semi-slug, *Phenacolimax major* , in its moist leaf-litter habitat.

Why be a slug?

Snails that sacrificed their ancestral shell presumably had something to gain. Shell-building uses calcium, hence the well-known affinity of snails for base-rich (alkaline) soils. Freed from this requirement, slugs can live on more acidic soils and adopt other diets. Without a shell, slugs are "leaner" and better able to squeeze into cracks; by losing the dead weight, they may be "fitter" too. Semi-slugs and agriolimacid slugs (*Deroceras* spp.) are probably our fastest-moving land molluscs.

The downsides of becoming a slug include increased evaporation from the exposed skin, and reduced defence against predators and parasites. By contracting to a hump slugs reduce surface evaporation. Some can endure an extreme degree of water loss (as much as 80% of the body weight) and recover. They can absorb moisture from the air or retain water in the lung. The large arionid slugs address both problems at once with their extraordinary mucus. It limits evaporation while repelling predators, in the case of carabid beetles and other would-be attackers, by "gluing" the mouth-parts together and restricting the normal cutting and mastication processes. The "alarm" mucus of some agriolimacids and limacids has a deterrent effect while at least one milacid slug, Tandonia budapestensis (p. 90), is poisonous . It has been suggested that the bright colours of some slugs warn predators away (e.g. Solem, 1976), although this has not been proven. Most share the neutral, possibly camouflaging patterns of their snail relatives.

Life as a slug

Our slugs are roughly synchronised with the plant growing season. Annual species overwinter in shelter as eggs (p. 122) or small juveniles, avoiding both frost and insect predators. They become active as soon as mild weather returns, which for some species means just above freezing. Feeding and mating activity generally peak in late summer but some slugs can reproduce all year in our climate. Summer dryness can limit activity and be fatal, but our nights are usually humid and dew is usually present even if rain is not.

Slugs are largely nocturnal, some emerging only well after dark. By day they may huddle together under cover, sometimes with other species, reducing collective evaporation. When active they waste little time. They detect food, moisture and potential mates by smell and taste (their eyesight is poor) through their tentacles, lips and sole. Slugs often follow the mucus trails of other slugs, reducing their need to produce mucus upon which to glide forwards. Arionids are sometimes seen rearing up off the ground, as if sniffing the air. It has been suggested that a plug of mucus in their tail pore (p. 10) advertises their maturity to mates (Barr, 1927; Van Mol *et al.*, 1970). Larger slugs can travel many metres a night, but often return to the same refuges each morning. Some have a homing ability based on smell, and perhaps also involving memory (South, 1992). The Tree Slug *Lehmannia marginata* (p. 74) is our most impressive climber while the Marsh Slug *Deroceras laeve* (p. 88) either climbs one step ahead of fluctuating water levels or takes the plunge. Concussion can kill slugs, and most species can lower themselves safely on a mucus thread (Kew, 1902), although this is seldom observed. Soil-dwellers, on the other hand, can travel almost their entire lives below ground through worm tunnels and root spaces.

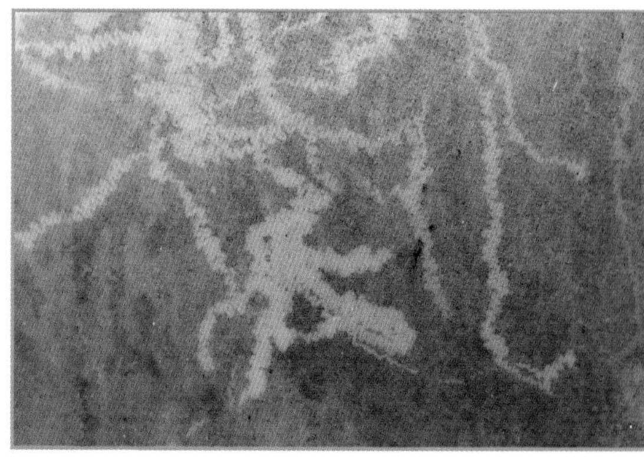

Feeding trails in algae.

Not all slugs eat live plants, and those that do, do not do so all the time (see the accounts for each species on p. 30-109). Many feed on decaying plant matter or fungi, and may be attracted to food waste and animal faeces. Most species will scavenge on other slugs and snails when they are dead or dying. Others specialise on algae and lichens, and a few are strict carnivores. Like snails, slugs feed by rasping their food with a radula (a ribbon bearing many tiny teeth) and a single, crescent-shaped jaw. Our smallest slugs have around 2,000 teeth on the radula, the largest nearly 8,000. In worm-killing slugs, the teeth are fewer in number but larger and longer, sometimes being barbed like harpoons. The larger, long-lived species like the Leopard Slug (*Limax maximus*, p. 62) are known to have some ability to learn and to develop food preferences (South, 1992). This species is also known for its apparent territoriality and incredible mating behaviour.

Two Leopard slugs, *Limax maximus,* mating. The intertwined genitalia hang below the bodies. (Photo: Wendy Ladd)

Mating is a complex business in slugs, which are hermaphrodites (both male and female simultaneously). It can last from under a minute to many hours, involving jockeying for position, stimulation, adhesion and one- or two-way sperm transfer. The structures involved, normally hidden inside the body, are sometimes the only way to distinguish species (p. 110-121). Outcrossing (fertilisation of and/or by a partner) is the clear preference of most species, but probably all have the ability to self-fertilise if necessary. A single slug can thus found an entire population. This has obvious implications for the control of pests and invasive species, although our worst pests are all normally outcrossers (Foltz *et al.*, 1984). Long dynasties of self-fertilisation, broken by occasional bouts of outcrossing, may cause some of the identification problems that slugs present (e.g. Geenen *et al.*, 2006). Also, slugs of some species groups can hybridise occasionally, cross-fertilising in at least one direction (e.g. Dreijers *et al.*, 2013; Rowson *et al.*, 2014).

Two Dusky Slugs, *Arion subfuscus,* mating. The genitalia of each partner make up the pale mass in the middle.

The native slug fauna

Our native slugs are those that arrived in Britain or Ireland without human help between 15,000 and 5,000 years ago (Kerney, 1999). Those that arrived later or with obvious assistance are considered introduced (this is a rather strict definition as compared to some other animal groups). Humans had established themselves in both Britain and Ireland by around 10,000 years ago at the end of the Devensian glacial (the last "ice age"). Ireland became an island around this time while Britain remained connected to the continent. The ice sheet, kilometres thick, would have wiped out terrestrial molluscs in Britain and Ireland. Any survivors either occupied the extreme south, coastal areas now covered by the shallow Celtic Sea and English Channel, or perhaps the tundra of Doggerland. Others survived only in continental Europe. As the climate warmed, they became free to spread north and west. Snail shells provide an excellent fossil record proving that at least 67 species are native and arrived this way (Kerney, 1999). Kerney estimated that at least 18 slug species had also done so, although fossil slug shells (p. 124) provide far less information.

This immigrant history explains why Britain and Ireland, despite being islands, have very few endemic native species (those that are found nowhere else). All our native slugs occur elsewhere in western Europe, with the possible exception of some *Arion* (*Kobeltia*) species (p. 48-59). The

Kerry Slug *Geomalacus maculosus* (p. 60) is a classic example of a species found in Ireland and Iberia but not in Britain, and its status has been long debated. A few other British and Irish arionids, and the semi-slug *Semilimax pyrenaicus* (p. 108), have their closest relatives in Iberia or the Pyrenees and pose similar questions. The status and origins of some other species, discovered only while researching this guide, are also uncertain.

Slugs and environmental history

Slugs occur in all our habitats from sea level to our highest mountain summits at around 1300m (Dance, 1969). Some species are habitat specialists, others more adaptable. Human clearance of forests, drainage, soil improvement and agriculture since the Neolithic (6,000 years ago, earlier in Ireland) has altered the landscape greatly. These habitat changes, referred to loosely as "disturbance" in this guide, have benefited some slugs and been detrimental to others (Boycott, 1934).

Species negatively affected by humans include four species useful as indicators of habitat history. The Lemon Slug *Malacolimax tenellus* (p. 72) is confined to continuously wooded areas between which it can now scarcely disperse. This makes it an excellent indicator of ancient woodland in Britain, as is the Greater Semi-slug *Phenacolimax major* (p. 108). The Ash-black Slug *Limax cinereoniger* (p. 64) is not quite as restricted and so less informative, except perhaps in Ireland where the preceding two do not occur. The Arctic Field Slug *Deroceras agreste* (p. 82) has potential as an indicator of ancient pasture or other less disturbed open habitats. In places, genetically "pure" populations of the Large Black Slug *Arion* (*A.*) *ater* (p. 30) are becoming similarly restricted. This species can hybridise with the similar Large Red Slug *A.* (*A.*) *rufus* (p. 32) which is either a native of the lowlands or an introduction. An analogy can be drawn with the two native oak species of Britain and Ireland. In both cases, populations of the two species and their hybrids reflect local geology, climate, and history.

Species benefiting from humans include agricultural pests (some of which would otherwise be less common) and synanthropes (other species living closely associated with humans). Many species in each category are introduced. The onset of agriculture is associated with a steady rise in agriolimacid shells in the archaeological record (Evans, 1972). The import of plants, soil and other goods is doubtless how many species were introduced, with many early (Roman?) introductions from the western Mediterranean area. The process continues, and many twentieth-century introductions are now established throughout Britain and Ireland. A particular development is the arrival of species from the Black Sea and Caucasus regions. These are beginning to interact with earlier introductions (see *Limacus maculatus*, p. 70).

Finding and recording slugs

The spread (or decline) of each slug species has been monitored largely by volunteer recorders, who have endured their share of disparaging comments over the years. More money is spent on say, dormouse and newt surveys every year than has ever been spent on slug recording. The maps in this guide are based on data in the UK's National Biodiversity Network (www.nbn.org.uk) and Ireland's National Biodiversity Data Centre (www.biodiversityireland.ie). The vast majority were

Slugs occur in all our habitats including allotments and urban areas, agricultural and farmland, and natural "undisturbed" areas such as ancient woodlands and mountainous habitats.

submitted through the Conchological Society of Great Britain and Ireland (established 1876; www.conchsoc.org). The Society has always taken great care over species identification and verification. Unfortunately some species are sometimes recorded as "aggregates" of similar species, for example "*Arion hortensis* agg." now meaning "*hortensis* or *distinctus* or *owenii* or maybe even one of the others". Such data is not very useful since most of the aggregates are widespread, while many of their "segregate" species are under-recorded. It is recommended that only records of confidently identified species are submitted. Photographs of live animals or reference specimens can be very useful for verification, especially important for what are currently less common species. Advice on preservation is given on p. 110.

Collecting slugs in leaf litter in wooded environments.

Collecting slugs at night.

Slugs can be found under stones or other objects, in leaf litter or soil, or among plants throughout the year. This may be difficult only in dry conditions. "Soft weather" of mist or drizzle is better than rain, in which slugs do not always emerge, perhaps unable to follow scents or trails or annoyed by the raindrops. Using torches in darkness (taking all safety precautions) can be rewarding even on dry nights. Early mornings, when slugs are still active in the dew, are also good. Note that it is very difficult to detect all the slug species present at a site, especially a potentially rich one, in a single visit. One of our gardens supports 14 slug species but they have never all been seen in any 24-hour period. Old woods can host 10 or more species.

Simple non-lethal trapping methods involve supplying horizontal or vertical refuges (planks or tiles) with or without bait (carrots, mushrooms, oats, chicken mash etc.). Beer traps kill slugs and may make them unidentifiable. Slug pellets contain powerful attractants, but slugs that have eaten them should not be handled. The "mustard extraction" method used to find earthworms may work for soil-dwelling slugs. More intensive methods are required to estimate abundances for ecological studies (South, 1992).

If necessary most slugs can be kept alive for several weeks in plastic margarine tubs containing a little soil. They need to be kept cool and moist. Crowded slugs of any species may kill and eat one another, or pass on diseases and parasites, so slugs that die should be removed. Soil-dwellers can be watched in plastic wormeries. If kept outdoors (e.g. in a cool shed) the whole life cycle can be observed.

Conservation

None of our native slug species is known to have been made extinct nationally. The rarer species may be threatened locally by the destruction, fragmentation or modification of habitats, pollution, persecution, and from competition or hybridisation with introduced relatives. Lichen feeders may be vulnerable to atmospheric pollution. None of the species has any legal status except *Geomalacus maculosus*, which is protected under Irish and European law. None is yet listed as a UK Biodiversity Action Plan Priority Species. *Limax cinereoniger*, *Tandonia rustica*, and *Testacella haliotidea* are considered Vulnerable in the Irish Red List (Byrne *et al.*, 2009), while *T. rustica* was listed as Insufficiently Known in the British Red Data Book (Bratton, 1991).

Slugs as pests

Slugs and plants in nature

In natural habitats slugs can be 'keystone species', that is species that can affect the structure of the community of plants and animals within which they live. Slugs do this by selective grazing, especially of seedlings. Slugs have a hierarchy of preferences; they will go for their favourites first, then when these are all eaten go for their next most favoured and so on. Thus the community of plants growing up from these seedlings will be a reflection of this weeding-out process. The community of mature plants that we see, therefore, is often in large part determined by slugs grazing (e.g. Allan & Crawley 2011). Overall slugs prefer young, fast-growing, broad-leaved plants containing low levels of the plant toxins that repel grazers. Some plants, such as white clover, an important forage plant for cattle and sheep, have evolved strains that contain cyanogenic compounds specifically evolved to deter grazing by slugs. These resistant strains dominate where there is a lot of slug grazing pressure (e.g. Horrill & Richards, 1986). There is a cost to the plants (genetic strains containing cyanogens are more frost susceptible, have fewer flowers and are more susceptible to fungal attacks) and therefore where there is little slug grazing non-cyanogenic strains predominate. Slugs can also affect the latitudinal and altitudinal range of plants. For example, the European wildflower *Arnica montana* (Compositae) grows perfectly happily in lowland gardens, as long as it is protected against slugs. In the wild it is only found at high altitude above the 'slug line', in areas too cold for slugs to survive (Bruelheide & Scheidel 1999).

Slugs as pests

Slugs become pests when they attack cultivated plants or their seeds. Some may also be pests of stored products. The importance of slugs (and snails) as pests is increasing in many parts of the world as the pest species spread, agricultural methods change, and other pests, such as insects, are brought under control (Barker, 2002). Curiously, it is the European slugs, spread by humans to other continents, that cause most of the damage.

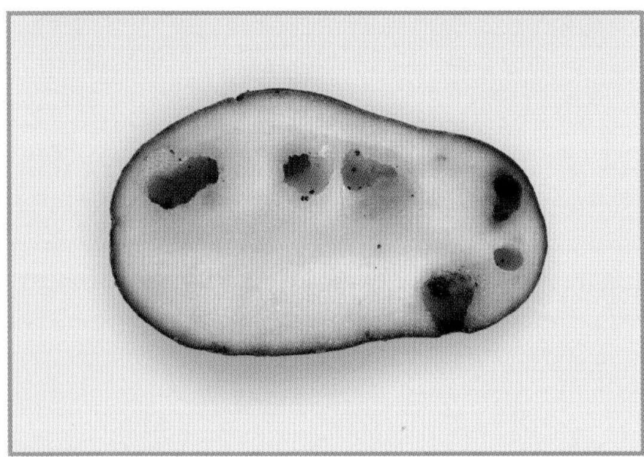

Slug damage to potatoes, probably caused by milacid slugs (*Tandonia* species, p. 90-95).

The highest densities of slugs are found in agricultural and horticultural fields, where plants that we have bred to grow fast and taste sweet have mostly lost any resistance their ancestors may have had to slug grazing. In arable fields slug numbers can sometimes be measured in the hundreds per square meter and can do massive economic damage, more than insect pests. However, the numbers of species that cause most of this damage are small. Few slug species specialise on eating living plant material. In arable fields the worst slug pest is usually *Deroceras reticulatum* (p. 80), often followed by *Arion* (*Kobeltia*) *distinctus* (p. 48), *A.* (*K.*) *hortensis* (p. 50) and (at least in terms of numbers present) *A.* (*K.*) *intermedius* (p. 58). These are all small species that can survive cultivation well and live all year round in open fields. Root crops are attacked in addition by subterranean species too, particularly milacid slugs amongst which *Tandonia budapestensis* (p. 90) is the most common. In gardens all of these slugs can be problematic, but in addition the rich mixture of garden environments can foster many other slug species, some of which can damage susceptible plants. In particular the larger Arionidae, which cannot survive in cultivated fields, can sometimes be very damaging, including *Arion* (*A.*) *rufus* (p. 32) and its hybrids. On the continent of Europe gardens can be devastated by the 'plague slug', *Arion* (*A.*) *vulgaris* (p. 36) but so far in the Britain and Ireland this species does not appear to be a serious problem. Slugs are so damaging because unlike many insect pests, such as aphids, they are not crop-specific, but attack most of our major and minor crops.

Slug numbers can vary considerably from year to year and population modelling has shown this to be mainly driven by the weather (both temperature and moisture) (Choi *et al.*, 2006). However, many other factors are involved including, in agriculture, crop rotations. Slug numbers build up rapidly in oilseed rape (a broad-leaved crop much favoured by slugs) followed, the next year, by major damage to developing crops of wheat or barley which are next in the rotation (Barker, 2002). Similar processes probably happen in vegetable gardens; crops sown in ground where slugs have been attacking a previous crop are likely to be attacked in turn.

Pest control

Perhaps the simplest form of slug control is the application of 'slug pellets'. These consist of cereal bait with a toxic ingredient. Three types of pellets are now widely available, based upon carbamates, metaldehyde, or ferric phosphate. Carbamates (e.g. methiocarb) are effective, but also kill the natural enemies of slugs, particularly carabid beetles. Metaldehyde is equally effective and, if applied thinly at recommended rates, is only problematic if vertebrates, such as dogs or hedgehogs, have access to large concentrations of the pellets. Ferric phosphate pellets are approved for use in organic growing, being based on a naturally-occurring chemical. This is relatively less toxic to vertebrates than the other molluscicides, although other ingredients in the pellets may increase its toxicity. All three types of pellet should be kept out of the reach of children. Hands should be washed, and crops carefully cleaned and checked for pellets before eating. In gardens, slug pellets should be seen as an emergency measure, needed to save a crop or flower bed under serious attack. They will also kill non-pest species of slugs and snails, as will the nematodes now available to control slugs (see Slugs and parasites, p. 8).

There are several other products available that mostly act as barriers, giving a measure of protection to susceptible plants. Traditionally soot was used as a barrier, but in quantity it is hard to find these days. Broken egg shells can also limit slug movements. Small areas can be protected by wooden barriers topped by wires through which a low-level electric current is passed, preventing slugs from crossing. Similarly copper tape, once it starts to oxidise, can be an effective barrier to slug movements. Barriers can work for a while, but they can also be subverted by slugs that travel through the soil underneath or hatch from eggs within the confined area.

Pest slugs can be controlled, where necessary, in a number of other ways, most of which can be used by those who prefer to use techniques compatible with organic growing or simply wish to protect other wildlife. Tillage can be very effective, particularly the use of rotavation which kills (or exposes to predators and the elements) most of the slugs in the upper few centimetres of soil (where most slugs live). Damage can be limited by creating firm seedbeds, preventing slugs from hiding in soil crevices to attack germinating seed.

A beer trap baited for slugs.

Wooden boards placed on the soil between crop rows attract slugs looking for daytime refuges and regular checking of the boards, and removal of the slugs, can be effective. These boards also provide refuges for the ground beetles (carabids) that are probably the most important insect predators of slugs in the UK, encouraging them to live within a crop. Slugs can also be trapped in traditional beer traps, using beer taken from pub drip trays or milk. However, these must be used at high density (about a metre apart) and may not be practical. They must also be set high so that the slugs are required to climb in; if set flush with the soil they also trap and drown useful ground beetle predators. Chicken mash, under a plant saucer or slate, can be used as a bait to attract and remove slugs if visited regularly. Such traps can also be used to simply monitor whether the slug population is increasing and give warning that action may need to be taken to control them. Many slugs are found living in lawns surrounding flower and vegetable beds. These slugs climb the grass stems at night and can be killed in large numbers by lawn mowing late in the evening as it gets dark (if this is safe and does not bother the neighbours).

Slugs are particularly attracted to damp areas of fields and gardens and it may be possible simply to avoid growing the most susceptible plants in such areas. Damp areas can be drained or the soil improved by addition of grit or compost. Manure and compost is less attractive to slugs when it is well rotted. Unfortunately, green manure crops and mulches are much beloved by slugs, both as food and refuges. Now that burning of straw in fields is banned, farmers are increasingly incorporating crop residues in the soil, which is good for soil fertility but has led to a marked increase in slug damage to the following crop. Weeds in crops are a mixed blessing. If all weeds are removed the slugs have nothing to eat except the crop that remains, resulting in greater damage. In some cases weeds are preferred by the slugs to the crop, offering some protection.

Plants vary considerably in their susceptibility to attack by slugs. Gardeners know all too well, for example, that plants such as hostas and Chinese cabbages will attract slugs from far and wide. What is less appreciated is that some varieties of plant are more resistant to slug attack than others. Even amongst hostas the blue-leaved varieties are less likely to be attacked than the variegated varieties. Some potato varieties, such a 'Kestrel', are excellent at resisting slug attack on the tubers. For example the Royal Horticultural society list 10 potato varieties that resist slug attack (www.rhs.org.uk). In general potatoes become more susceptible to slug attack as they mature, when sugars are turned into starch, thus early potato crops are often free from slug damage. Plants that are highly susceptible to slug attack can be used more cunningly as trap crops, to attract slugs away from more valued plants that one wishes to protect. Further simple ideas for controlling slugs in the garden can be found in Symondson (1990).

Encouraging natural enemies

The natural enemies of pest slugs can be encouraged in both fields and gardens. Many birds, including blackbirds, thrushes, crows, starlings and robins will take slugs. In the tropics ducks are used to control slugs and snails. Even chickens, if confined to a run, can clear an area of slugs rapidly. Mammals such as hedgehogs and badgers have slugs as a primary part of their diets, although their role in slug control has sometimes been exaggerated. Frogs and other amphibians eat slugs too, another good reason to have a garden pond. Slow worms, the most common reptile in British gardens, eat large numbers of slugs.

The ground beetle *Pterostichus niger* (Carabidae); a slug predator common in gardens.

Many insects attack slugs, including the snail-killing flies (Sciomyzidae), whose larvae live inside the body of slugs. However, the main slug predators are probably ground beetles (Carabidae). These are the fast moving black beetles often found under stones. Research has shown that the larger the species of ground beetle, the more likely it is to take slugs and/or snails, and many of the large woodland species such as *Cychrus caraboides* are mollusc specialists. Slugs are also eaten by many other beetles including large rove beetles (Staphylinidae), the snail-eating *Silpha* (Silphidae), and glow-worms (Lampyridae). Encouraging as many as possible of these natural enemies into your garden will go a long way to keeping pest slugs in check without resort to pesticides. Further specialised information on natural enemies of slugs can be found in Barker (2004).

Slugs and parasites

Like all wildlife, slugs and snails harbour parasites. The tiny bloodsucking mite *Riccardoella limacum* is often seen running over their skins and into and out of the breathing pore. Several protozoan (single-celled) slug parasites are known, at least one with potential in pest control (South, 1992). A parasitic nematode worm, *Phasmarhabditis hermaphrodita*, is now widely available as a method of control. This is a native species and a natural regulator of slug populations. The microscopic nematodes are watered onto susceptible crops and seek out slugs in the soil. They enter the mantle through the breathing pore, carrying bacteria which kill the slug while the parasites reproduce, feeding on the bacterial soup. Infected slugs may be recognised by their swollen mantle. The juvenile worms may then go on to invade further slugs. This method is particularly effective at killing the small species that do most harm, but is relatively ineffective against mature large arionids. These nematodes are considered harmless to non-molluscan wildlife.

Slugs and snails are also the intermediate hosts of a range of other parasitic worms that complete their complex life cycles in mammals, birds or other animals. These include trematode and cestode platyhelminths (flukes and tapeworms), and nematodes (roundworms) of the genera *Angiostrongylus* and *Crenosoma*. The well-known sheep liver fluke *Fasciola hepatica*, whose usual intermediate host in Europe is the lymnaeid snail *Galba truncatula*, is not among the species infecting slugs.

Awareness and treatment of lungworm or French heartworm, a potentially fatal disease of dogs and foxes, has increased in recent years (Morgan & Shaw, 2010). It is caused by *Angiostrongylus vasorum*, a nematode whose larvae are ingested by eating slugs or snails (of apparently any species) or possibly food contaminated with their mucus. The worms lay eggs that hatch in the lungs and are expelled as larvae in dog or fox faeces to infect other molluscs. First recognised in France and arriving in southern Britain in the 1980s, *A. vasorum* is increasingly reported further north and is spreading worldwide. This could lead to renewed attempts at garden slug control (although this is unlikely to have much real impact on infection risk). The dangerous tropical species *A. cantonensis* (rat lungworm) and *A. costaricensis*, which can cause meningitis or abdominal disease in humans, are not known in wild molluscs in Britain or Ireland.

About this guide

This guide aims to supersede the last AIDGAP guide on slugs (Cameron *et al.*, 1983). The monographs by Taylor (1902-7) and Quick (1960) provide additional detail on anatomy and other matters. The names used and species treated (as in Kerney & Cameron [1979] and Kerney [1999] which also treat snails) are out-of-date. The most up-to-date checklist of non-marine molluscs of Britain and Ireland (currently Anderson, 2008) is maintained by the Conchological Society (http://www.conchsoc.net/). A website associated with the present guide (http://naturalhistory.museumwales.ac.uk/slugs) is intended to be periodically updated as necessary.

Only slug species established outdoors, and apparently naturalised (sustaining their populations by breeding) are included here. We have not included "adventives" or intercepted introductions. Records of past adventives include slugs of the families Parmacellidae and Veronicellidae (Ellis, 1969).

Species accounts

After the keys, a detailed account and image plate is given for each species. The plates show three annotated views of a "typical" individual and as much variation as it has been possible to show. For most species it is impossible to be comprehensive, so many individuals will not resemble any of the variants shown. Annotations in red brackets **[····]** correspond to particularly distinctive features.

Unless otherwise indicated, all images on a plate are to scale. Several are shown at actual size. For the others, grey silhouettes represent the actual size of a mature adult specimen.

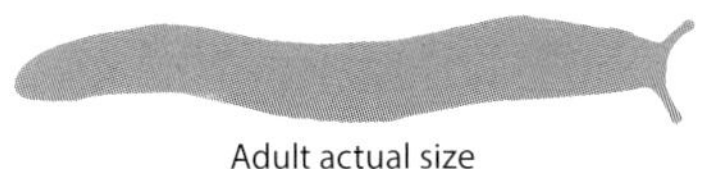

Adult actual size

The codes next to each illustrated specimen (PYC4, DF23, etc.) correspond to locality details in the Appendix (p. 136). Photographs are not necessarily typical of populations in different regions.

The maps show records from both the UK's NBN and Ireland's NBDC datasets. A few records, mainly of the recently discovered species, have been added but remain to be submitted and processed.

Symbols

We have tried to avoid unnecessary symbols in this guide. However some people's priority may be to categorise which species are generally considered plant pests. Some explanation is given in the species accounts, but the shorthand symbols used are:

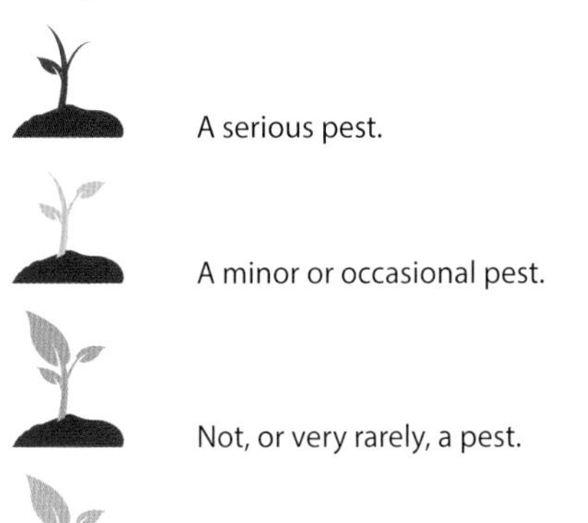

A serious pest.

A minor or occasional pest.

Not, or very rarely, a pest.

Pest status not known at present.

Notes on names

This guide assumes readers are familiar with two-part scientific names, as in *Tyrannosaurus rex* and *T. rex*. Most of our arionid slugs are grouped in one genus, *Arion*, which is divided into four subgenera. These subgenera are useful and have a sound evolutionary basis, but result in three-part names, as in *Arion* (*Arion*) *ater* or *Arion* (*Mesarion*) *subfuscus*. The subgenus name appears in brackets. Either the genus or subgenus name can be abbreviated, hence *Arion* (*A.*) *ater*, or *A.* (*Mesarion*) *subfuscus*. Subgenera also appear in the names of other slugs.

English names are given for each species. A panoply of these has been used in different parts of the world, with the same name sometimes used for different species (e.g. Garden Slug, Bourguignat's Slug). As those who loathe such names know, no English name is official or correct in taxonomy, but they can be useful. Here we supply our recommendation along with any others we have encountered. In particular we have avoided the term "Garden Slug", since almost any slug could occur in a British or Irish garden. An index to scientific names (p. 136) and English names (p. 133) is provided.

External features of slugs

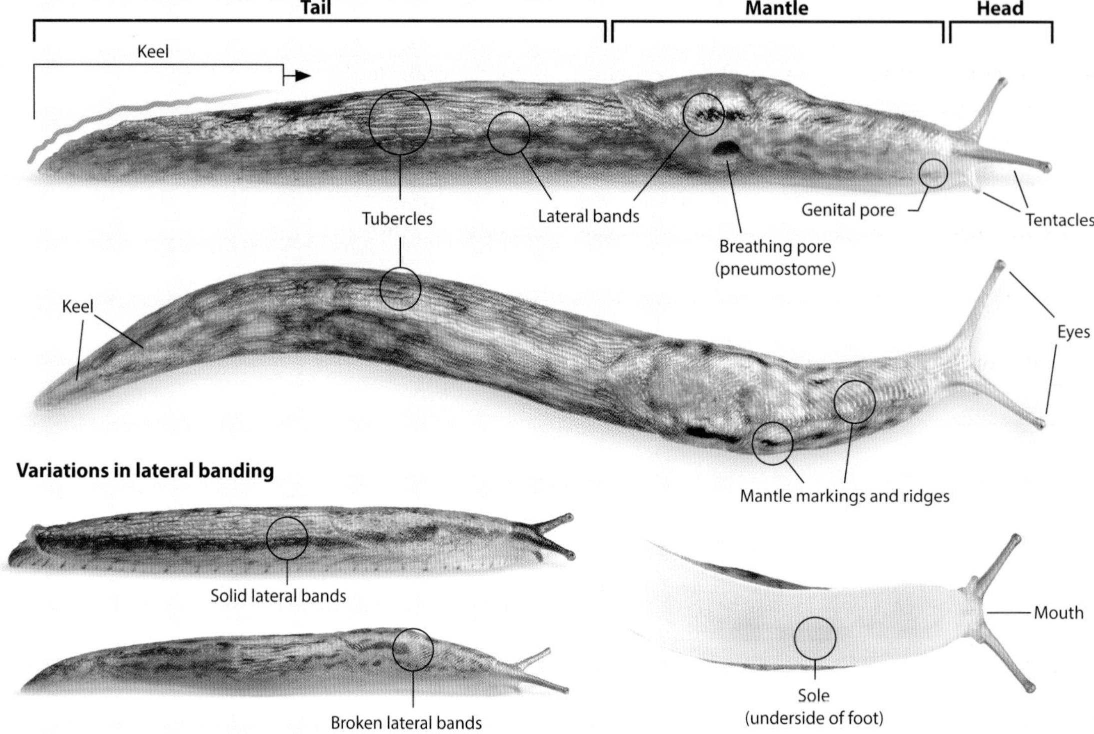

Mantle. Note texture and presence of grooves and ridges, as well as any markings and banding.

Tentacles. Note colour. Slugs may need to be handled or disturbed to extend tentacles.

Breathing pore (pneumostome).
On the right-hand side of the body. Note whether rim is noticeably paler or darker than body sides.

Lateral bands. Note whether present on mantle and/or tail. Note also intensity, whether broad or narrow, and whether high or low on body sides.

Tubercles. Note whether numerous and small/fine, or few and large/coarse. Dark pigment may be present in the grooves between tubercles.

Keel (raised ridge along tail). Note length and whether sloping sharply to the tip of tail. Beware markings that may exaggerate or obscure the length of the keel.

Sole (underside of foot). Note colour and any patterning. The sole in most slugs is tripartite i.e. there are three fields running in parallel the length of the animal. Note whether the central field is a different shade from those at the sides.

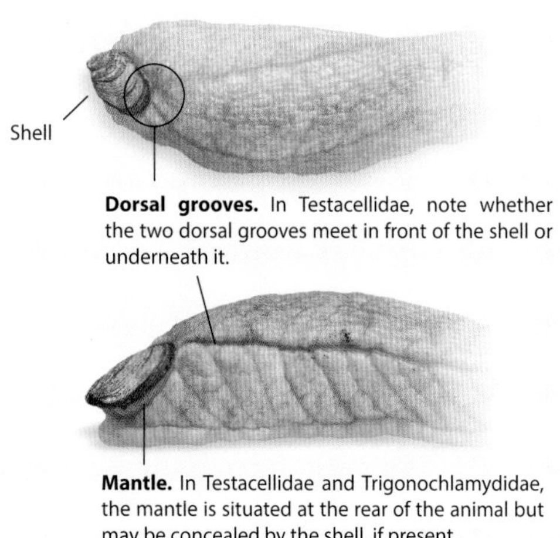

Dorsal grooves. In Testacellidae, note whether the two dorsal grooves meet in front of the shell or underneath it.

Mantle. In Testacellidae and Trigonochlamydidae, the mantle is situated at the rear of the animal but may be concealed by the shell, if present.

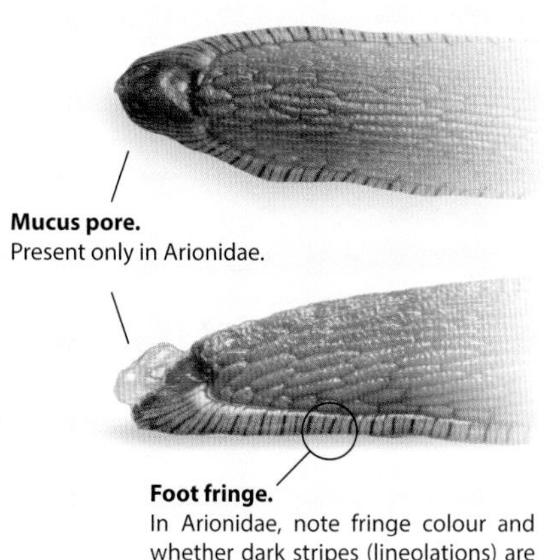

Mucus pore.
Present only in Arionidae.

Foot fringe.
In Arionidae, note fringe colour and whether dark stripes (lineolations) are present or not.

Identifying slugs

Living, adult slugs are the easiest to identify. Live slugs differ in the shapes they adopt when contracted, and their behaviour when disturbed. They may need to be examined closely, especially if small (a lens is recommended). White tissue or paper is useful to check the colour of the mucus. **Always wash your hands after handling slugs**. Many species can be identified from good photographs provided these show enough of the key features. The right-hand side of the body is most informative since it shows the breathing pore and the position of other features in relation to it. Dead slugs (e.g. from beer or pitfall traps) may become difficult to identify as shapes distort and colours fade. **Some species have to be killed and dissected for accurate identification** (see p. 110) in which case any observations or photographs of the live animal need to be taken first.

There are two main problems with slug identification. Firstly, many species are **extremely variable in appearance**. In particular, size, colour and markings can vary between localities and habitats and even among slugs from a single clutch of eggs. Colour and markings often change radically as slugs grow.

Secondly, **juveniles of some species may resemble the adults of others**. Some species have a loosely-defined adult season, but juveniles can be encountered at any time of year. Without experience there is no easy way to distinguish a juvenile of a large species from an adult of a small species. Most slugs of 50 mm or more long will be mature enough to identify, but some species become adult at just 15 mm. Of course, slugs encountered mating or laying eggs will be adult. In some species the genital pore also becomes subtly swollen in adults. Juveniles may have noticeably bigger eye tentacles, relative to their body size.

These problems make it difficult to construct and use a dichotomous key (a key that presents only two options at a time). We have therefore adopted charts or tabular keys that show several options at once. Where possible, the identification charts emphasize shape, texture and behavioural features over size, colour, and markings. They are designed to work for both adults and (as far as possible) juveniles.

Using the identification charts

This book contains both identification charts and species accounts. We recommend that inexperienced users first try the charts for identification. **They draw attention to important features and away from distracting ones.** The charts are designed to work without the species accounts, although these should be consulted for additional features, species variation and useful background information to confirm identifications.

Most of the charts offer several identification options at once. Species (or groups of species) and identification features are arranged in vertical columns or horizontal rows. The rows sometimes run across two pages. Where a feature is shared by more than one species (or group of species) the box is spread across columns or rows.

It is important to examine all the features in a row or column, ruling out as many species as possible each time. Boxes with a red outline highlight particularly distinctive features that may often work as shortcuts to the right identification.

If the slug being identified does not correspond with all features, try returning to an earlier chart to check it is in the right group of species. Other species may be found in Britain and Ireland in future, but the vast majority of slugs will belong to the known species.

Some externally similar slug species cannot be distinguished without dissection. Such cases are indicated in the charts.

For encouragement, remember that:

- **Not every single slug you find will be identifiable**, at least at first. Juveniles especially are often not distinctive enough to identify to species.
- With practice, especially as one encounters more species, identification becomes easier. This is motivation to keep exploring.

Adult size range

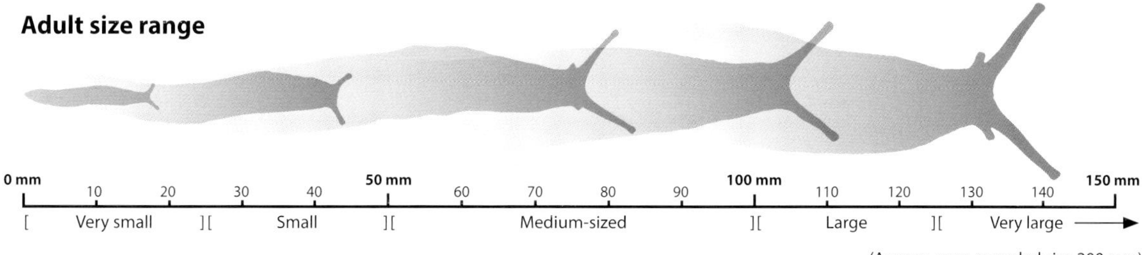

(Approx. max. recorded size 200 mm)

1a. External shell		Group
Shell spiral and obvious, even if thin and transparent. Animal able to retract fully into shell. Mantle virtually hidden within shell.		**Snails** For identification, see the AIDGAP guide by Cameron (2008).
Shell a loosely coiled spiral, very thin, transparent. Animal snail-like, but unable to retract fully into shell. Mantle mainly hidden within shell, but with mantle lobes overlapping shell edge.		**Semi-slugs (Vitrinidae)** Go to Chart 15, p. 29.
Shell virtually uncoiled, flattened and fingernail-like, covering only part of the rear end of the animal. Mantle virtually hidden beneath shell.		**Shelled Slugs (Testacellidae)** Go to Chart 14, p. 28.
No visible external shell.		**Other Slugs** Go to 1b.

1b. Mantle Position		Group
Mantle tiny, disc-shaped, at the very rear of the animal.		**Ghost Slug (Trigonochlamydidae)** p. 106. Note: in extremely rare cases, Testacellidae (p. 100-105) have been found alive but lacking a shell.
Mantle cloak-like or shield-like, covering the neck and "shoulders" of the animal. Mantle is of a different texture from rest of body with breathing pore on right side.		**Other slugs** Go to Chart 2, p. 13.

2.	Round-backed Slugs (Arionidae)	Long-keeled Slugs (Milacidae, Boettgerillidae)	Short-keeled Slugs (Limacidae)	Short-keeled Slugs (Agriolimacidae)
Breathing pore	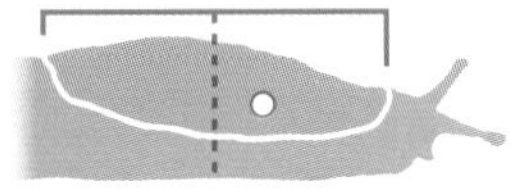 Breathing pore in front half of mantle.	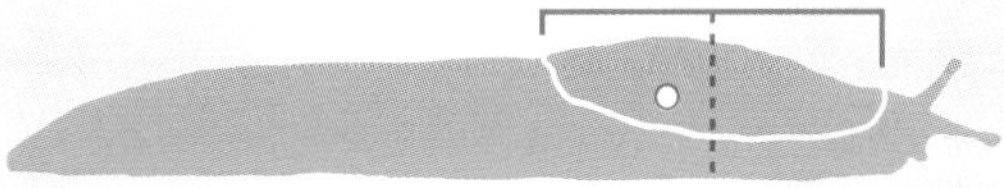 Breathing pore in rear half of mantle.		
Keel (raised ridge)	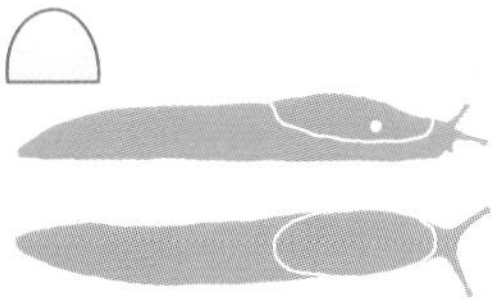 No keel. Animal round-backed. Note: a very weak keel is present in some species , especially when young.	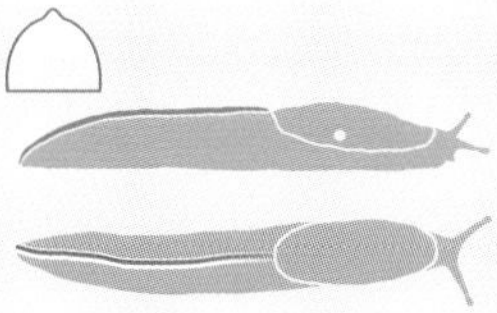 Keel long, running all the way to the rear mantle edge.	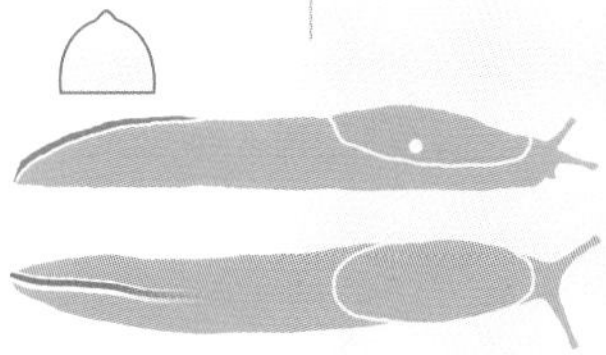 Keel short, petering out well before the rear mantle edge. May be the same colour as the body and therefore inconspicuous.	
Tail tip	 Rounded, with a mucus pore visible.	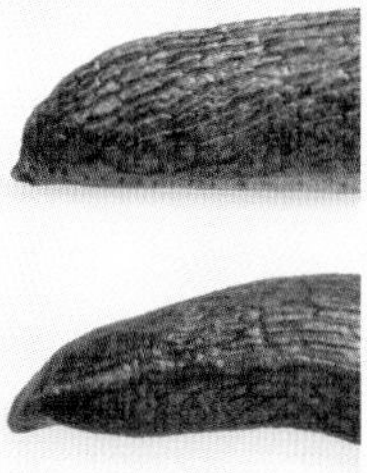 Pointed, with no mucus pore. Keel sloping sharply to tail tip.	 Pointed, with no mucus pore. Keel sloping gradually to tail tip.	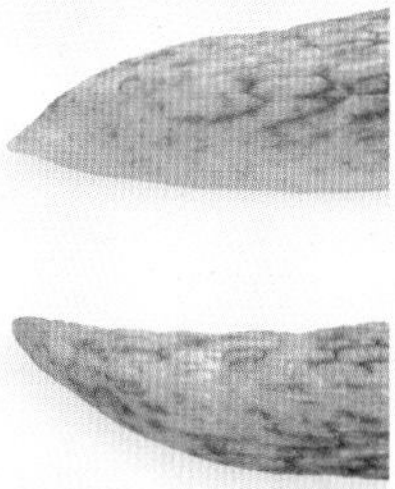 Pointed, with no mucus pore. Keel sloping sharply to tail tip.
Mantle texture	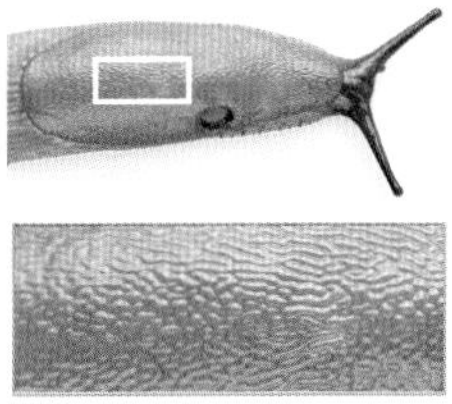 Mantle finely granular ("shagreened").	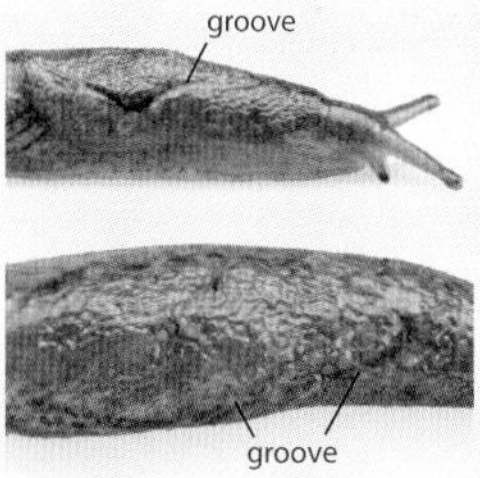 groove groove Mantle texture variable. A deep ⊃ shaped groove is usually present, but often inconspicuous.	 Mantle with fine concentric ridges, like a fingerprint. Ridges centred around the midpoint of the back.	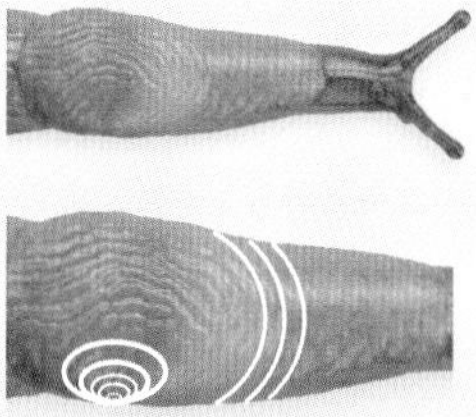 Mantle with fine concentric ridges, like a fingerprint. Ridges centred around the breathing pore.
Adult size & behaviour	15 - 140 mm. Usually rather sluggish and less willing to extend when handled. Mostly poor climbers. Mucus may be very sticky and staining.	25 - 75 mm. Reasonably active when handled. Particularly poor climbers, usually found on or in the ground. Do not produce much mucus.	35 - 200 mm. Active when handled. Strong climbers, often found well off the ground. Mucus may be thin and runny.	15 -50 mm Especially active, extending readily in the hand. Not very strong climbers. Mucus may be thin and milky.
Families	**Round-backed Slugs** (Arionidae) Go to Chart 3, p. 14.	**Long-keeled Slugs** (Milacidae, Boettgerillidae) Go to Chart 8, p. 20.	**Short-keeled Slugs** (Limacidae) Go to Chart 9, p. 22.	**Short-keeled Slugs** (Agriolimacidae) Go to Chart 13, p. 27.

3.	***Geomalacus***	***Arion* (*Kobeltia*)**	***Arion* (*Carinarion*)**	***Arion* (*Mesarion*)**	***Arion* (*Arion*)**
Adult size	Medium-sized (60 - 90 mm).	Very small to small (15 - 45 mm).	Small (30 - 45 mm).	Medium-sized (50 - 70 mm).	Medium-sized to very large (60 - 140 mm).
Tubercles	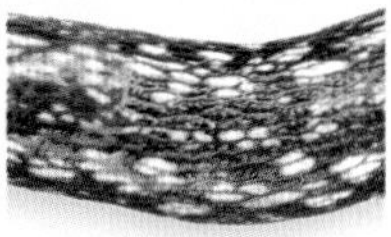 Small/fine; even more so than in many smaller species.	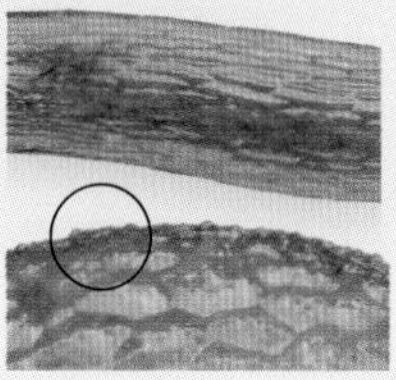 Varying between species. May appear prickly when contracted.	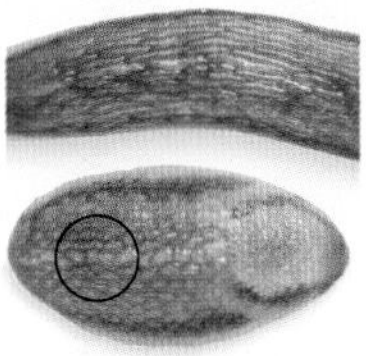 Small/fine; central row often paler, giving the impression of a keel (a "false keel").	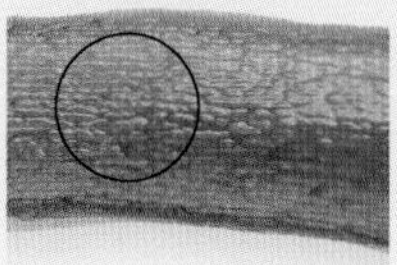 Small/fine, even more so than in many smaller species.	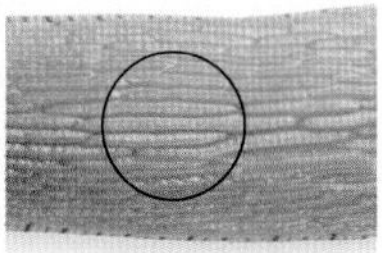 Large/coarse; slugs nearly always rough or warty to the naked eye.
Contracted shape	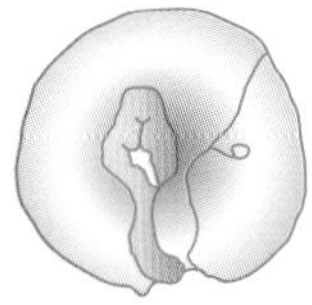 A ball, formed by bending the sole in half.	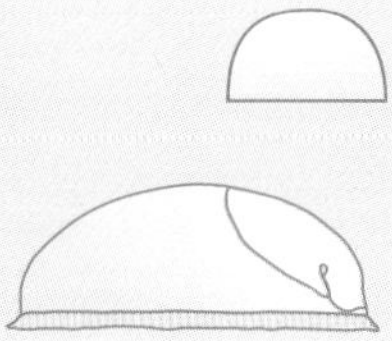 Varies from a dome to elongate; less flattened than in subgenus *Carinarion*.	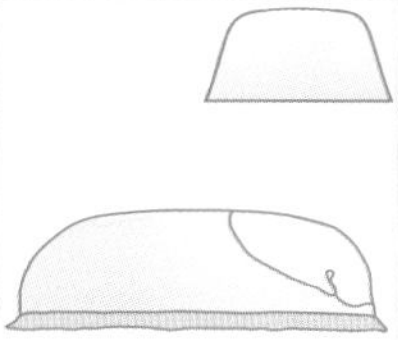 A flattened dome, bell-shaped in cross-section.	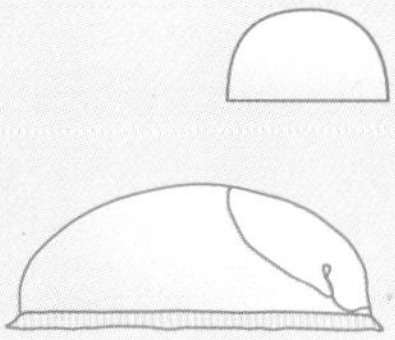 An elongate dome, very seldom hemispherical.	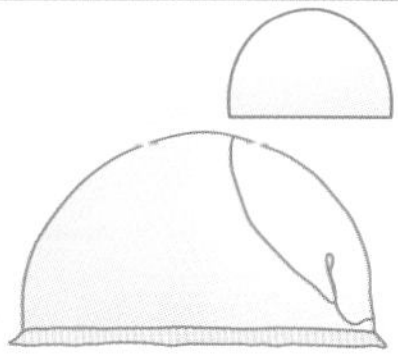 A near- hemispherical dome. May squirm or rock from side to side if disturbed.
Mucus	Mucus colourless.	Mucus yellow-orange, at least on the sole, staining fingers or paper.	Mucus colourless.	Mucus yellow-orange, staining fingers or paper.	Mucus thick, sticky and hard to remove, usually colourless.
Other features	 Back covered with pale spots. W & SW Ireland only.	Sole coloured yellow-orange. 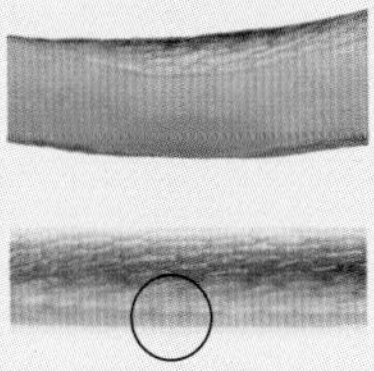 Foot fringe usually without stripes.	Sole pale grey to white, never dark. 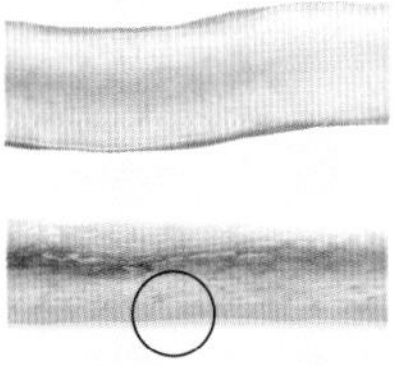 Foot fringe usually without stripes.	Sole pale grey to white, never dark. 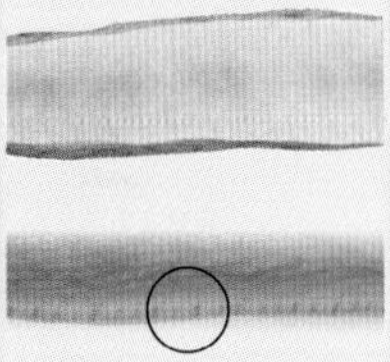 Foot fringe with narrow stripes from front to rear.	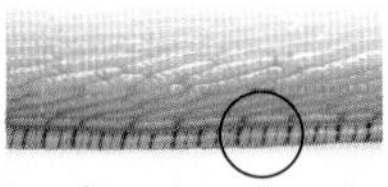 Foot fringe broadly and clearly striped from front to rear.
Genus (subgenus)	***Geomalacus maculosus*** 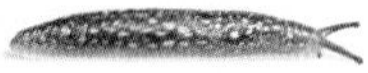 p. 60.	***Arion* (*Kobeltia*)** 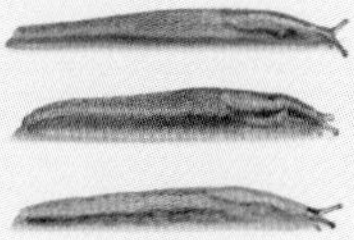 Go to Chart 4, p. 15.	***Arion* (*Carinarion*)** 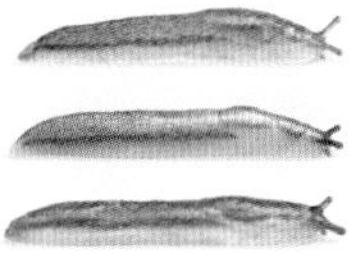 Go to Chart 5, p. 16.	***Arion* (*Mesarion*)** 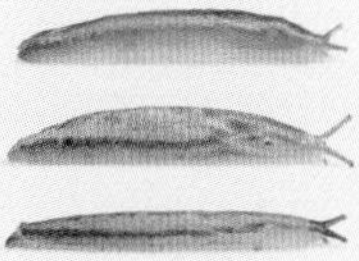 Go to Chart 6, p. 17.	***Arion* (*Arion*)** 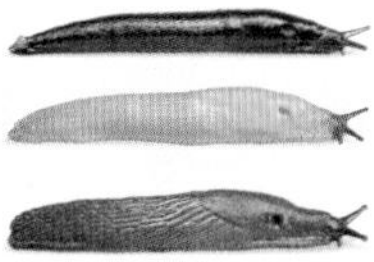 Go to Chart 7, p. 18.

4.	***A.* (*Kobeltia*) *intermedius***	***A.* (*Kobeltia*) *occultus* / cf. *fagophilus***	***A.* (*Kobeltia*) *owenii***	***A.* (*Kobeltia*) *distinctus***	***A.* (*Kobeltia*) *hortensis***
Adult size	Very small (15 - 20 mm).	Small (35 - 40 mm).	Small (25 - 40 mm).	Small (25 - 40 mm).	Small (20 - 35 mm).
Body (contracted)	Dome-shaped.	A flattened dome, not elongated.	Flattened, often slightly elongated. May form a (shape.		
Tubercles	Coarse, sometimes drawn to slight points giving a "prickly" appearance in dry or cold conditions.	Coarse, giving a rough or warty appearance, especially in drier conditions.		Tubercles fine, not giving a warty appearance.	Tubercles fine, not giving a warty appearance. Bottom row of tubercles often contrastingly white.
Body colour & markings	More variable than other *Kobeltia*: white to orange or blue-grey. Often a dull yellow-brown with darker head.	Yellow-brown, yellow-grey, or pale blue-grey.	Tawny yellow-brown to rich warm brown. Usually with obvious diffuse dark pigment along centre of back.	Dark grey-brown, suffused with a trace of yellow or putty- coloured pigment on back. Never blue-grey.	Dark blue-grey to black, with little or no trace of yellow. Often bluish when young.
Lateral bands	Often absent; if present, faint and high on body.	High on body, not diffusing gradually down to foot fringe.	High on body, usually diffusing down to the foot fringe.	Low on body sides, almost reaching foot fringe.	Moderately low on body sides, almost reaching foot fringe.
Tentacles	Variable, seldom black.	Black to cold blue-black.	Black to purplish-brown.	Black to cold blue-black.	Black to warm red-black.
Other features	Sole mucus: Season: Adults all year round.	Sole mucus: Season: Adults mainly in spring.	Sole mucus: Season: Adults mainly in summer.	Sole mucus: Season: Adults mainly in spring and summer.	Sole mucus: Season: Adults mainly in autumn and winter, later than *A. distinctus*.
Species	***A.* (*Kobeltia*) *intermedius*** p. 58.	***A.* (*Kobeltia*) *occultus*** or ***A.* (*Kobeltia*) cf. *fagophilus*** (see species accounts) p. 54 & p. 56.	***A.* (*Kobeltia*) *owenii*** p. 52.	***A.* (*Kobeltia*) *distinctus*** p. 48.	***A.* (*Kobeltia*) *hortensis*** p. 50.

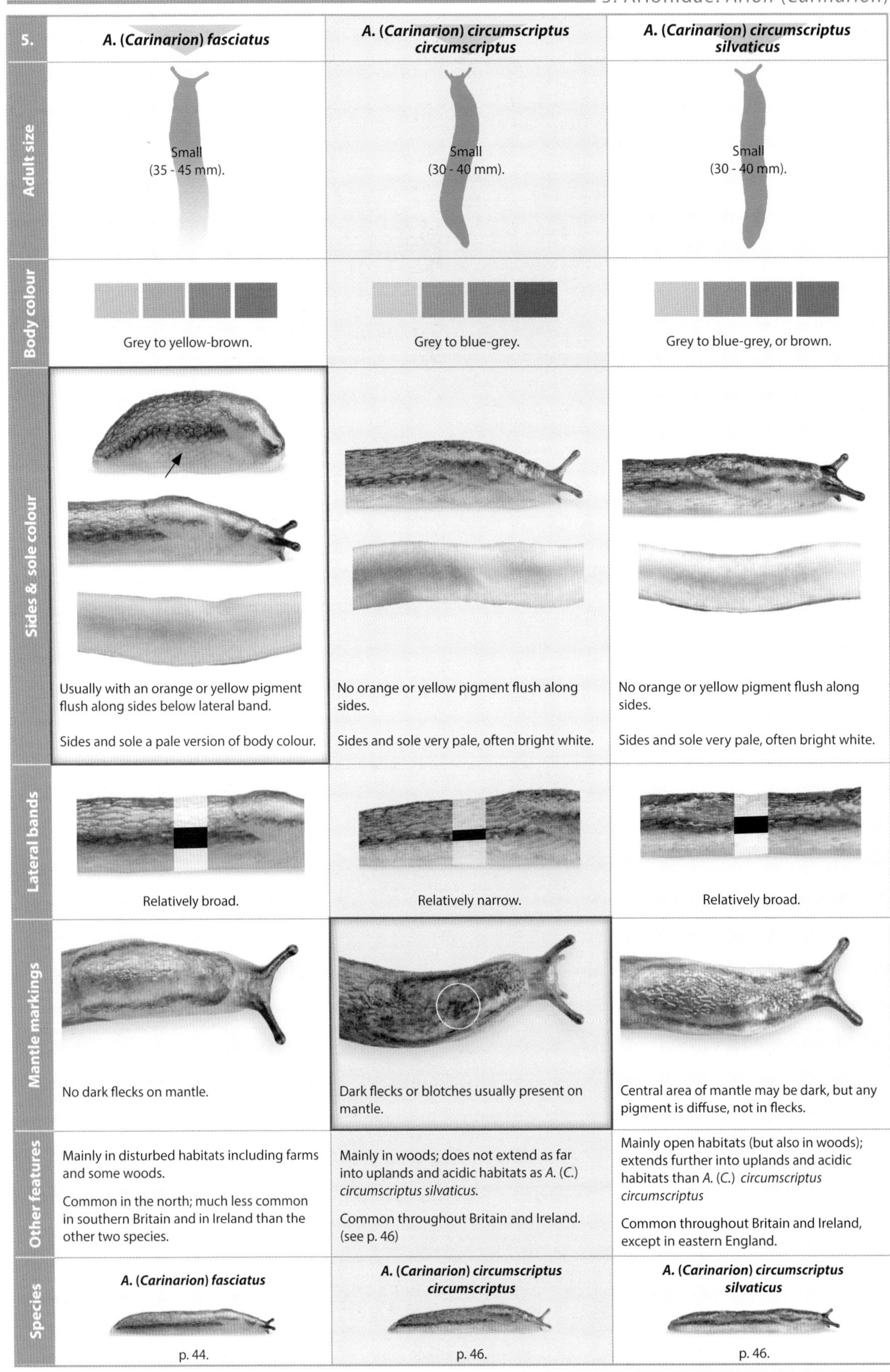

5.	***A.* (*Carinarion*) *fasciatus***	***A.* (*Carinarion*) *circumscriptus circumscriptus***	***A.* (*Carinarion*) *circumscriptus silvaticus***
Adult size	Small (35 - 45 mm).	Small (30 - 40 mm).	Small (30 - 40 mm).
Body colour	Grey to yellow-brown.	Grey to blue-grey.	Grey to blue-grey, or brown.
Sides & sole colour	Usually with an orange or yellow pigment flush along sides below lateral band. Sides and sole a pale version of body colour.	No orange or yellow pigment flush along sides. Sides and sole very pale, often bright white.	No orange or yellow pigment flush along sides. Sides and sole very pale, often bright white.
Lateral bands	Relatively broad.	Relatively narrow.	Relatively broad.
Mantle markings	No dark flecks on mantle.	Dark flecks or blotches usually present on mantle.	Central area of mantle may be dark, but any pigment is diffuse, not in flecks.
Other features	Mainly in disturbed habitats including farms and some woods. Common in the north; much less common in southern Britain and in Ireland than the other two species.	Mainly in woods; does not extend as far into uplands and acidic habitats as *A.* (*C.*) *circumscriptus silvaticus*. Common throughout Britain and Ireland. (see p. 46)	Mainly open habitats (but also in woods); extends further into uplands and acidic habitats than *A.* (*C.*) *circumscriptus circumscriptus* Common throughout Britain and Ireland, except in eastern England.
Species	***A.* (*Carinarion*) *fasciatus*** p. 44.	***A.* (*Carinarion*) *circumscriptus circumscriptus*** p. 46.	***A.* (*Carinarion*) *circumscriptus silvaticus*** p. 46.

6.	***A.* (*Mesarion*) cf. *iratii***	***A.* (*Mesarion*) *fuscus***	***A.* (*Mesarion*) *subfuscus***
Adult size	Medium-sized (50 - 70 mm).	Medium-sized (50 - 70 mm).	Medium-sized (50 - 70 mm).
Body colour	Pale orange-brown to dark grey.	Pale orange-brown.	Variable, even within populations: from bright orange-yellow, through brown and grey to (in uplands) purple-black.
Body markings	Dark lateral bands present, low on body sides, with black spots or speckles usually present on back.	Dark smudge present on "cheeks" below mantle edges seems to persist in adults. Dark lateral bands present, low on body sides.	Dark lateral bands nearly always present, though may be faint, or obscured in dark individuals. Usually high on the body sides.
Body mucus	Orange or yellow.	Orange, yellow, or colourless.	Orange or yellow.
Other features	Known only from upland woodlands, mainly larch plantations, in South Wales.	Known only from woodlands in the Cairngorms and Sherwood Forest area; also from near Cannock Chase and Thetford Forest. Records from Ireland require confirmation.	Common throughout Britain and Ireland, except East Anglia. In almost all habitats, including woodlands and gardens.
Species	***A.* (*Mesarion*) cf. *iratii*** p. 42.	***A.* (*Mesarion*) *fuscus*** Dissection is recommended to confirm the identity of this species (p. 115). p. 42.	***A.* (*Mesarion*) *subfuscus*** p. 40.

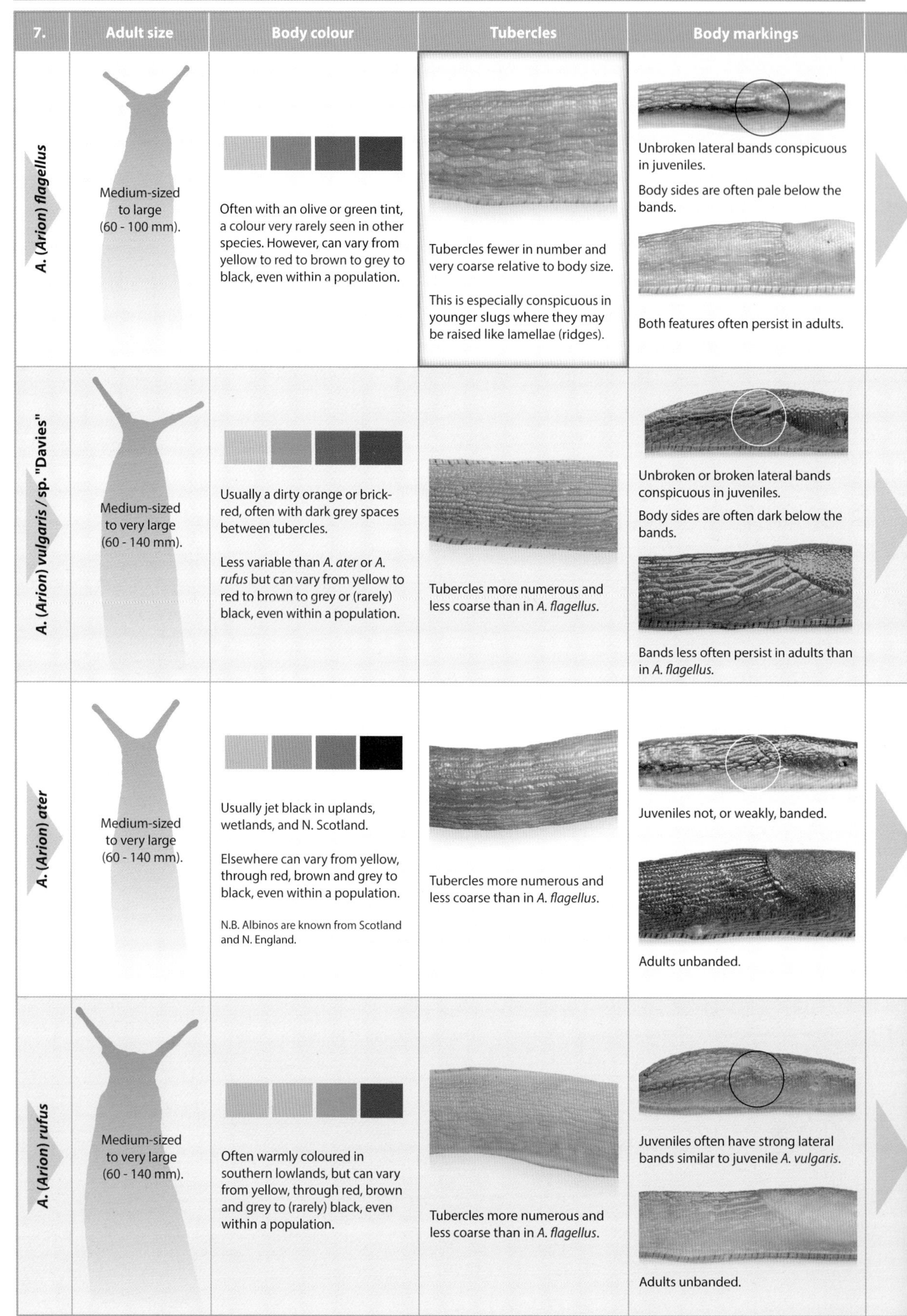

7.	Adult size	Body colour	Tubercles	Body markings
A. (Arion) flagellus	Medium-sized to large (60 - 100 mm).	Often with an olive or green tint, a colour very rarely seen in other species. However, can vary from yellow to red to brown to grey to black, even within a population.	Tubercles fewer in number and very coarse relative to body size. This is especially conspicuous in younger slugs where they may be raised like lamellae (ridges).	Unbroken lateral bands conspicuous in juveniles. Body sides are often pale below the bands. Both features often persist in adults.
A. (Arion) vulgaris / sp. "Davies"	Medium-sized to very large (60 - 140 mm).	Usually a dirty orange or brick-red, often with dark grey spaces between tubercles. Less variable than *A. ater* or *A. rufus* but can vary from yellow to red to brown to grey or (rarely) black, even within a population.	Tubercles more numerous and less coarse than in *A. flagellus*.	Unbroken or broken lateral bands conspicuous in juveniles. Body sides are often dark below the bands. Bands less often persist in adults than in *A. flagellus*.
A. (Arion) ater	Medium-sized to very large (60 - 140 mm).	Usually jet black in uplands, wetlands, and N. Scotland. Elsewhere can vary from yellow, through red, brown and grey to black, even within a population. N.B. Albinos are known from Scotland and N. England.	Tubercles more numerous and less coarse than in *A. flagellus*.	Juveniles not, or weakly, banded. Adults unbanded.
A. (Arion) rufus	Medium-sized to very large (60 - 140 mm).	Often warmly coloured in southern lowlands, but can vary from yellow, through red, brown and grey to (rarely) black, even within a population.	Tubercles more numerous and less coarse than in *A. flagellus*.	Juveniles often have strong lateral bands similar to juvenile *A. vulgaris*. Adults unbanded.

Foot fringe colour	Sole colour	Other features	Species	
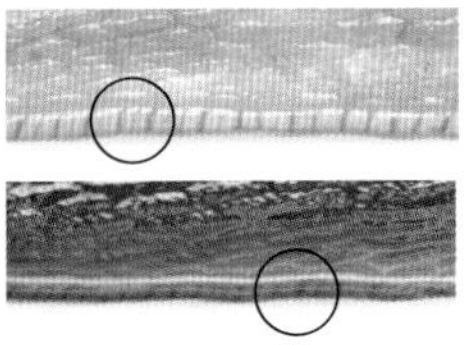 Usually same as body sides, or a dirty orange.	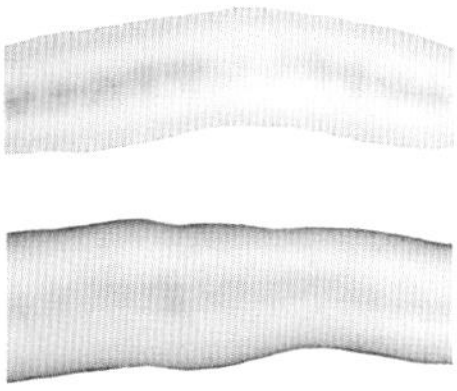 Always as pale or paler than body sides, and often with an olive or green tinge, a colour very rarely seen in other species. Dark fringe lines never reach far into centre of sole.	Sometimes appears more flattened than other species. Does not squirm from side to side when contracted and stroked firmly with a finger.	***A.* (*Arion*) *flagellus*** 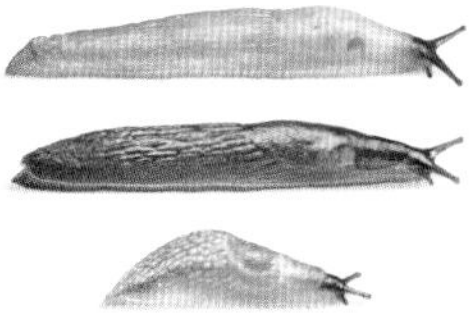 p. 34.	**These species are readily distinguished from *A. ater* and *A. rufus*, even as juveniles, by dissection.**
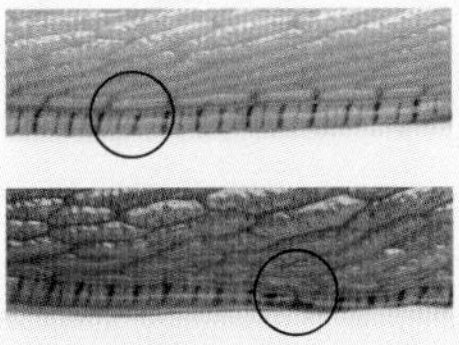 Usually same as body sides, or a dirty orange.	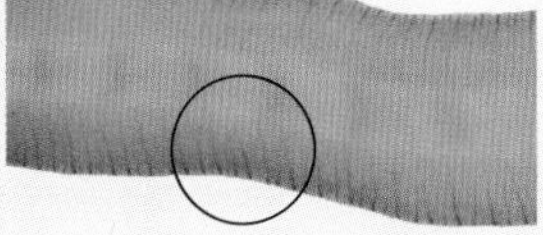 Often a dark sooty grey, darker than the body sides. This is diagnostic, although paler soles often occur in the same populations. Dark fringe lines often reach far into centre of sole, which may also have an orange flush.	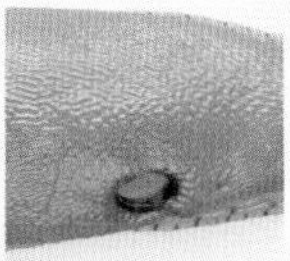 The rim around the breathing pore is often dark or black. Does not squirm from side to side when contracted and stroked firmly with a finger.	***A.* (*Arion*) *vulgaris*** p. 36.  or 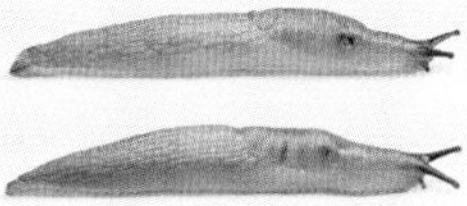 ***A.* (*Arion*) sp. "Davies"** p. 38.	***A. vulgaris* and *A.* sp. "Davies" are only reliably distinguished by dissection (p. 114).**
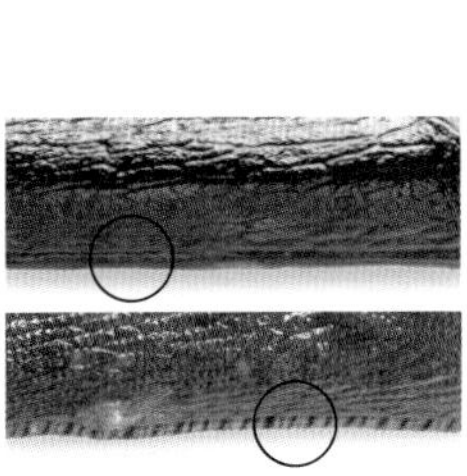 Usually a darker or duller colour than body sides. May be a dirty orange.	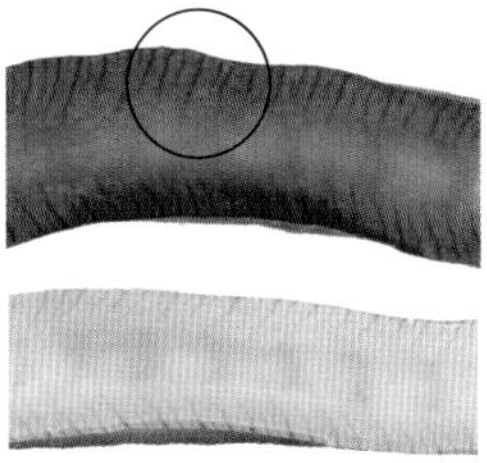 As dark or paler than body sides, never darker. Dark fringe lines often reach far into centre of sole.	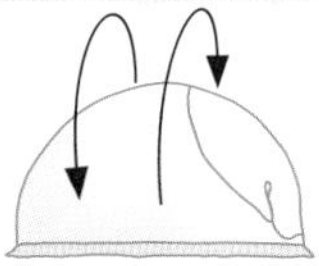 Adults *usually* squirm from side to side when contracted and stroked firmly with a finger. Less likely to be seen mating than other species.	***A.* (*Arion*) *ater*** 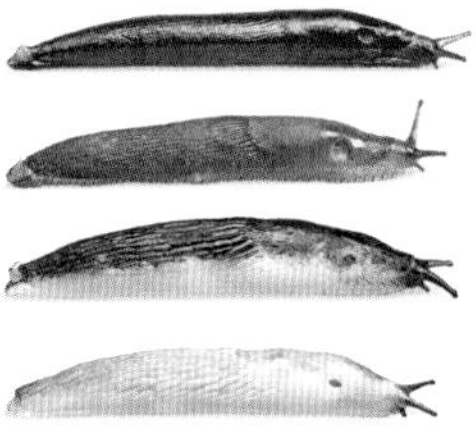 p. 30.	***A. ater* and *A. rufus* cannot always be distinguished externally, or even after dissection (p. 114).**
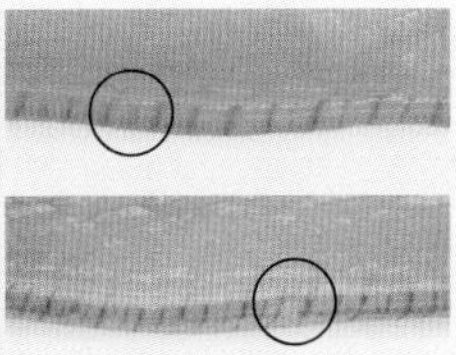 Often brighter than body sides, bright orange or orange-red being common, but like other species may be a dirty orange.	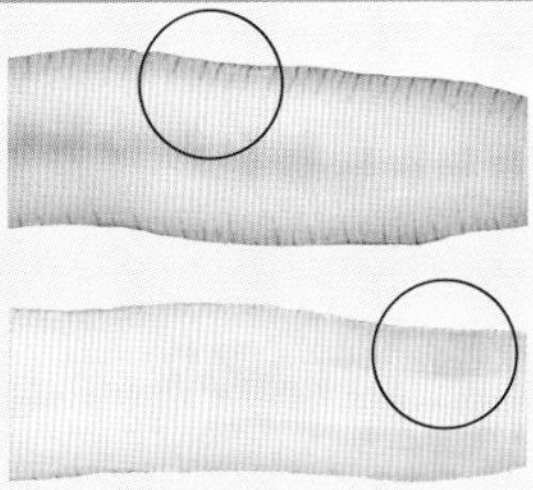 As dark or paler than body sides, never darker. Dark fringe lines often reach far into centre of sole, which may also have an orange flush.	Adults *occasionally* squirm from side to side when contracted and stroked firmly with a finger. Mucus may have a faint orange tinge.	***A.* (*Arion*) *rufus*** 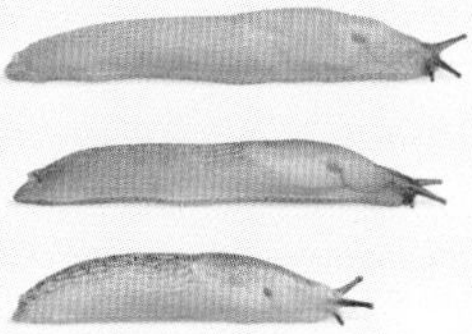 p. 32.	

8.	Adult size	Body colour	Mucus	Keel colour	Sole colour
Boettgerilla pallens	Small to medium-sized (35 - 55 mm).	Body white to pale blue-grey or lilac-grey, becoming paler at sides.	Colourless.	Same as body or slightly darker.	Uniformly pale (although dark gut contents may show through translucent central strip).
Milax gagates	Small to medium-sized (45 -55 mm).	Body elephant-grey to brown or black, becoming paler at sides.	Colourless.	Same as body or slightly darker.	Uniformly pale (although dark gut contents may show through translucent central strip).
Tandonia cf. cristata	Small (25 - 35 mm).	Body light yellow-grey to brown- or blue-grey, becoming paler at sides.	Colourless.	Lighter than body, yellow-white.	Uniformly pale (although dark gut contents may show through translucent central strip).
Tandonia budapestensis	Medium-sized (50 -70 mm).	Body elephant-grey to dark grey-brown. Mantle usually brown.	Colourless.	Usually lighter than body, often dirty yellow-orange.	With pale sides and dark pigment in the central strip.
Tandonia sowerbyi	Medium-sized (60 - 75 mm).	Body yellow-grey to dark grey-brown.	Yellow to orange.	Usually lighter than body, often dirty yellow-orange.	Uniformly pale.
Tandonia rustica	Medium-sized (50 -70 mm).	Body warm yellow-brown to pale pinkish-brown.	Colourless.	Lighter than body, yellow-white.	Uniformly pale.

Markings	Body shape (extended)	Body shape (Contracted)	Rim of breathing pore	Species
 Body unmarked, appearing relatively smooth.	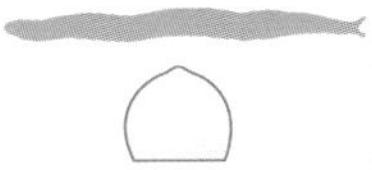 Very slender and elongate, wormlike. Round in cross-section.	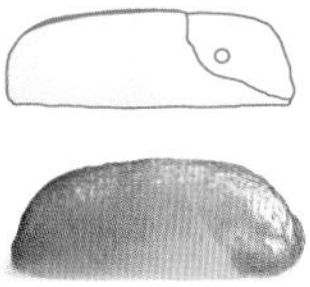 Cylindrical.	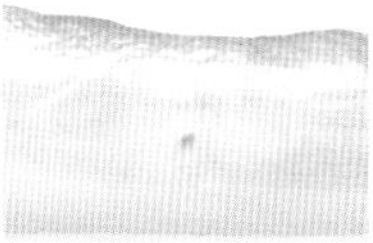 Not contrastingly paler than body sides.	***Boettgerilla pallens***  p. 98.
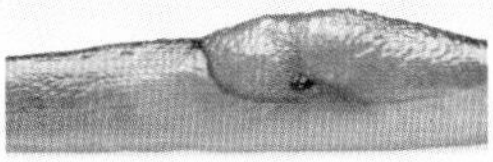 Body unmarked, appearing relatively smooth.	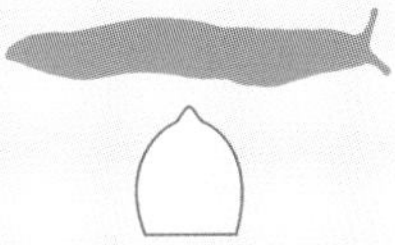 Less slender than other species. Round to oval in cross-section.	 Hump-shaped with keel raised.	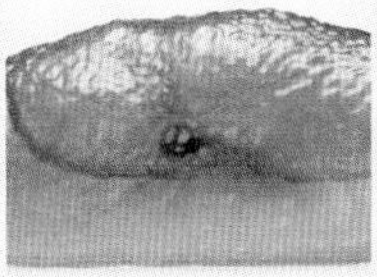 Usually darker than body sides.	***Milax gagates***  p. 96.
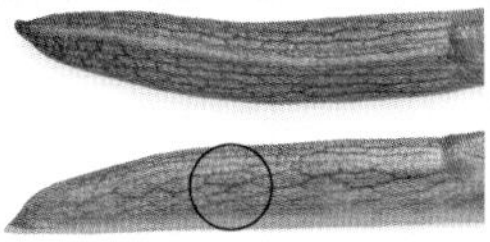 Dark pigment confined to grooves between tubercles, forming a uniform reticulate (fishnet) pattern on tail and sides.	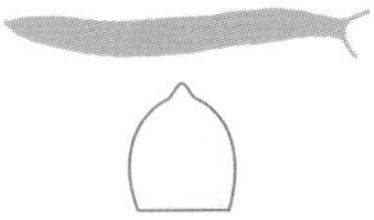 Slender, elongate. Round to oval in cross-section.	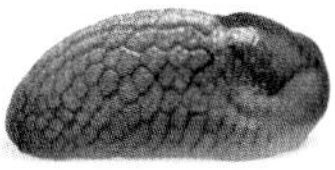 Elongate hump-shaped or forming a C or U-shape at rest.	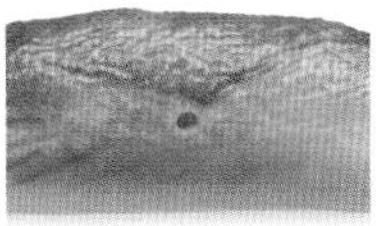 Not contrastingly paler than body sides.	***Tandonia* cf. *cristata*** 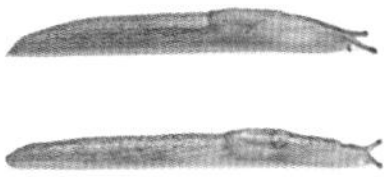 p. 92.
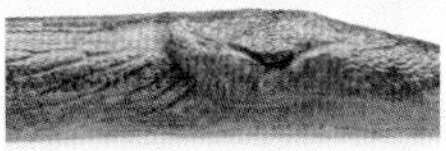 Whole body densely "speckled" with minute dark spots. Dark pigment in mantle grooves may form narrow black lines.	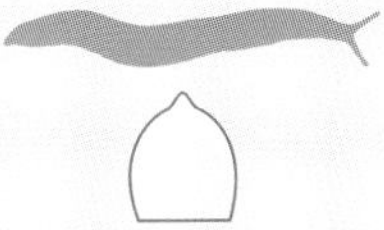 Slender, elongate. Round to oval in cross-section.	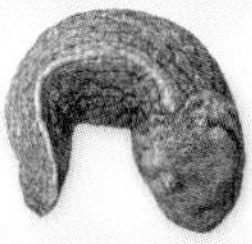	 Not contrastingly paler than body sides.	***Tandonia budapestensis***  p. 90.
 Whole body densely "speckled" with minute dark spots. Dark pigment in mantle grooves may form narrow black lines.	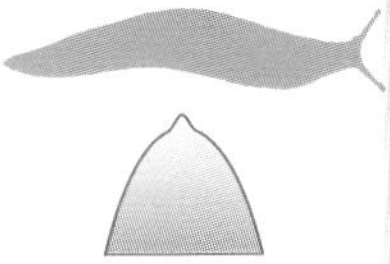 Less slender than other species. Triangular in cross-section.	 Hump-shaped, with keel raised and sometimes crinkled.	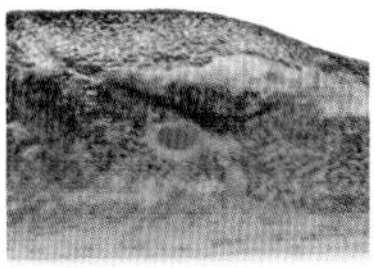 Usually contrastingly paler than body sides.	***Tandonia sowerbyi*** 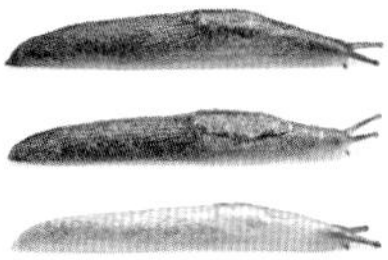 p. 94.
 Whole body lightly speckled with large black spots. Prominent lateral bands on the mantle.	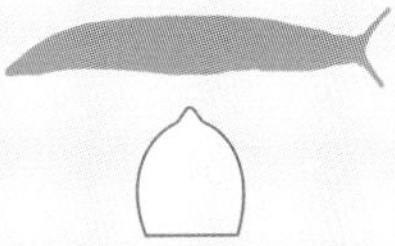 Less slender than other species. Round to oval in cross-section.	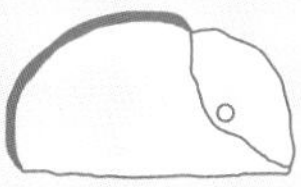 Hump-shaped.	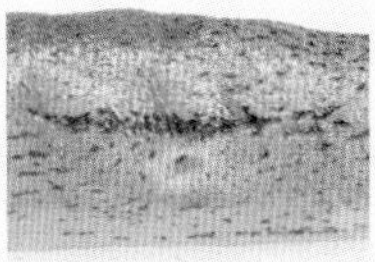 Usually contrastingly paler than body sides.	***Tandonia rustica***  p. 94.

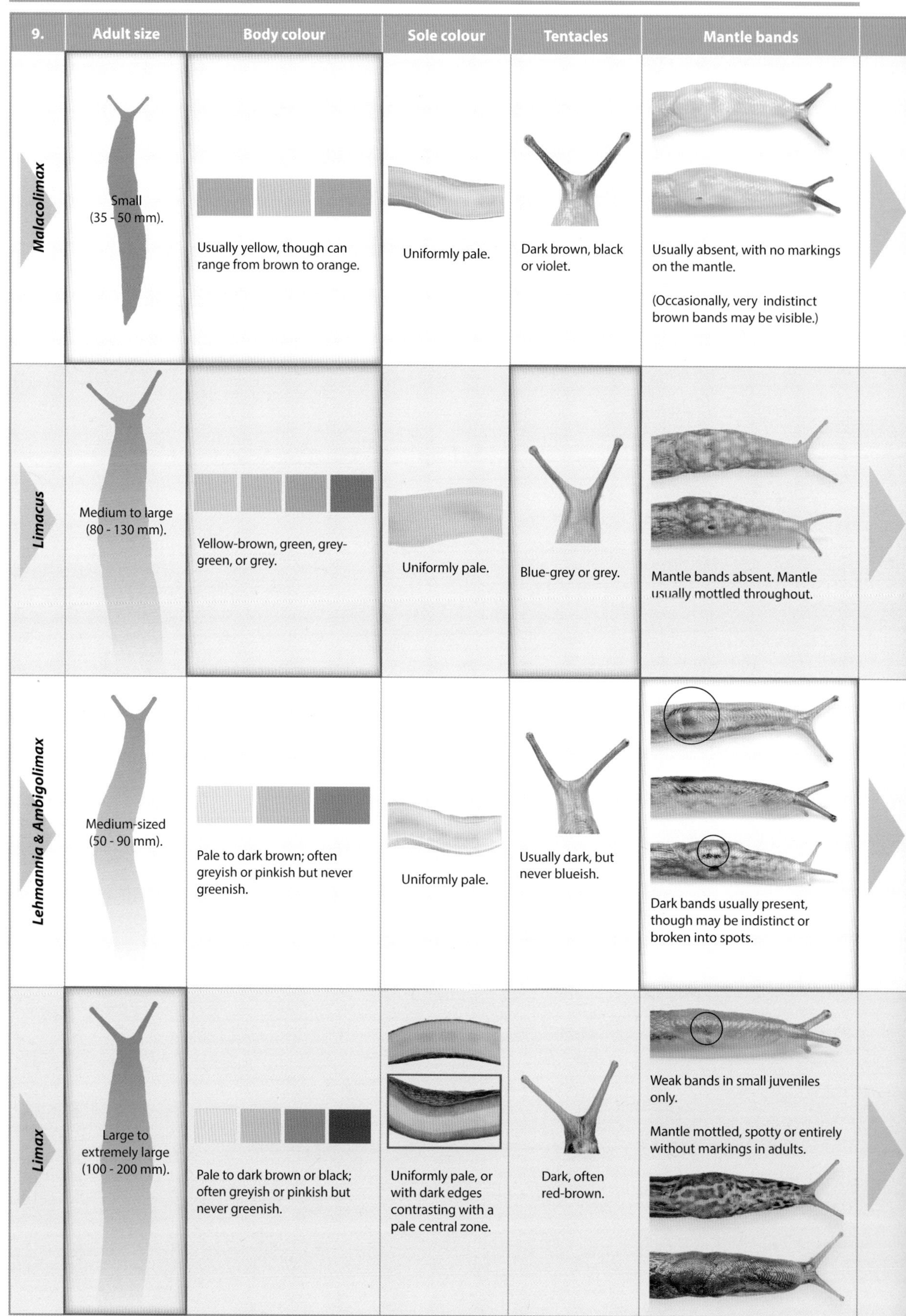

9.	Adult size	Body colour	Sole colour	Tentacles	Mantle bands
Malacolimax	Small (35 - 50 mm).	Usually yellow, though can range from brown to orange.	Uniformly pale.	Dark brown, black or violet.	Usually absent, with no markings on the mantle. (Occasionally, very indistinct brown bands may be visible.)
Limacus	Medium to large (80 - 130 mm).	Yellow-brown, green, grey-green, or grey.	Uniformly pale.	Blue-grey or grey.	Mantle bands absent. Mantle usually mottled throughout.
Lehmannia & Ambigolimax	Medium-sized (50 - 90 mm).	Pale to dark brown; often greyish or pinkish but never greenish.	Uniformly pale.	Usually dark, but never blueish.	Dark bands usually present, though may be indistinct or broken into spots.
Limax	Large to extremely large (100 - 200 mm).	Pale to dark brown or black; often greyish or pinkish but never greenish.	Uniformly pale, or with dark edges contrasting with a pale central zone.	Dark, often red-brown.	Weak bands in small juveniles only. Mantle mottled, spotty or entirely without markings in adults.

Other markings	Mucus & body texture	Other features	Genus / species
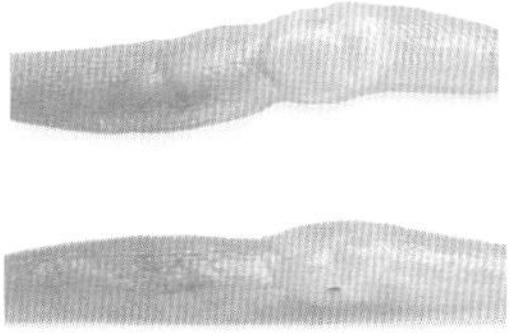 Body unmarked.	 Mucus lightly tinged yellow or orange. Body noticeably soft and flaccid.	Only in old woodlands, including those replanted with conifers, or (rarely) in ancient wood-pasture. Not yet known from Ireland.	***Malacolimax tenellus*** 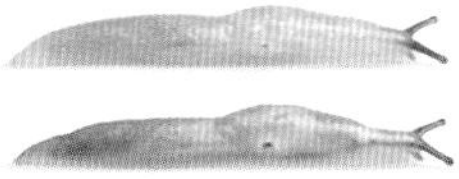 p. 72.
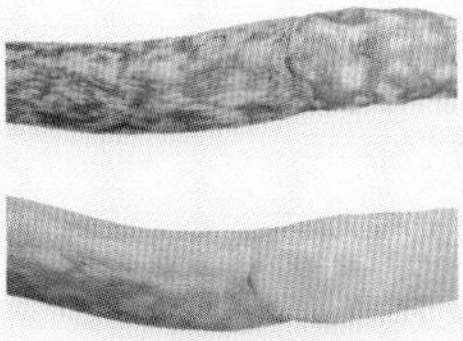 Mantle and tail heavily blotched and spotted with green, grey-green or darker grey.	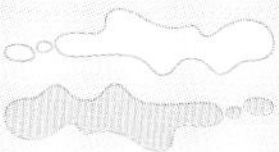 Mucus colourless, or (mainly near head) tinged yellow or orange. Body firm and muscular.	Occurs in most habitats; sometimes found indoors.	***Limacus***  Go to Chart 10, p. 24.
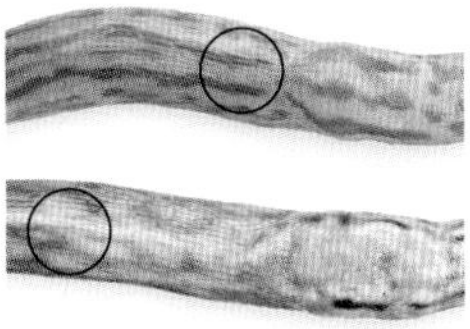 Often heavily blotched, banded or spotted with dark brown, grey or black.	Mucus colourless and watery (even enough to make the slug slip around in the hand). Body noticeably soft and flaccid.	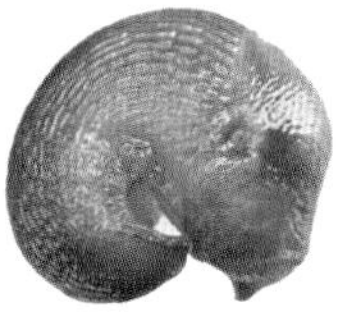 May curl into a near ball-shape, tail folded towards head, when handled. Occurs in most habitats.	***Lehmannia* & *Ambigolimax*** 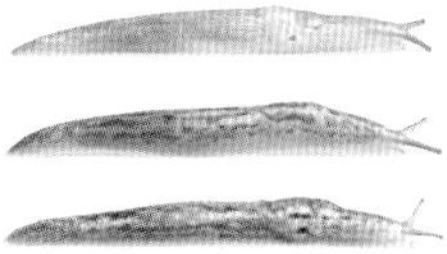 Go to Chart 11, p. 25.
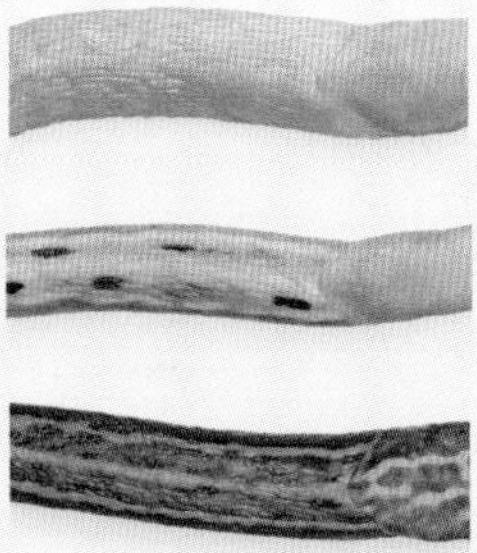 Body unmarked to strongly marked with dark or black spots, blotches and stripes.	 Mucus colourless or very light yellow, and sticky rather than watery. Body firm and muscular.	Occurs in most habitats; sometimes found indoors.	***Limax*** 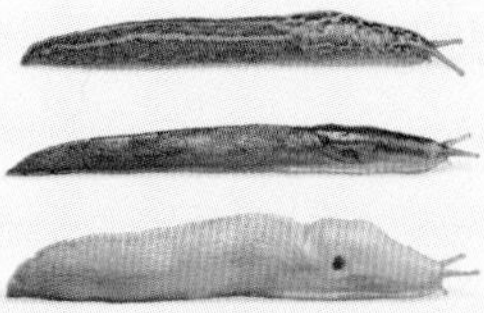 Go to Chart 12, p. 26.

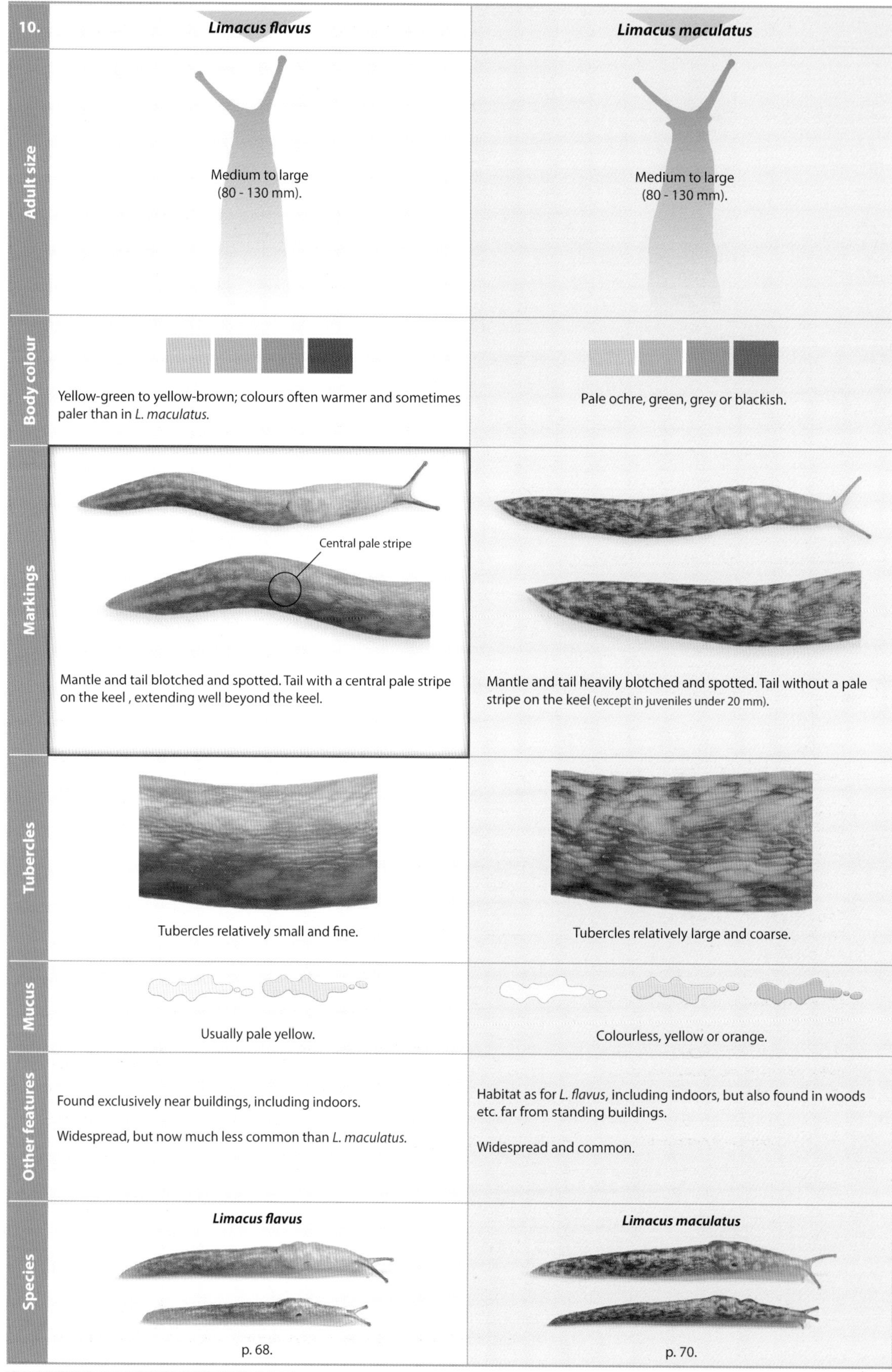

10.	***Limacus flavus***	***Limacus maculatus***
Adult size	Medium to large (80 - 130 mm).	Medium to large (80 - 130 mm).
Body colour	Yellow-green to yellow-brown; colours often warmer and sometimes paler than in *L. maculatus*.	Pale ochre, green, grey or blackish.
Markings	Central pale stripe Mantle and tail blotched and spotted. Tail with a central pale stripe on the keel , extending well beyond the keel.	Mantle and tail heavily blotched and spotted. Tail without a pale stripe on the keel (except in juveniles under 20 mm).
Tubercles	Tubercles relatively small and fine.	Tubercles relatively large and coarse.
Mucus	Usually pale yellow.	Colourless, yellow or orange.
Other features	Found exclusively near buildings, including indoors. Widespread, but now much less common than *L. maculatus*.	Habitat as for *L. flavus*, including indoors, but also found in woods etc. far from standing buildings. Widespread and common.
Species	***Limacus flavus*** p. 68.	***Limacus maculatus*** p. 70.

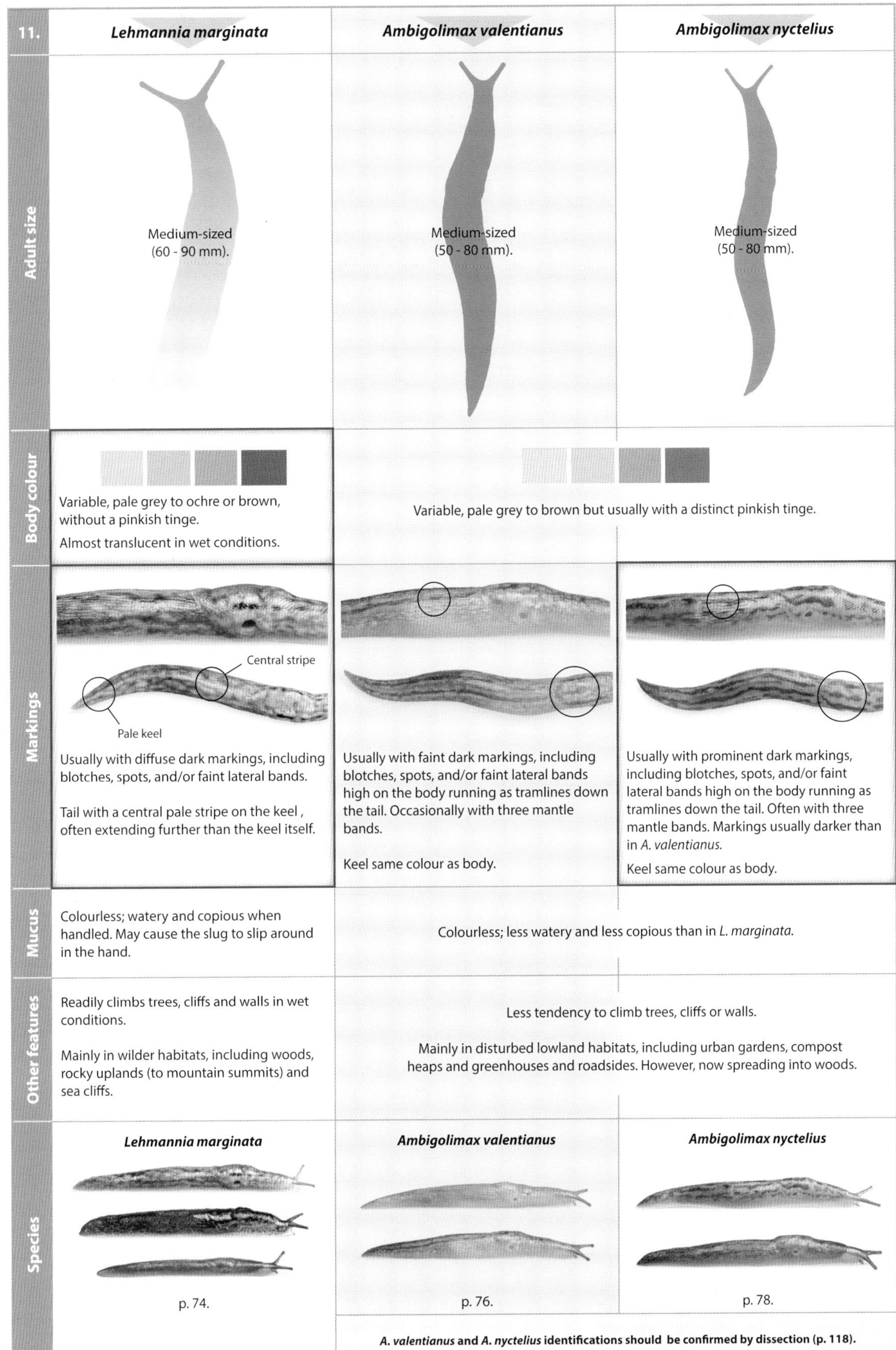

11.	***Lehmannia marginata***	***Ambigolimax valentianus***	***Ambigolimax nyctelius***
Adult size	Medium-sized (60 - 90 mm).	Medium-sized (50 - 80 mm).	Medium-sized (50 - 80 mm).
Body colour	Variable, pale grey to ochre or brown, without a pinkish tinge. Almost translucent in wet conditions.	Variable, pale grey to brown but usually with a distinct pinkish tinge.	
Markings	Central stripe Pale keel Usually with diffuse dark markings, including blotches, spots, and/or faint lateral bands. Tail with a central pale stripe on the keel , often extending further than the keel itself.	Usually with faint dark markings, including blotches, spots, and/or faint lateral bands high on the body running as tramlines down the tail. Occasionally with three mantle bands. Keel same colour as body.	Usually with prominent dark markings, including blotches, spots, and/or faint lateral bands high on the body running as tramlines down the tail. Often with three mantle bands. Markings usually darker than in *A. valentianus*. Keel same colour as body.
Mucus	Colourless; watery and copious when handled. May cause the slug to slip around in the hand.	Colourless; less watery and less copious than in *L. marginata*.	
Other features	Readily climbs trees, cliffs and walls in wet conditions. Mainly in wilder habitats, including woods, rocky uplands (to mountain summits) and sea cliffs.	Less tendency to climb trees, cliffs or walls. Mainly in disturbed lowland habitats, including urban gardens, compost heaps and greenhouses and roadsides. However, now spreading into woods.	
Species	***Lehmannia marginata*** p. 74.	***Ambigolimax valentianus*** p. 76.	***Ambigolimax nyctelius*** p. 78.
		A. valentianus **and** ***A. nyctelius*** **identifications should be confirmed by dissection (p. 118).**	

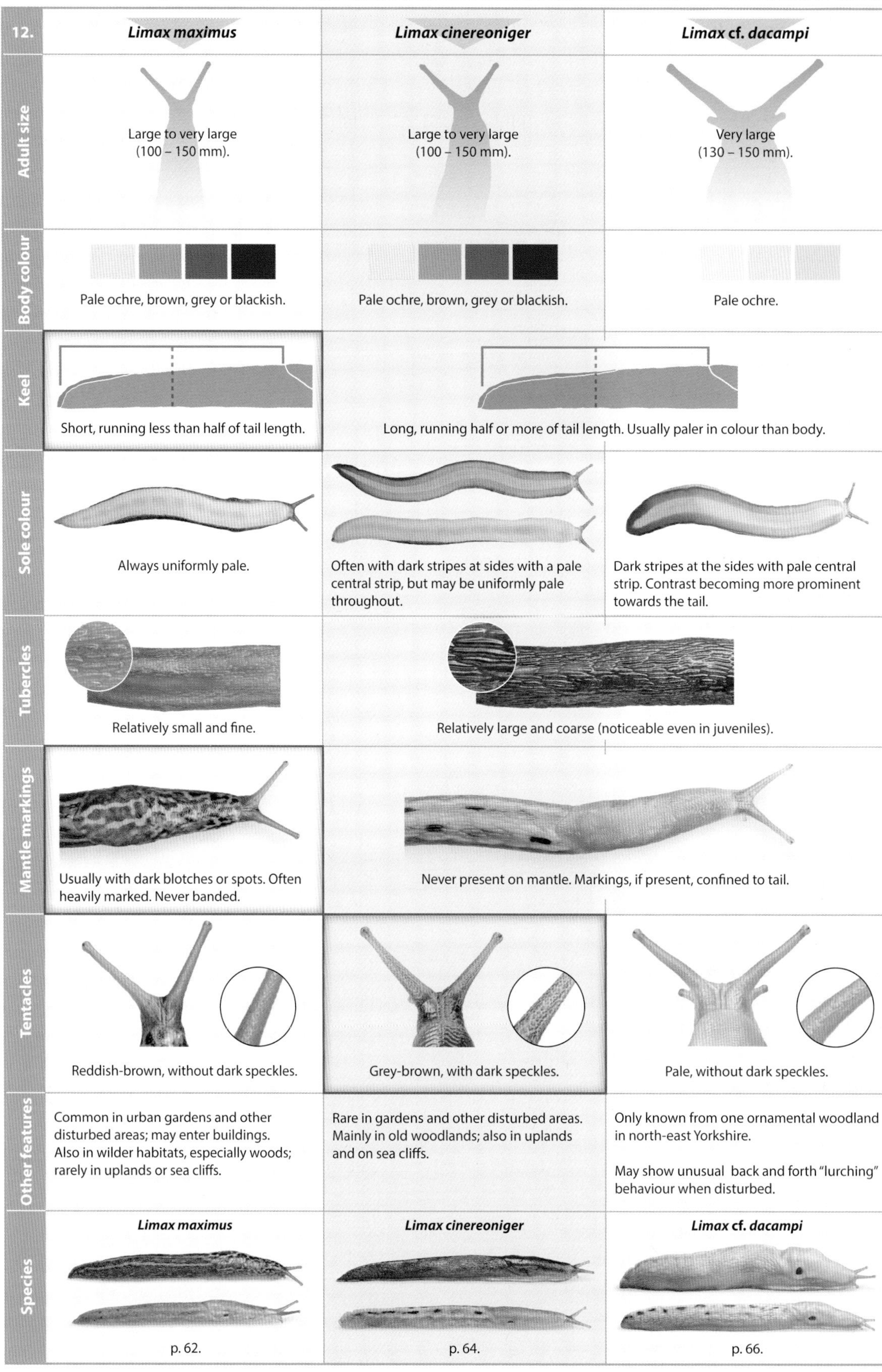

12.	***Limax maximus***	***Limax cinereoniger***	***Limax* cf. *dacampi***
Adult size	Large to very large (100 – 150 mm).	Large to very large (100 – 150 mm).	Very large (130 – 150 mm).
Body colour	Pale ochre, brown, grey or blackish.	Pale ochre, brown, grey or blackish.	Pale ochre.
Keel	Short, running less than half of tail length.	Long, running half or more of tail length. Usually paler in colour than body.	
Sole colour	Always uniformly pale.	Often with dark stripes at sides with a pale central strip, but may be uniformly pale throughout.	Dark stripes at the sides with pale central strip. Contrast becoming more prominent towards the tail.
Tubercles	Relatively small and fine.	Relatively large and coarse (noticeable even in juveniles).	
Mantle markings	Usually with dark blotches or spots. Often heavily marked. Never banded.	Never present on mantle. Markings, if present, confined to tail.	
Tentacles	Reddish-brown, without dark speckles.	Grey-brown, with dark speckles.	Pale, without dark speckles.
Other features	Common in urban gardens and other disturbed areas; may enter buildings. Also in wilder habitats, especially woods; rarely in uplands or sea cliffs.	Rare in gardens and other disturbed areas. Mainly in old woodlands; also in uplands and on sea cliffs.	Only known from one ornamental woodland in north-east Yorkshire. May show unusual back and forth "lurching" behaviour when disturbed.
Species	***Limax maximus*** p. 62.	***Limax cinereoniger*** p. 64.	***Limax* cf. *dacampi*** p. 66.

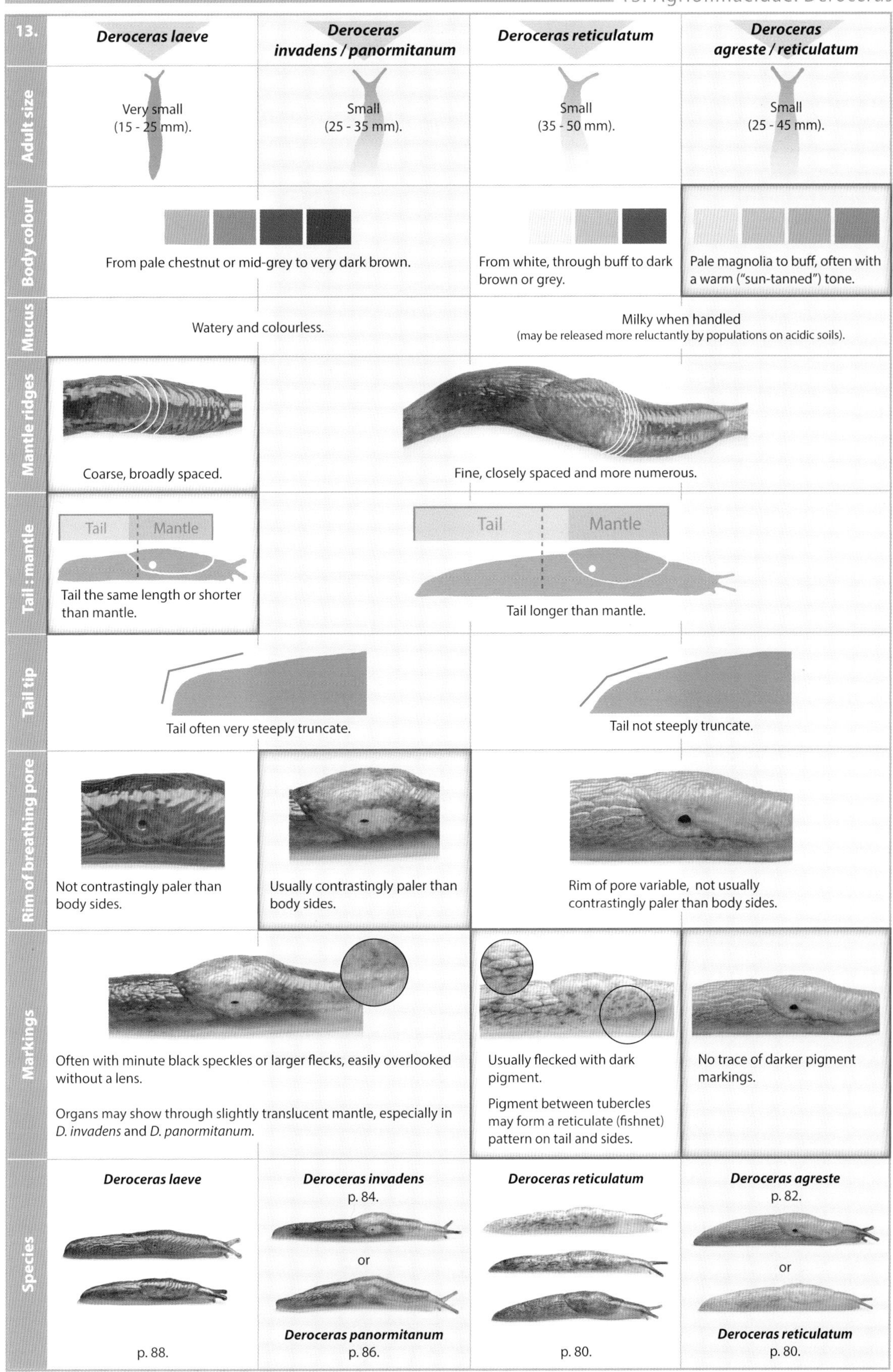

13.	***Deroceras laeve***	***Deroceras invadens / panormitanum***	***Deroceras reticulatum***	***Deroceras agreste / reticulatum***
Adult size	Very small (15 - 25 mm).	Small (25 - 35 mm).	Small (35 - 50 mm).	Small (25 - 45 mm).
Body colour	From pale chestnut or mid-grey to very dark brown.		From white, through buff to dark brown or grey.	Pale magnolia to buff, often with a warm ("sun-tanned") tone.
Mucus	Watery and colourless.		Milky when handled (may be released more reluctantly by populations on acidic soils).	
Mantle ridges	Coarse, broadly spaced.	Fine, closely spaced and more numerous.		
Tail : mantle	Tail / Mantle Tail the same length or shorter than mantle.	Tail / Mantle Tail longer than mantle.		
Tail tip	Tail often very steeply truncate.		Tail not steeply truncate.	
Rim of breathing pore	Not contrastingly paler than body sides.	Usually contrastingly paler than body sides.	Rim of pore variable, not usually contrastingly paler than body sides.	
Markings	Often with minute black speckles or larger flecks, easily overlooked without a lens. Organs may show through slightly translucent mantle, especially in *D. invadens* and *D. panormitanum*.		Usually flecked with dark pigment. Pigment between tubercles may form a reticulate (fishnet) pattern on tail and sides.	No trace of darker pigment markings.
Species	***Deroceras laeve*** p. 88.	***Deroceras invadens*** p. 84. or ***Deroceras panormitanum*** p. 86.	***Deroceras reticulatum*** p. 80.	***Deroceras agreste*** p. 82. or ***Deroceras reticulatum*** p. 80.

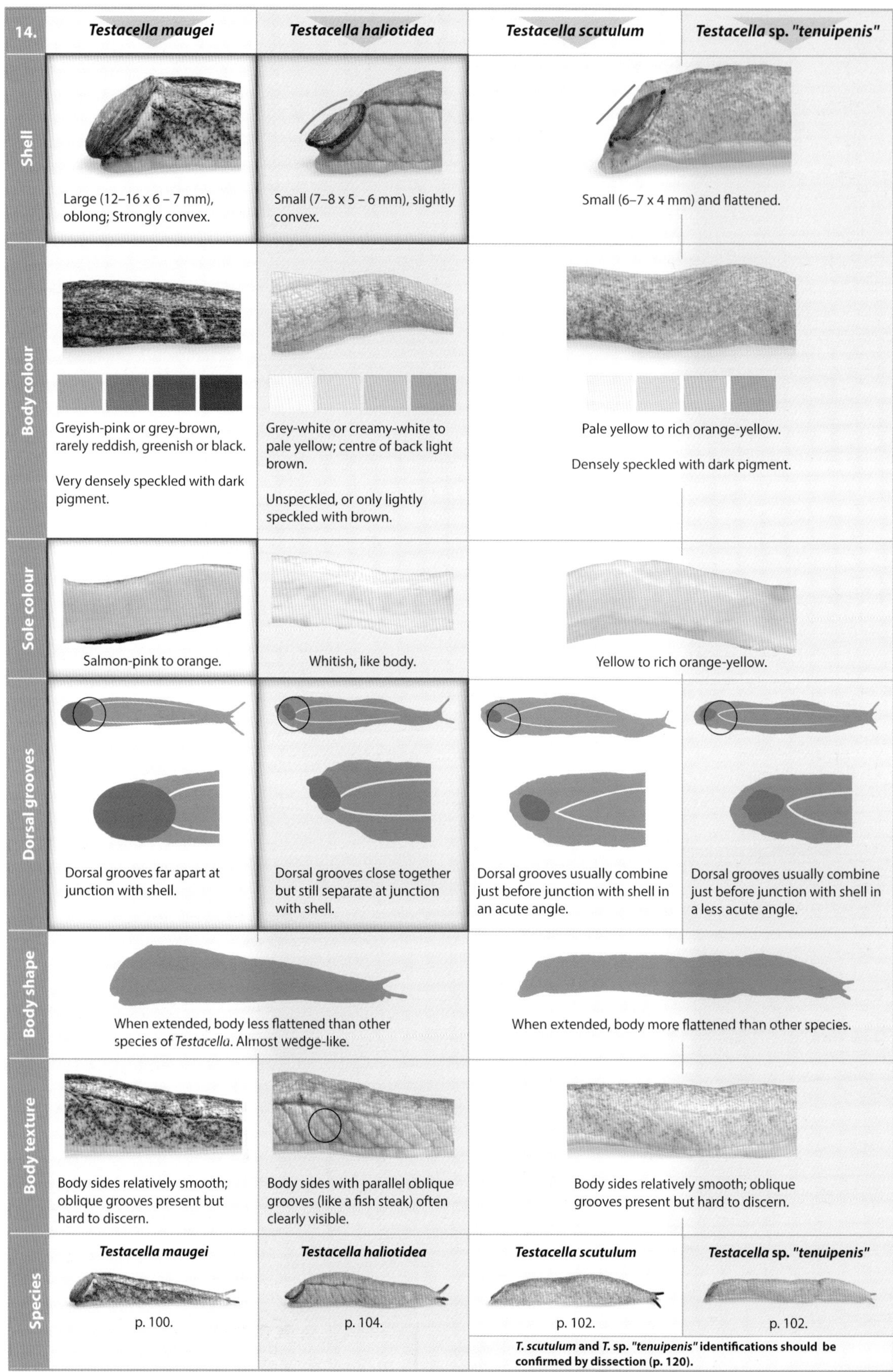

14.	*Testacella maugei*	*Testacella haliotidea*	*Testacella scutulum*	*Testacella* sp. "*tenuipenis*"
Shell	Large (12–16 x 6 – 7 mm), oblong; Strongly convex.	Small (7–8 x 5 – 6 mm), slightly convex.	Small (6–7 x 4 mm) and flattened.	
Body colour	Greyish-pink or grey-brown, rarely reddish, greenish or black. Very densely speckled with dark pigment.	Grey-white or creamy-white to pale yellow; centre of back light brown. Unspeckled, or only lightly speckled with brown.	Pale yellow to rich orange-yellow. Densely speckled with dark pigment.	
Sole colour	Salmon-pink to orange.	Whitish, like body.	Yellow to rich orange-yellow.	
Dorsal grooves	Dorsal grooves far apart at junction with shell.	Dorsal grooves close together but still separate at junction with shell.	Dorsal grooves usually combine just before junction with shell in an acute angle.	Dorsal grooves usually combine just before junction with shell in a less acute angle.
Body shape	When extended, body less flattened than other species of *Testacella*. Almost wedge-like.		When extended, body more flattened than other species.	
Body texture	Body sides relatively smooth; oblique grooves present but hard to discern.	Body sides with parallel oblique grooves (like a fish steak) often clearly visible.	Body sides relatively smooth; oblique grooves present but hard to discern.	
Species	*Testacella maugei* p. 100.	*Testacella haliotidea* p. 104.	*Testacella scutulum* p. 102.	*Testacella* sp. "*tenuipenis*" p. 102.

***T. scutulum* and *T.* sp. "*tenuipenis*" identifications should be confirmed by dissection (p. 120).**

15.	*Semilimax pyrenaicus*	*Vitrina pellucida*	*Phenacolimax major*
Adult size	Very small (up to 16 mm).	Very small (up to10 mm).	Very small (up to 16 mm).
Shell	Ear-like, flattened.	More snail-like than *S. pyrenaicus.* (for further details see AIDGAP snails key (Cameron,2008))	
Mantle	Mantle Mantle lobe Mantle pale grey to brown and mottled. Mantle lobe covers apex of shell.	Mantle Mantle lobe Mantle nearly always pale and often pale grey, never black or mottled. Mantle lobe barely extends on to shell.	Mantle Mantle lobe Mantle usually dark and mottled. Mantle lobe extends well onto shell, nearly reaching apex.
Other features	Widespread but local in Ireland (not in Britain).	Common and widespread throughout Britain and Ireland. Adults living mainly in winter.	Rare; generally ancient woodlands in southern Britain (not in Ireland). Adults living mainly in summer.
Species	*Semilimax pyrenaicus* p. 108.	*Vitrina pellucida* p. 108.	*Phenacolimax major* p. 108.

Arion (Arion) ater (Linnaeus, 1758)

Large Black Slug (Great Black Slug, Black Slug, Black Arion, Black Snail)

Identification. Up to 60-140 mm extended. A medium-sized to very large, heavily-built slug with coarse tubercles. The mucus is thick, sticky and usually colourless. It can contract to a near-hemisphere and readily squirms from side to side when disturbed. Colour is very variable, even within populations, and can range from yellow to black. The jet-black form of uplands, wetlands and northern Scotland is characteristic but black examples of other *A.* (*Arion*) species can also occur. Albinos are occasionally encountered in the north and pale specimens elsewhere. The foot fringe is lineolated (striped) and does not strongly contrast in colour with the body sides, usually being darker or duller. The sole is as dark as the body sides or paler, never darker. Faint, dark lateral bands are occasionally present in juveniles, never in adults. Juveniles are often much paler than adults (pale yellow juveniles often become jet black adults).

Similar species. Generations of naturalists have struggled to consistently distinguish *A.* (*A.*) *ater* from *A.* (*A.*) *rufus*. This guide treats them as two occasionally hybridising species in which most, but not all, individuals can be assigned to one or the other, especially by dissection. Those that cannot may include hybrids. For the distinction of other *A.* (*Arion*) species from *A.* (*A.*) *ater*, see those species accounts.

Arion (*A.*) *ater* is generally duller, or darker, in colour than *A.* (*A.*) *rufus*, although the colour ranges overlap. In particular, the foot fringe of *A.* (*A.*) *ater* is dark or dull, not bright orange as in *A.* (*A.*) *rufus*.

The squirming response (also called "rocking", or "rolling"; Quick, 1960) is shown only by *A.* (*A.*) *ater* and *A.* (*A.*) *rufus* when they are half-grown to adult. To test consistently for the squirming response, push the back of a contracted slug firmly from head to tail with a finger. In *A.* (*A.*) *ater* it is generally shown more readily than in *A.* (*A.*) *rufus,* is more intense, and continues for longer (tens of minutes in some cases) (Davies, 1987).

Arion (*A.*) *ater* is less likely to be seen copulating (June-October; Adams, 1910; Quick, 1947) than other *A.* (*Arion*) species and may mainly self-fertilise (Burnet, 1972; Foltz *et al.*, 1982).

Juveniles of *A.* (*A.*) *ater* usually lack lateral bands, or the bands are faint. Hatchlings and younger animals are invariably a uniform pale yellow. Very young *A. rufus* are similar but medium-sized juveniles of *A.* (*A.*) *rufus* have stronger bands, rather similar to those of *A.* (*A.*) *vulgaris*.
Colour forms with a dark back and strikingly paler sides (some are figured here for each species) were once given names like *albolateralis*, *bicolor*, and *salmolateralis* (Taylor, 1902-7; Roebuck, 1919). Noble & Jones (1996) said that *bicolor* was the only colour form seen exclusivly in *A.* (*A.*) *ater* x *A.* (*A.*) *rufus* hybrids, while *albolateralis* could occur in hybrids and pure *A.* (*A.*) *ater*. Cain & Williamson (1958) suggested *salmolateralis* was also of hybrid origin.

Dissection of mature individuals can help distinguish *A.* (*A.*) *ater* and *A.* (*A.*) *rufus* where doubt exists and can rule out other species (p. 114).

Pest status. See *A.* (*A.*) *rufus*.

Range. Very widespread throughout Britain and Ireland. The map's patchiness probably reflects different recorders' willingness to discriminate *A.* (*A.*) *ater* and *A.* (*A.*) *rufus*. The map for undifferentiated records would have dots in virtually every 10km square (Kerney, 1999).

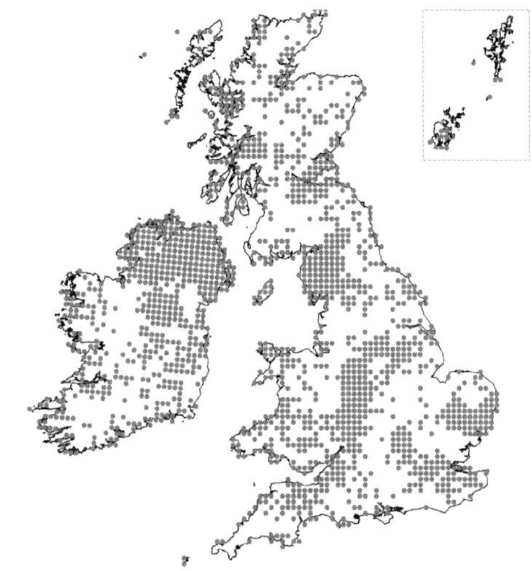

A native species present throughout northern and western Europe. Populations genetically like the British and Irish *A.* (*A.*) *ater* are known from Norway to Spain (Rowson *et al.*, 2014).

Habitat. Almost all habitats, including woods, peatlands and fen margins (e.g. in Wicken Fen, Cambs. and the Broads). Characteristic of acid upland grassland and bogs, but also common in lowlands including gardens, at least in the west. Compare with *A.* (*A.*) *rufus*.

Biology. See *A.* (*A.*) *rufus*. Scharff (1891) suggested that in cool, frost-free parts of western Ireland, populations of *A.* (*A.*) *ater* took two years to reach maturity. Details of copulation are lacking in this species because it has been observed so rarely (in Britain and Ireland).

Actual size

I32

Foot fringe striped, usually a darker or duller colour than body sides.

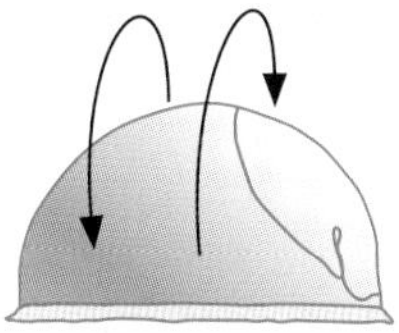

Adults usually squirm from side to side when contracted and disturbed.

Dark fringe lines often reach far into centre of sole.

K3

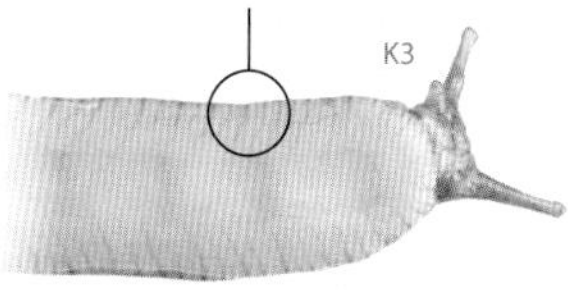

Sole as dark or paler than body sides, never darker.

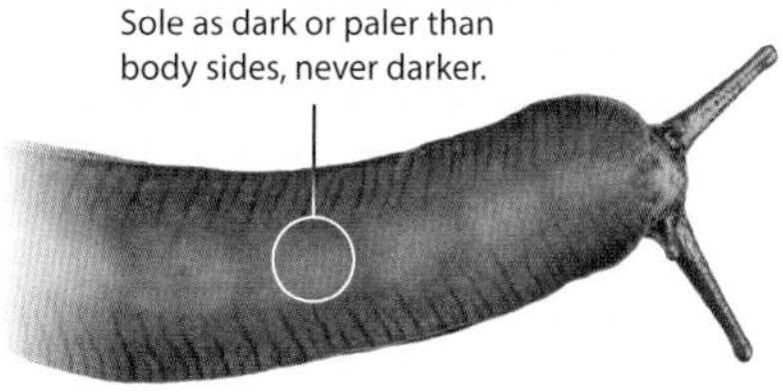

Juveniles and subadults

12misc2

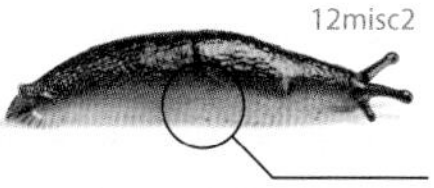

Body sides often paler than back.

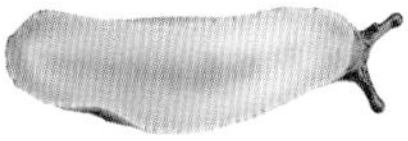

DF6

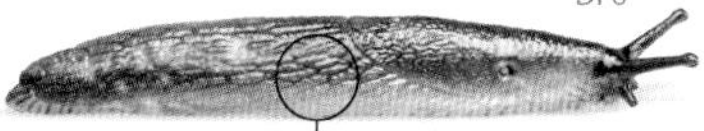

Juveniles not, or weakly, banded.

Y37

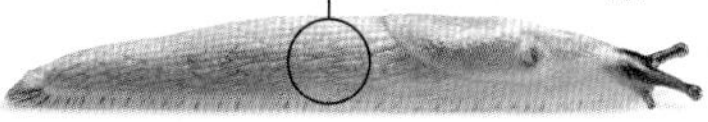

L1

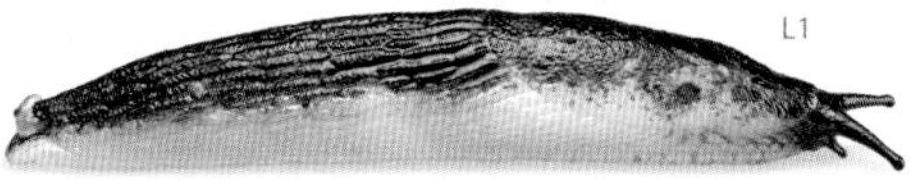

albolateralis form

Variation

SN1

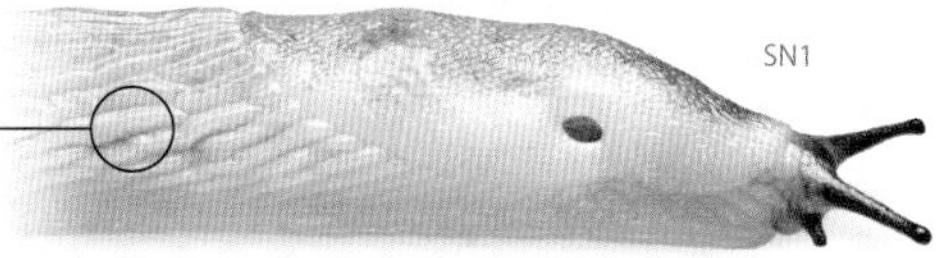

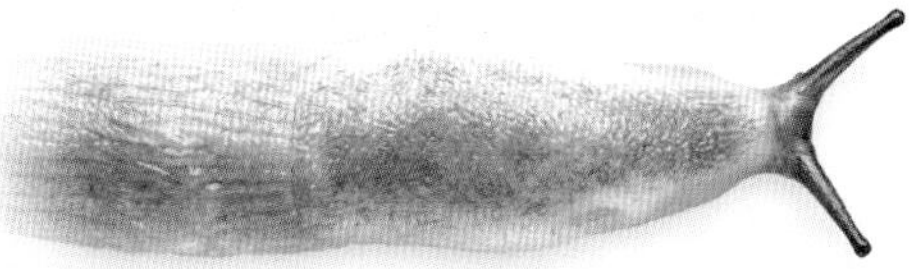

I13

K3

Additional features

Mucus

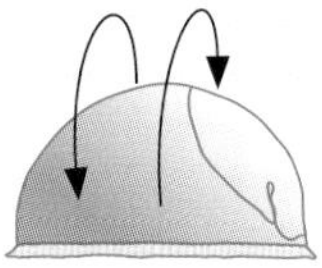

Contracted shape

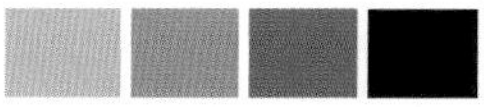

Body colour

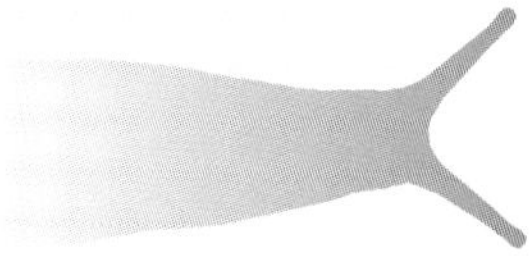

Adult size

Arion (*Arion*) *rufus* (Linnaeus, 1758)

Large Red Slug (Great Red Slug, Red Slug, Chocolate Arion)

Identification. Up to 60-140 mm extended. A medium-sized to very large, heavily-built slug with coarse tubercles. The mucus is thick, sticky and colourless, or with an orange tinge. It can contract to a near-hemisphere and occasionally squirms from side to side when disturbed. Colour is very variable, even within populations, and can range from yellow to (rarely) black. The warmer coloured, yellow-grey or pale orange forms of southern lowlands are characteristic, but pale examples of other *A.* (*Arion*) species can also occur. Forms with the body sides paler than the back occur in this species, but also in others. The foot fringe is lineolated (striped) and characteristically often brighter in colour than the body sides. Bright orange or orange-red fringes are common. The sole is often paler than the body sides or with an orange flush. It may be as dark as the body sides but never darker. Lineolations can extend in some forms from the foot fringe right across the sole but are obvious only when the sole is pale. This has been suggested as a species characteristic but such extended lineolations ocuur occasionally also in *A. ater*. Dark lateral bands are often present in juveniles, and sometimes subadults, but never in adults.

Similar species. See comments under *A.* (*A.*) *ater*. The two species are notoriously difficult, sometimes impossible, to distinguish as adults. For the distinction of other *A.* (*Arion*) species, see those species accounts.

Pest status. *Arion* (*A.*) *rufus* and *A.* (*A.*) *ater* are often considered relatively unimportant as pests (e.g. Godan, 1983; South, 1992). Being large and conspicuous by day (their thick mucus limits desiccation) they are readily blamed for damage caused at night by other slug species. They are omnivores (Taylor, 1902-7; Quick, 1960; South, 1992) and can be useful composters of dead plant matter, food waste and pet faeces. However, they also attack tender parts of plants and seedlings, especially – inevitably – in spring. In horticulture they are thus a potential pest for part of the year and a potential asset at others.

Range. Widespread in southern Britain and Ireland, including offshore islands in the west of Ireland. In Britain mainly in the southern lowlands and more local elsewhere, although present in the Outer Hebrides and the Lake District, etc. Likely to be underrecorded as records are often lumped with *A.* (*A.*) *ater*. Probably a native species, although Quick (1960) considered it introduced. Populations genetically like the British and Irish *A.* (*A.*) *rufus* are known in Brittany, France (Barr *et al.*, 2009; Rowson *et al.*, 2014). Linnaeus' name "*rufus*" applies to this form (Quick, 1947; Altena, 1963).

Arion (*A.*) *rufus* is believed native across western and central Europe (e.g. Quick, 1960; Welter-Schultes, 2012), although this may include additional species that do not occur or have only recently arrived in Britain or Ireland (e.g. Chevallier, 1981; Noble & Jones, 1996; Quinteiro *et al.*, 2005; Rowson *et al.*, 2014). The name *empiricorum* Férussac, 1819 has sometimes been used for these (e.g. Simroth, 1885). At least one form of *A.* (*A.*) *rufus* or *A.* (*A.*) *ater* is established in North America (Chichester & Getz, 1973; Barr *et al.*, 2009; Grimm *et al.*, 2010). According to Noble & Jones (1996), *ater* x *rufus* hybrids have also been introduced to other continents.

Habitat. Almost all lowland habitats including gardens, allotments, woods, etc., but also in uplands (e.g. Grass Wood, Yorks.). Compare with *A.* (*A.*) *ater*. Either (or both) species can occur in coastal grassland, dunes or even lowland mires.

Biology. Like *A.* (*A.*) *ater*, an annual species in which juveniles often overwinter. Mating and egg-laying occurs between August and October, eggs hatching in the autumn or the following spring (Taylor, 1902-7; Quick, 1947; Davies, 1987).

Arion (*A.*) *rufus* and *A.* (*A.*) *ater* appear to hybridise occasionally (e.g. Cain & Williamson, 1958; Burnet, 1972; Foltz *et al.*, 1982; Rowson *et al.*, 2014). Some authors argue that *A.* (*A.*) *ater* and *A.* (*A.*) *rufus* should be considered subspecies of a single species, known as *A.* (*A.*) *ater* (e.g. Quick, 1960; Burnet, 1972; Evans, 1986). An east-west hybrid zone, of which Britain and Ireland form part, may separate the European ranges of the two (Noble & Jones, 1996). *Arion* (*A.*) *rufus* also seems able to hybridise with *A.* (*A.*) *vulgaris* (see species account) and perhaps other *A.* (*Arion*) species.

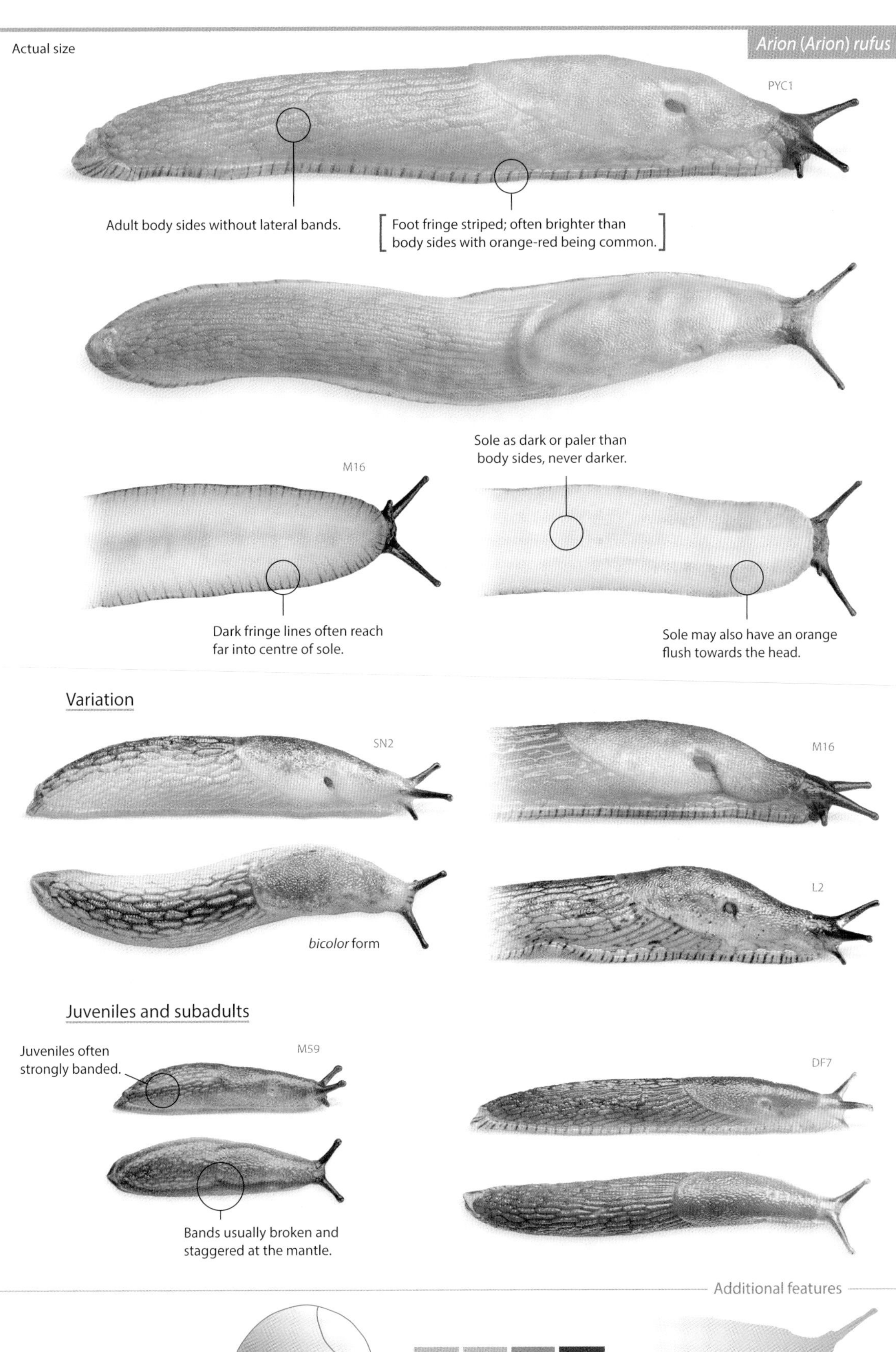
Actual size
PYC1
Adult body sides without lateral bands.
Foot fringe striped; often brighter than body sides with orange-red being common.
M16
Sole as dark or paler than body sides, never darker.
Dark fringe lines often reach far into centre of sole.
Sole may also have an orange flush towards the head.
Variation
SN2
M16
L2
bicolor form
Juveniles and subadults
Juveniles often strongly banded.
M59
DF7
Bands usually broken and staggered at the mantle.
Additional features
Mucus
Contracted shape
Body colour
Adult size

Arion (Arion) flagellus Collinge, 1893

Green-soled Slug (Spanish Stealth Slug, Durham Slug)

Identification. Up to 60-100 mm extended. A medium-sized to large, heavily-built slug with characteristically coarse tubercles (the coarsest of any British or Irish species). The crests of the tubercles often appear to have been "highlighted" yellow or light brown, especially in juveniles. The mucus is thick, sticky and usually colourless. It can contract to a near-hemisphere but never squirms from side to side when disturbed. When contracted it is sometimes more flattened than other large arionids (*A.* (*Arion*) species), especially when young.

The ground colour is very variable, even within populations, and can range from yellow to black. Characteristically, however, the sole is always as pale or paler than the body size and shows a greenish or olive-green tint. This colour is very rarely seen in other *A.* (*Arion*) species. The foot fringe is lineolated (striped) and usually does not contrast strongly in colour with the body sides. The lineolations never reach far into the centre of the sole.

Dark lateral bands are often present, especially in juveniles. The area between the bands is often more warmly or brightly coloured, again most conspicuously in juveniles.

Similar species. *Arion* (*A.*) *flagellus* is arguably the most distinctive of the *A.* (*Arion*) group. The green tint, tendency to remain banded as an adult, and coarse tubercles are characteristic. On the back just behind the mantle, there are usually fewer than 9-10 tubercles between the lateral bands of an adult *Arion* (*A.*) *flagellus*. In slugs of other *Arion* (*Arion*) species at a similar size, there are usually 10 or more tubercles in the same region. *A.* (*A.*) *flagellus* usually reaches a smaller size than the other species.

The strongly banded juveniles are superficially similar to those of *A.* (*A.*) *vulgaris* and some *A.* (*A.*) *rufus*. In *A.* (*A.*) *flagellus* the lateral bands usually run continuously across the rear edge of the mantle onto the tail, whereas in *A.* (*A.*) *vulgaris* they are usually staggered or interrupted. The body sides below the bands are often dark in juvenile *A.* (*A.*) *vulgaris*, but are usually less so in juvenile *A.* (*A.*) *flagellus*.

Dissection is only occasionally necessary to identify this species (p. 114).

Pest status. Not well understood. *A.* (*A.*) *flagellus* can reach high densities in allotments and gardens. It has been observed feeding on garden flowers and their seedheads, but any preference for live (rather than dead) plants and its importance relative to other abundant slugs in the same localities is unclear.

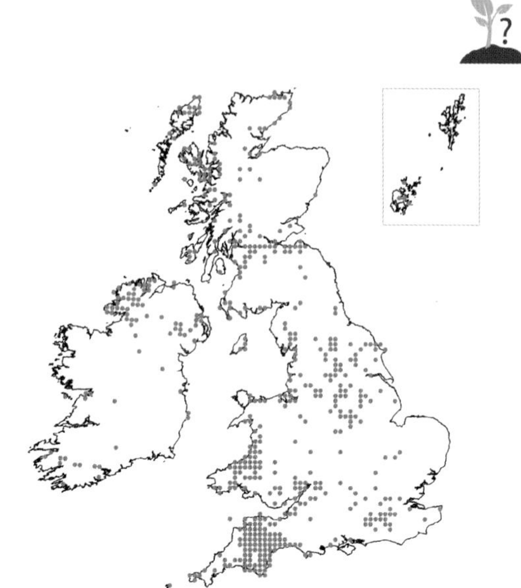

Range. Widespread in much of Ireland and western Britain, generally more local in the east.

Arion (*A.*) *flagellus* remains poorly recorded but is probably spreading. Originally described from Co. Cork, it went unrecorded for many years and was dismissed by Taylor (1902-7) as a variety of *A.* (*M.*) *subfuscus*. It was recorded in Durham in 1952 by Quick (1952) (hence "Durham Slug"). It was then confused with *A.* (*A.*) *vulgaris*, then known as *A.* (*A.*) *lusitanicus*, by Quick (1960). The "Durham species" was, however, distinguished in Cameron *et al.*'s key (1983) and in some detail by Davies (1987). It was later recorded from northwest Iberia (Castillejo, 1992). This may be its original range (Quinteiro *et al.*, 2005) and it remains unrecorded elsewhere in Europe (Welter-Schultes, 2012). It is potentially an ancient introduction to Ireland that has only recently begun to spread (Noble & Jones, 1996; Rowson *et al.*, 2014). It may do so at the expense of other *A.* (*Arion*) species (Noble & Jones, 1996).

Habitat. Disturbed habitats with rich soils and sufficient shelter, including urban areas, but also well into other habitats including rocky moorland, woodlands, and clear-felled conifer plantations.

Biology. This species breeds by outcrossing, apparently with an annual cycle much like *A.* (*A.*) *vulgaris*. Like that species, it can lay larger clutches of smaller eggs than *A.* (*A.*) *ater* or *A.* (*A.*) *rufus*. Adults may continue laying some time into the winter (Davies, 1987).

This species is relatively distantly related to our other *A.* (*Arion*) species (Quinteiro *et al.*, 2005) and does not seem to hybridise with them (Rowson *et al.*, 2014), although an attempted mating with *A. rufus* has been observed (RA).

10mm

Faint bands may persist in adults.

I9

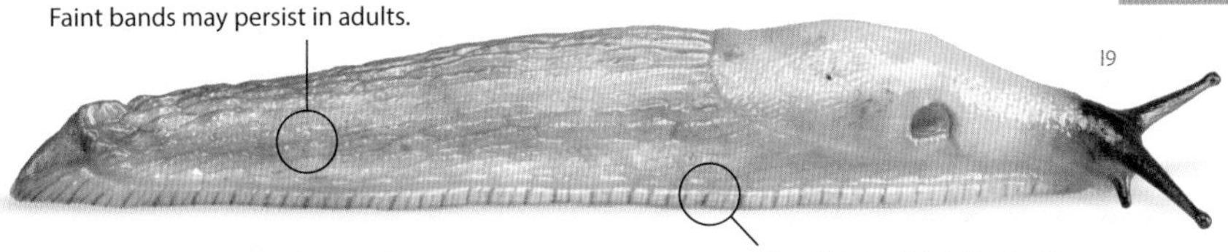

Foot fringe striped and not contrasting with body sides.

[Tubercles characteristically coarse relative to body size.]

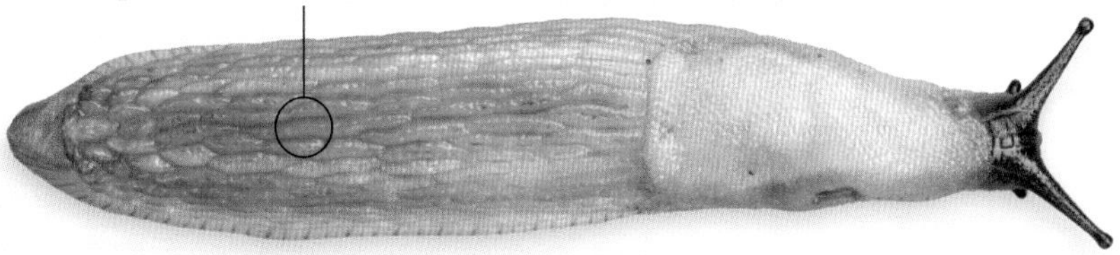

[Sole as pale or paler than body sides, often with a green tinge.]

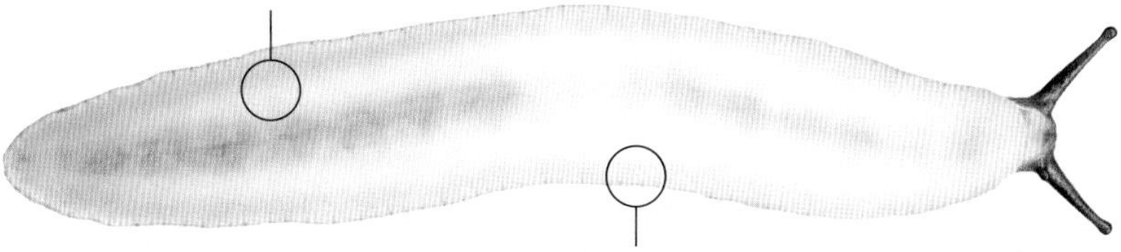

Fringe lines never reach far into centre of sole.

Juveniles and subadults

Bands run continously from mantle to tail tip.

S25

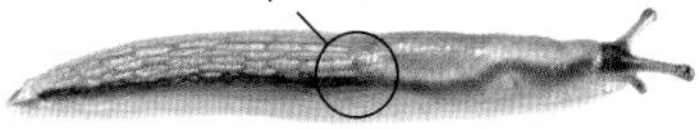

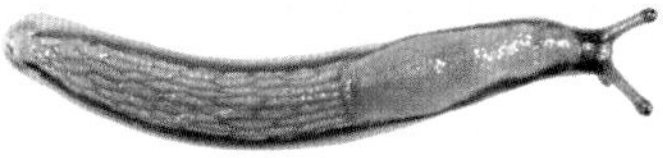

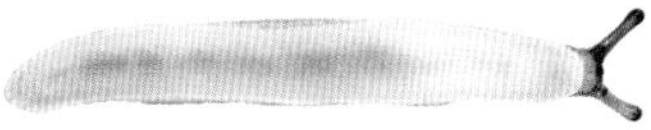

PYC2

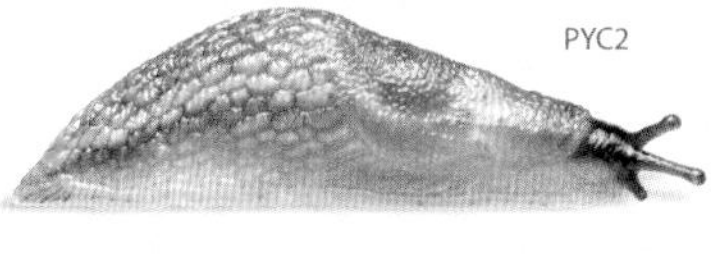

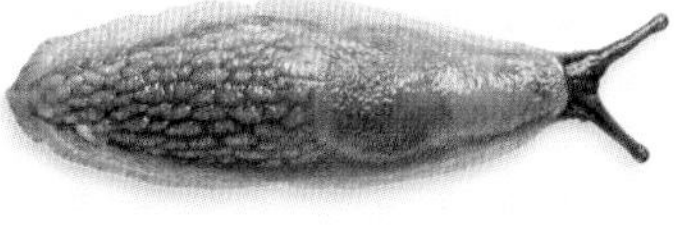

Variation

Tubercles may seem "highlighted" with yellow or light brown.

DN1

K5

PYC4

Additional features

Mucus

Contracted shape

Body colour

Adult size

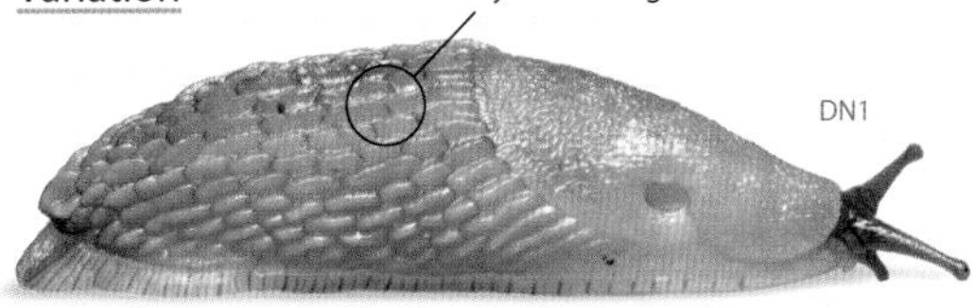

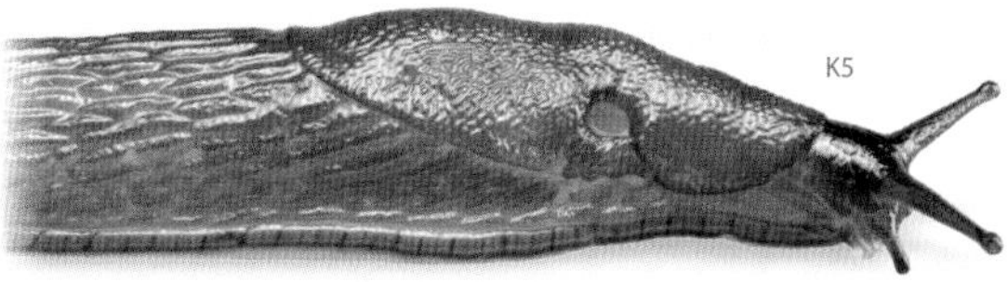

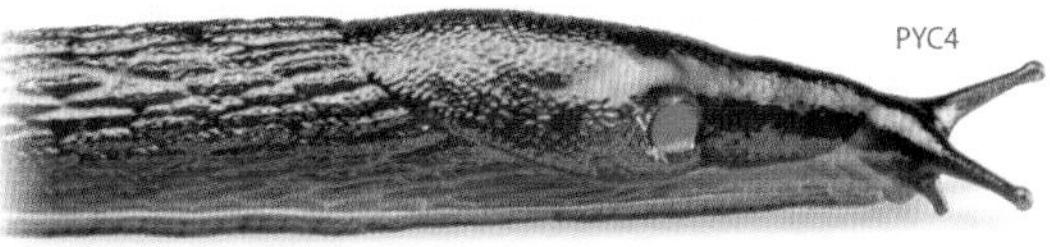

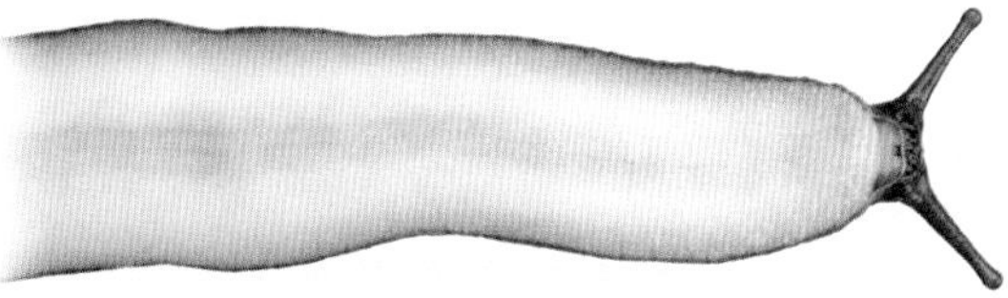

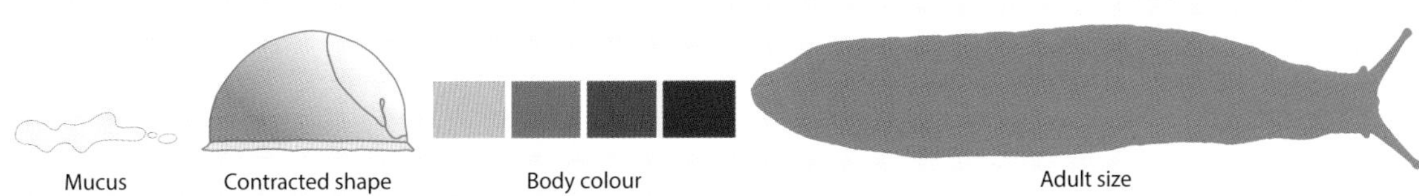

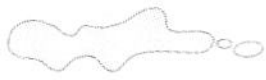

Arion (Arion) vulgaris Moquin-Tandon, 1855

Vulgar Slug (Spanish Slug, Iberian Slug, Lusitanian Slug, False Lusitanian Slug, Plague Slug)

Identification. Up to 60-140 mm extended. A medium-sized to very large, heavily-built slug with coarse tubercles. The mucus is thick, sticky and usually colourless. It can contract to a near-hemisphere but virtually never squirms from side to side when disturbed (there is a single recorded observation of this: Davies, 1987).

Colour is very variable, even within populations, and can range from yellow to black. However adults are commonly brick-red, dirty orange or brown with dark sooty-grey spaces between the tubercles. When present, this characteristic dark colour makes both the sole and the rim of the breathing pore dark grey or black. It also shows where exposed by bites from other slugs (such wounds are pale in *A. (A.) rufus*). The foot fringe is lineolated (striped) and usually does not strongly contrast in colour with the body sides.

Juveniles are usually strongly banded, with the body sides below the bands dark, and the area between them more warmly coloured or pale at the edges. Bands gradually fade and rarely persist in adults.

Similar species. *Arion (A.) vulgaris* is regularly confused with other *A. (Arion)* species. Their ranges of colour variation partially overlap and two or more species may occur at the same site. Individuals with a dark grey sole, darker than the body sides, that do not squirm when contracted and disturbed, are a reliable indicator that *A. (A.) vulgaris* is present. Individuals showing the squirming behaviour or with a strongly contrasting foot fringe are likely to be *A. (A.) ater* or *A. (A.) rufus* respectively. Unfortunately, this is not completely foolproof – at least one rare colour form of *A. (A.) rufus* has dark spaces between the tubercles and at the rim of the breathing pore (e.g. photo L2, p. 33). Individuals seen copulating are more likely to be *A. (A.) vulgaris* or *A. (A.) rufus* than *A. (A.) ater*.

Arion (A.) vulgaris and *A. (A.) flagellus* were almost universally confused with one another prior to Davies (1987) but are quite distinct. *Arion (A.) flagellus* usually has coarser tubercles and often has bands and/or a green tinge. This tinge is also present in the banded juveniles of *A. (A.) flagellus*, which may otherwise be superficially similar to those of *A. (A.) vulgaris*. Juveniles of *A. (A.) vulgaris* may be indistinguishable from banded juveniles of *A. (A.) rufus*.

Dissection is strongly recommended to confirm the occurrence of this important species (p. 114). Internally, it is clearly distinct from *A. (A.) rufus* and *A. (A.) ater*, even when young. Adults are also internally distinct from those of *A. (A.)* sp. "Davies" and *A. (A.) flagellus*.

Pest status. Godan (1983) considered this an emerging pest at that time. It is now a notorious pest in central and northern Europe, damaging plant shoots, roots and fruit near the soil surface. It also attacks stored produce. It has even been known to attack the leaves of broadleaved tree saplings and understorey plants in woodland (von Proschwitz, 1997). In arable fields damage may be limited to the margins where this large species can shelter (Frank, 1998). However it can reach densities above 50 slugs per square metre in some fruit and vegetable crops (Kozłowksi, 2007). Such conspicuous "plagues" have other effects including the contamination of fodder and compost, and causing heightened awareness and alarm that may result in increased efforts at control. On the continent, local populations of other *A. (Arion)* species often decline or vanish following the establishment of *A. (A.) vulgaris* (e.g. Welter-Schultes, 2012) although the reasons for this are uncertain. *Arion (A.) vulgaris* also seems able to establish in habitats in which no *A. (Arion)* species was already common.

Range. Scattered records throughout Britain and Ireland; more widespread in some areas, notably Devon.

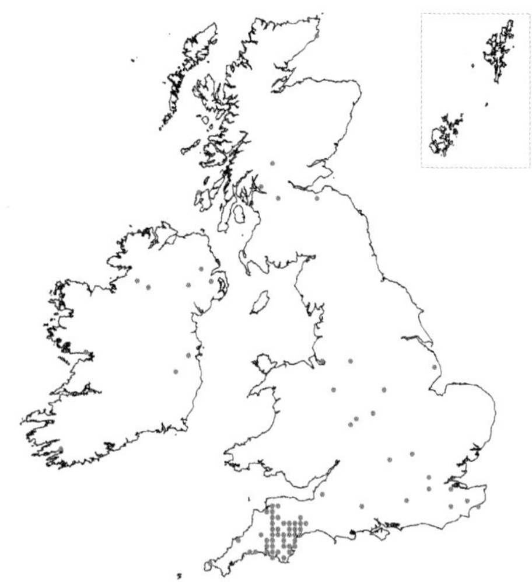

Though still underrecorded, *A. (A.) vulgaris* seems to be spreading and/or being bolstered by new introductions. The first records from large areas (including Yorkshire, East Anglia, Sussex and Co. Cork) were made in 2012. In Devon it is already widely recorded (though is not ubiquitous). The earliest vouchered records are from 1964-1967 (Penzance, Exeter, Salisbury and Kent) (Davies, 1987). It may have been in Warwickshire since 1952 or 1954 (Cain & Williamson, 1958; Kerney, 1999). Much earlier, Scharff (1891) figured a "common" brown *Arion* from Leeson Park, Dublin, resembling *A. vulgaris* (the juveniles might alternatively represent *A. (A.) flagellus*). These records are at least as old as those from other northern European

(continued overleaf)

Actual size

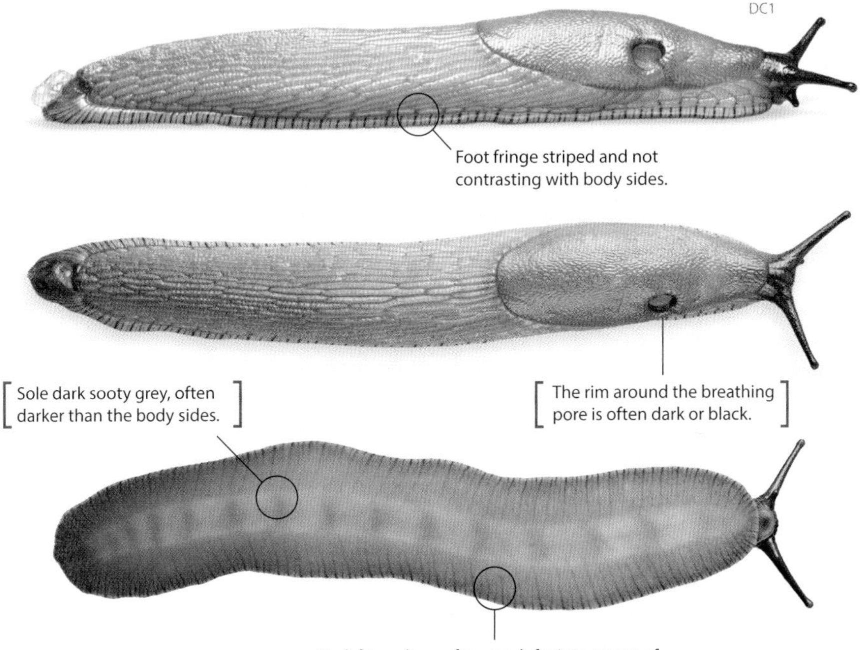

Juveniles and subadults

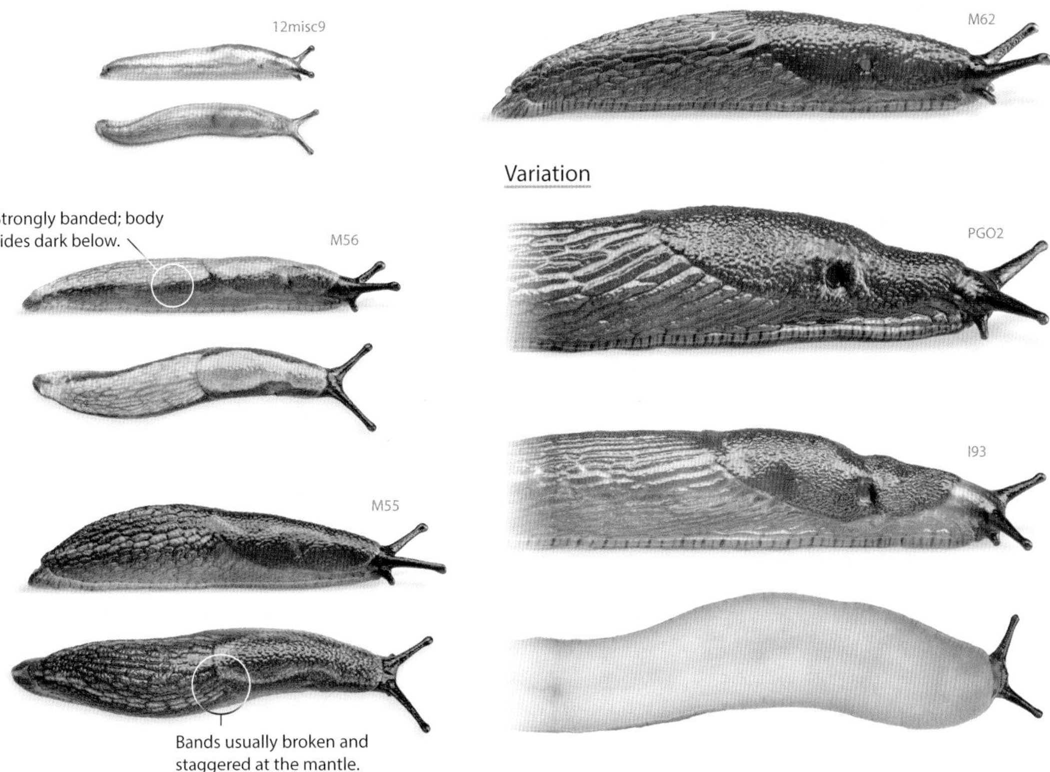

Additional features

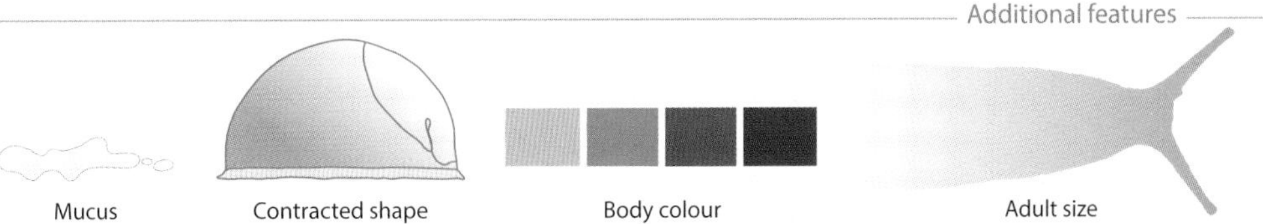

countries, through which the species has spread rapidly. It was first reported from Switzerland in 1955 and Germany in 1969 (Schmid, 1970). It remains doubtful that it is native to Britain or Ireland. *Arion (A.) vulgaris* was first described from France (Moquin-Tandon, 1855) but its original, presumably southern European, range is not clear.

Some workers use the name *Arion lusitanicus* for this species. The true *A. lusitanicus* Mabille, 1868 is however a Portuguese species genetically more similar to *A. (A.) flagellus* than to *A. (A.) vulgaris* (Quinteiro *et al.*, 2005).

Habitat. Disturbed habitats with rich soils and sufficient shelter, including roadsides, parks, gardens, and arable field margins. It has also been recorded at the margins of semi-natural habitats including woodlands.

Biology. *Arion (A.) vulgaris* is annual, reproducing sexually (Foltz *et al.*, 1982) and slightly earlier in the year than other large *Arion* species (June to August). The eggs are laid in soil in several clutches from September and are smaller and more numerous than in *A. (A.) rufus* or *A. (A.) ater*. The total per individual was found (in Poland) to average around 400 eggs. The species can also self-fertilise, although the resulting eggs have a low hatching rate. The winter is passed mainly in the egg or small juvenile stage, bar occasional adults. Briner & Frank (1998) and Kozłowski (2007) give more details.

There has been much interest in whether *A. (A.) vulgaris* hybridises with other *Arion (Arion)* species, potentially aiding its spread. Successful mating and sperm exchange with *A. (A.) rufus* has been proven (Dreijers *et al.*, 2013), but early suggestions that hybrids with *A. (A.) ater* had better cold tolerance now seem unlikely (Slotsbo *et al.* , 2012). It is not certain how hybrids can be recognised, except by their DNA. Hybridisation could play a role in displacing other *Arion (Arion)* species. Frequently, *A. (A.) vulgaris* is referred to as a "cannibal" or "killer" slug. Like most slugs it will scavenge on carrion, including dead slugs, but it is unclear whether it is especially aggressive. This may be an effect of high population densities. Although it has been suggested that its mucus is particularly unpalatable to predators, the species is still eaten by common ground beetles when young (Hatteland *et al.*, 2010) and by birds (Hagnell *et al.*, 2006).

Arion (Arion) sp. "Davies"

Stella Davies' Slug

Identification. Up to 100 mm long. A medium-sized to large, heavily-built slug with coarse tubercles. The mucus is thick, sticky and colourless. It can contract to a near-hemisphere but never squirms from side to side when disturbed. Colour is very variable, even within populations, and can be grey to blue-grey, dirty orange or grey-brown. The foot fringe is striped and often a brighter orange than the body sides. The sole is usually pale, but occasionally darker than the body sides.

Juveniles are strongly banded, with the body sides below the bands dark, and the area between them bronze or more warmly coloured. This pattern gradually fades, but faint bands occasionally persist in adults.

Similar species. Note that this species will not key out as distinct using Chart 7 (p. 18). Externally it is usually indistinguishable from pale-soled individuals of *A. (A.) vulgaris* and some individuals of *A. (A.) rufus*. Brown adults might be confused with *A. (A.) ater*, but they do not show the squirming reflex. The grey to blue-grey colouration is unusual, occurring otherwise only in some *A. (A.) rufus*. A subtle tendency for the tubercles to appear to align in narrow edged rows in *A. (A.)* sp. "Davies" seems an unreliable feature. Juveniles resemble those of *A. (A.) vulgaris* in particular, but

can be more bronze in colour. The species potentially differs from *A. (A.) vulgaris* in seasonality (adults persisting later in the year) and in reproductive behaviour, but further study is required.

It can be recognised with certainty only by dissection (p. 114), leaving possible confusion only with *A. (A.) vulgaris* and *A. (A.) flagellus*. It differs from these species in the form of the ligula.

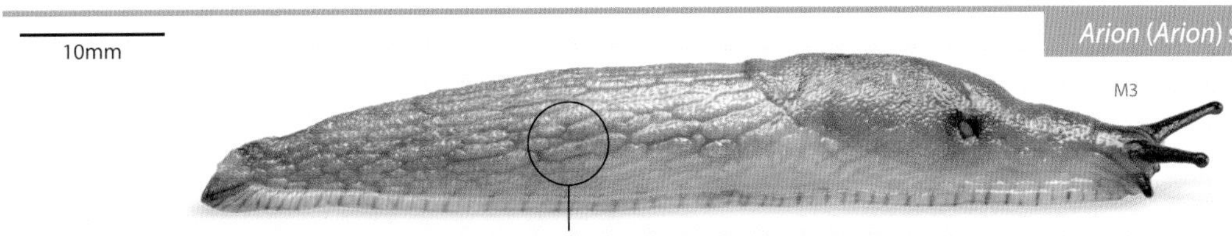

10mm

M3

Faint bands may persist in adults.

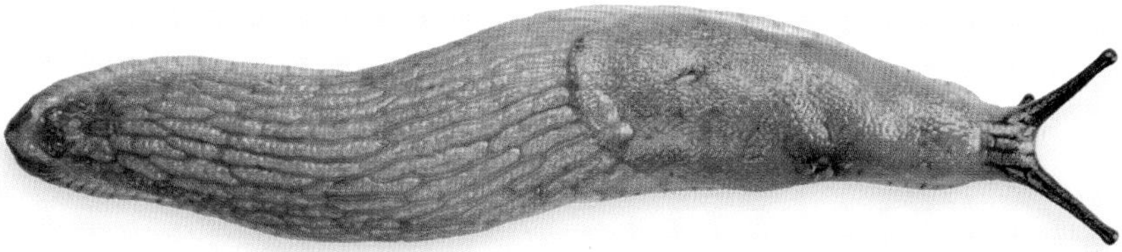

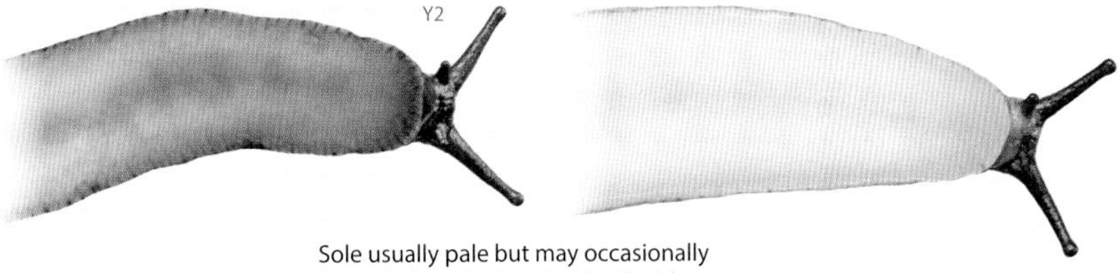

Y2

Sole usually pale but may occasionally be as dark, or darker, than body sides.

Variation

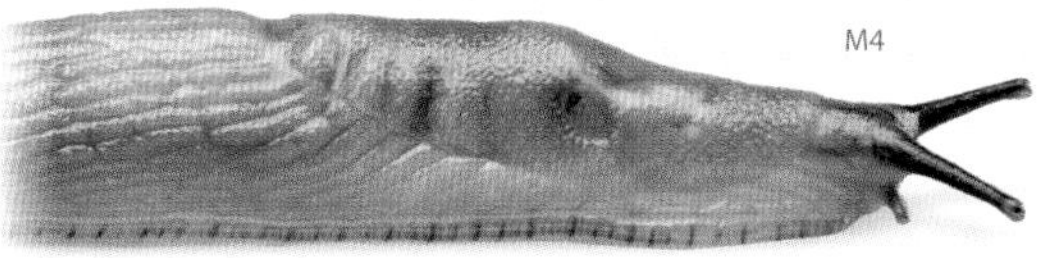

M4

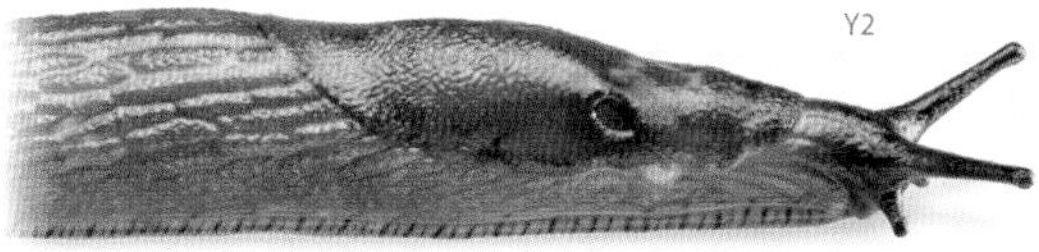

Y2

Additional features

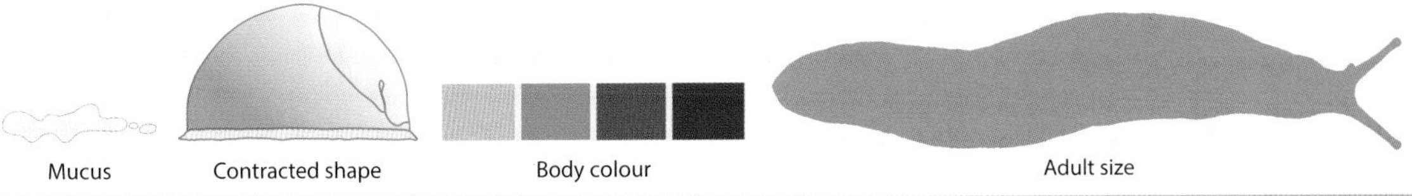

Pest status. Not known, but the obvious comparisons to make are with *A.* (*A.*) *vulgaris* and *A.* (*A.*) *rufus*.

Range. A few records in the eastern half of England. These are in Yorks. (Buttercrambe near York, and Menston near Leeds), Cambs. (Wicken village), Kent (Blean near Canterbury, and near Maidstone) and Surrey (the Sanderstead-Croydon area, where *A.* (*A.*) *vulgaris* is also common). *Arion* (*A.*) sp. "Davies" is likely to occur between these areas, however, and potentially beyond. Its native or introduced status and its continental range are not known. Genetically similar species have been found in the USA (Rowson *et al.* 2014).

Habitat. Records are from disturbed lowland habitats including gardens. The Kent records are from the margins of large woodlands and the Buttercrambe record is from a conifer plantation where the species was abundant.

Biology. Little is known about this species. Further research may yet show it to be a form of *A.* (*A.*) *vulgaris* or another continental species. Indeed it would have been treated as an English form or subspecies of *A.* (*A.*) *vulgaris* had genetic analysis not shown it to be genetically as distinct from the other British species as they were from one another (Rowson *et al.*, 2014). From a British perspective at least, it seems worth recording and studying as a separate entity, and so is included in this guide.

This appears not to be the species first recorded from Devon as "*A. lusitanicus*" by A. E. Ellis (Davies, 1987), which was probably typical *A.* (*A.*) *vulgaris*. However, some of the late Stella Davies' (1987) observations in and around Surrey may relate to this species rather than *A.* (*A.*) *vulgaris*.

Arion (Mesarion) subfuscus (Draparnaud, 1805)

Dusky Slug (Dusky Arion)

Identification. Up to 50-70 mm long. A medium-sized slug with small, fine tubercles, finer than in many smaller arionids and sometimes appearing almost smooth. The body contracts to an elongate dome rather than a hemisphere, but is not strongly flattened. It does not squirm from side to side. The body varies from grey or yellow to purple-brown or black, but is usually some shade of brown, glazed orange by the body mucus. Two dark lateral bands, fairly high on the body, are usually present but may be faint or obscured. The sole is pale grey to white, never dark. The foot fringe is the same colour as the sole or body and usually has narrow dark stripes. The head and tentacles are usually purple-brown. The body mucus, especially on the mantle, is usually characteristically yellow to deep orange. This readily stains the fingers even though it is less sticky than that of larger species. The sole mucus is colourless. Juveniles are more strongly banded than adults, and may have additional dark smudge markings along the body sides.

Similar species. As a group, the *A.* (*Mesarion*) species group is relatively easy to recognise at all life stages. The combination of fine tubercles, pale sole, and orange mucus is distinctive. For the distinction of *A.* (*M.*) *subfuscus* from the two rarer *A.* (*Mesarion*) species see p. 42.

The strongly banded juveniles of *A.* (*Mesarion*) species may be mistaken for juvenile *A.* (*Arion*) species but these never have orange mucus and have coarser tubercles. As noted by Quick (1960) the lateral bands are relatively far apart, at the head end, in juvenile *A.* (*Mesarion*) species compared to juvenile *A.* (*Arion*) species. *Arion* (*Kobeltia*) species have orange or yellow mucus on the sole, but never on the body, are more flattened than *A.* (*Mesarion*) species and reach a smaller size.

Dissection is not required to distinguish the *A.* (*Mesarion*) species from other arionid subgenera. If necessary, the ovotestis can be relatively quickly examined to rule out *A.* (*M.*) *fuscus* (p. 115).

Pest status. This is difficult to categorise. Has a broad diet including, at times, live plant material. It is apparently of minor importance in British arable fields although it has been recorded causing damage in horticulture (South, 1992). It can damage conifer seedlings in forestry (Godan, 1983). Welter-Schultes (2012) considers it a pest of agriculture and gardens, but apparently only since 1990. In North America it is considered a pest (e.g. McDonnell *et al.*, 2009; Grimm *et al.*, 2010). The pest status of other *A.* (*Mesarion*) species is unkown.

Range. Widespread and common almost throughout Britain and Ireland, yet markedly local in East Anglia where it is mainly recorded from woodlands (Taylor 1902-7; Killeen, 1992; Kerney, 1999).

Introduced to eastern and western North America, where it was once considered native (Grimm *et al.*, 2010). Genetic studies suggest that American populations are of both British/Irish and continental origin, suggesting at least two introduction events (Pinceel *et al.*, 2005b). The species was erroneously recorded from New Zealand in the past (Barker, 1999).

Habitat. Found in virtually all habitats, disturbed or natural, including gardens, sand dunes, and conifer plantations. Darker animals predominate in upland grassland above 500 m. It is very tolerant of acid soils (Waldén, 1981).

Biology. This species can self-fertilise but often outcrosses (Foltz *et al.*, 1982). It mates mainly in the spring (Quick, 1960), much earlier than the larger arionids. Ellis (1969) suggested it may live for two years (arionids are generally annual). It shows a much stronger tendency to climb trees than other arionids, especially when young.

The population genetics of this species across Europe have been mapped in detail (e.g. Pinceel *et al.*, 2005a; Jordaens *et al.*, 2010). At least two genetic lineages within *A.* (*M.*) *subfuscus* are widespread in Britain and Ireland. Detailed research would be required to determine whether they differ in their biology. They currently seem indistinguishable, and should not be confused with the two other *A.* (*Mesarion*) species recognised in this guide.

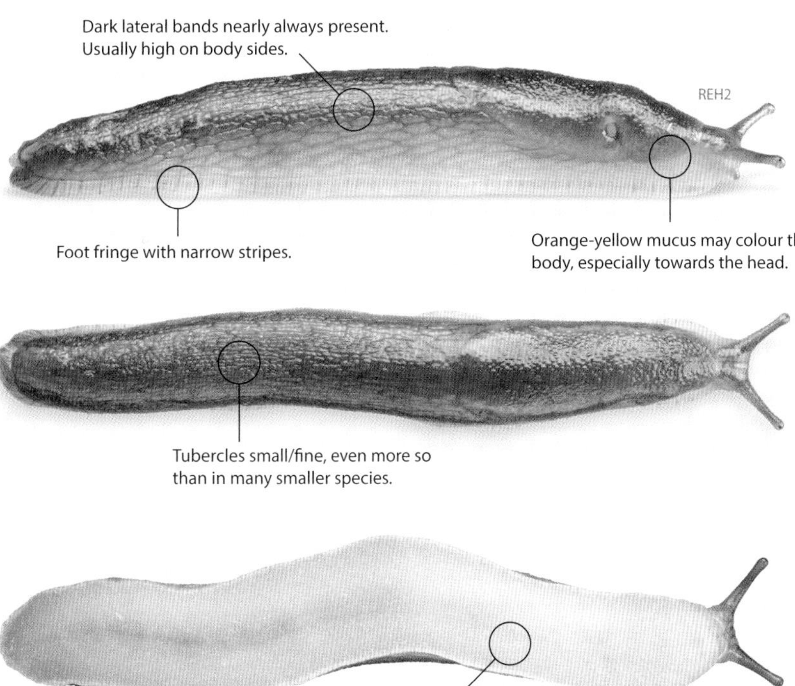

Juveniles and subadults

Variation

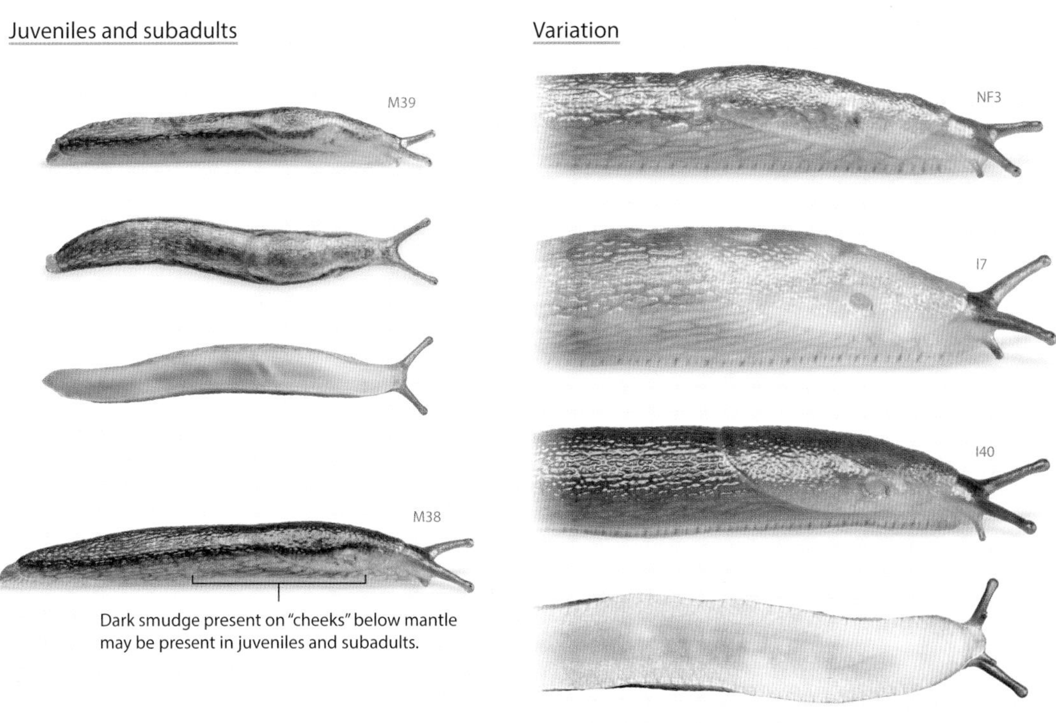

Additional features

Mucus

Contracted shape

Body colour

Adult size

Arion (*Mesarion*) *fuscus* (O. F. Müller, 1774)

Northern Dusky Slug

Identification. Up to 50-70 mm extended. Resembling *A.* (*M.*) *subfuscus* in all respects except markings. The dark lateral bands are low on the body. A dark smudge is present on the body sides or "cheeks" below the mantle. The stripes on the foot fringe are indistinct.

Similar species. Similar markings occasionally occur in *A.* (*M.*) *subfuscus*, especially in juveniles. Dissection is therefore required to distinguish this species with certainty (p. 115).

Pest status. Unknown; see *A.* (*M.*) *subfuscus*.

Range and habitat. Far less common and widespread than *A.* (*M.*) *subfuscus* in Britain. It is known from only four sites: woodlands in the Cairngorms (Dulnain Bridge) and the Sherwood Forest area (Clumber Park), near Cannock Chase (Rugeley) and Thetford Forest (Feltwell) (Jordaens *et al.*, 2010; Rowson et al., 2014). These genetically confirmed populations are all in or near forestry plantations, in areas with a long woodland history. It has also been reported from Clare Island, Co. Mayo and Cloontypruglish, Co. Leitrim, but these require confirmation. It is widespread in northern continental Europe including Scandinavia. Its native status in Britain and Ireland is therefore uncertain.

Biology. This species may be found to be much more variable than suggested here, but this can only be established when more populations are known. Jordaens *et al.* (2010) found that across europe it was scarcely distinguishable from *A.* (*M.*) *subfuscus* externally. Further study of life histories and behavioural preferences might reveal additional differences.

Arion (*Mesarion*) cf. *iratii* Garrido, Castillejo & Iglesias, 1995

Pyrenean Dusky Slug

Identification. Up to 50-70 mm extended. Resembling *A.* (*M.*) *subfuscus* in all respects except markings. Black spots or speckles are present on the back between the lateral bands. When the speckles are very small a "grizzled" or "salt-and-pepper" appearance can result. Darker specimens may be indistinguishable from dark *A.* (*M.*) *subfuscus*.

Similar species. Dissection allows *A.* (*M.*) *fuscus* to be ruled out (p. 115). Apart from the markings, *A.* (*M.*) cf. *iratii* resembles *A.* (*M.*) *subfuscus* even after dissection.

Pest status. Unknown; see *A.* (*M.*) *subfuscus*.

Range and habitiat. Far less common and widespread than *A.* (*M.*) *subfuscus* in Britain. Known only from upland woodlands, mainly larch plantations, in the Brecon Beacons and upper South Wales Valleys. The species was described from the Basque Country in the western foothills of the Pyrenees (Garrido *et al.*, 1995). Its native status in Britain is therefore uncertain.

Biology. British populations are genetically much closer to *A.* (*M.*) cf. *iratii* and other speckled Pyrenean species described by Garrido *et al.* (1995) than to either *A.* (*M.*) *subfuscus* or *A.* (*M.*) *fuscus*. Speckled or spotted *subfuscus*-like species are also known from the Alps (Welter-Schultes, 2012).

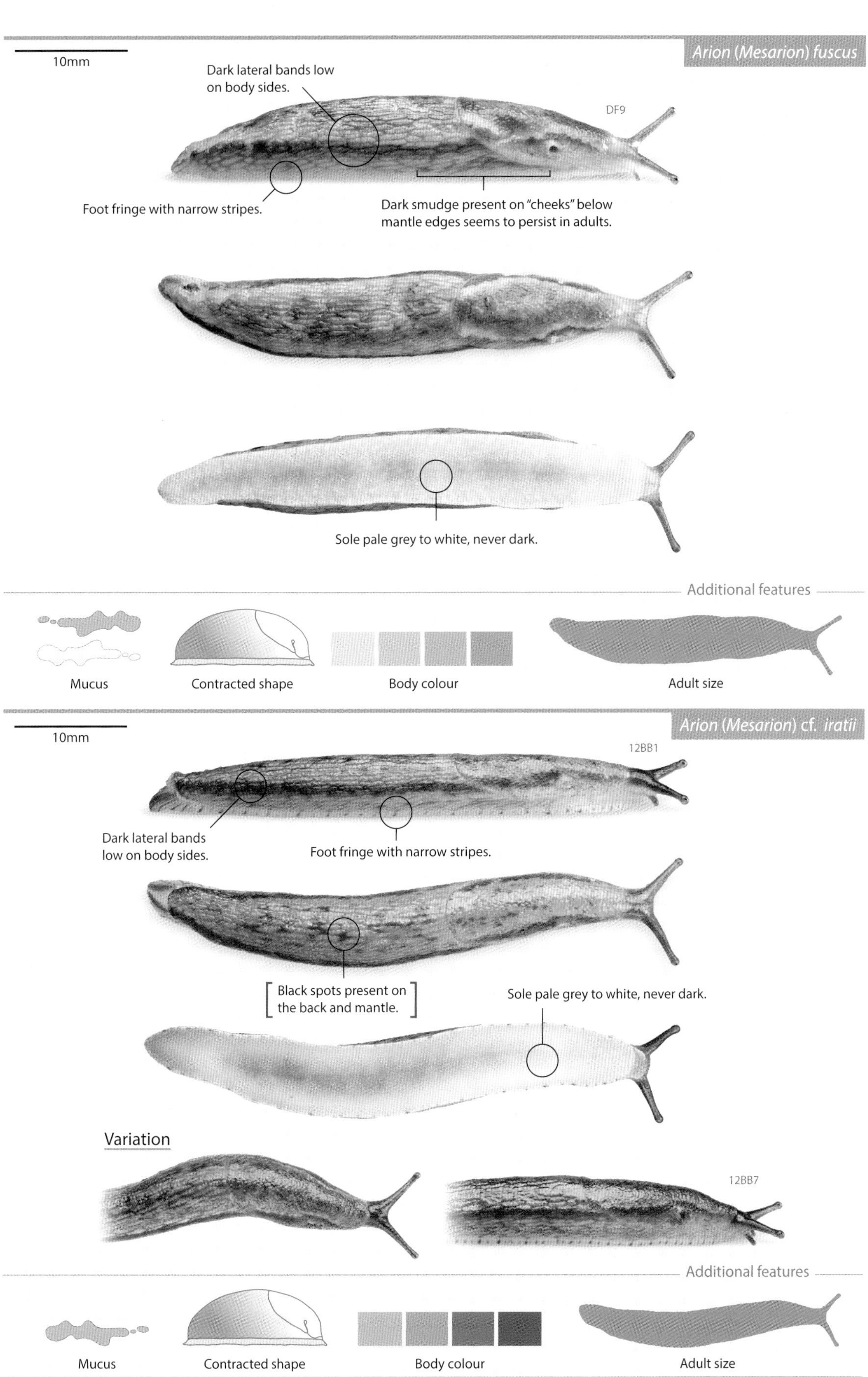
Arion (Mesarion) fuscus
10mm
Dark lateral bands low on body sides.
DF9
Foot fringe with narrow stripes.
Dark smudge present on "cheeks" below mantle edges seems to persist in adults.
Sole pale grey to white, never dark.
Additional features
Mucus
Contracted shape
Body colour
Adult size
Arion (Mesarion) cf. iratii
10mm
12BB1
Dark lateral bands low on body sides.
Foot fringe with narrow stripes.
[Black spots present on the back and mantle.]
Sole pale grey to white, never dark.
Variation
12BB7
Additional features
Mucus
Contracted shape
Body colour
Adult size

Arion (Carinarion) fasciatus (Nilsson, 1823)

Rusty False-keeled Slug (Banded Slug, Orange-banded Arion, Bourguignat's Slug)

Identification. Up to 35-45 mm extended. A small, slightly flattened, slow-moving slug, bell-shaped in cross-section, with a "false keel" along the back, particularly when young. It contracts to a flattened dome, sometimes superficially resembling a woodlouse. The mucus is colourless. The back is grey to yellow-brown, with relatively broad dark lateral bands. There is usually an orange or yellow "rusty" pigment flush along the sides below the band. The sole is a pale, opaque version of the body colour. Juveniles resemble adults.

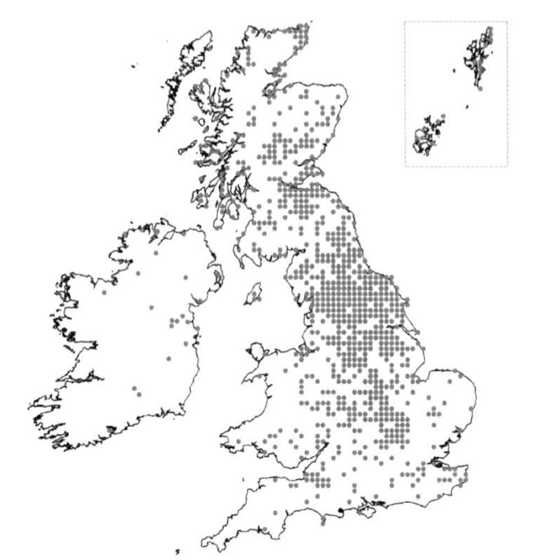

Similar species. Young individuals of *Arion* (*Mesarion*) species can be ruled out by their orange or yellow mucus. The sole is more translucent in *A.* (*Mesarion*) species than in *A.* (*Carinarion*) where it is opaque and often white. The small species of *Arion* (*Kobeltia*) can be distinguished by their yellow or orange soles. Neither of these groups have a false keel and are less flattened than *A.* (*Carinarion*) species especially when contracted.

Arion (*C.*) *fasciatus* is perhaps the easiest of the *Arion* (*Carinarion*) species to recognise. It reaches a larger size than the others, which also lack the orange or yellow pigment flush. The overall body colour is frequently warmer, yellower or browner in *A.* (*C.*) *fasciatus* than in the others.

Dissection may be useful in doubtful cases (p. 115).

Pest status. Not normally considered a serious pest but was one of few slug species found to occur in numbers in arable fields in northern Britain. South (1992) suggested this could indicate that *A.* (*C.*) *fasciatus* was a pest. Species of the *A.* (*Carinarion*) group were cited as occasional pests by Godan (1983).

Range. Widespread throughout northern and central England and the lowlands of Scotland. In Ireland and southern and western Britain it is much less widespread and strongly associated with disturbed habitats, perhaps indicating a recent spread into these areas.

Kerney (1999) considered this species native, but it seems plausible that it is actually an accidental introduction, especially in Ireland. It was first distinguished in Britain in the 1960s (Ellis, 1969; Kerney, 1999). Geenen *et al.* (2006) found genetic evidence for a recent population expansion in this species across its range, which includes most of northern and eastern Europe south to Bulgaria. In contrast to other *A.* (*Carinarion*) it is apparently absent from much of the Atlantic part of the continent (Welter-Schultes, 2012). Like them it has been introduced to North America (Chichester & Getz, 1973; Grimm *et al.*, 2010).

Habitat. Often in highly disturbed habitats such as roadsides, waste ground, gardens and arable land but also (in northern Britain especially) woodlands and scrub. Remarkably, it has also been found living submerged and grazing aquatic algae in well-oxygenated streams (Haro et al., 2004).

Biology. Species in the *A.* (*Carinarion*) group seem to mature relatively early in the year in Britain, as early as May or June (Taylor, 1902-7; Quick, 1960).

The *A.* (*Carinarion*) group has been studied genetically by Geenen *et al.* (2006) and others. The patterns of variation suggest that reproduction by self-fertilisation predominates (see also Foltz *et al.*, 1982), but that interbreeding can occur even between quite distantly-related lineages within the group. *Arion* (*C.*) *fasciatus* is genetically the most distinct lineage, while British and Irish populations of the other two commonly recorded species appear so closely related we consider them to be subspecies of *A.* (*C.*) *circumscriptus* (Rowson *et al.*, 2014).

Experiments have shown that the orange or yellow flush normally characteristic of *A.* (*C.*) *fasciatus* can be influenced by diet (Jordaens *et al.*, 2001). In captivity, the flush was induced by a diet of nettles or lettuce in *A.* (*C.*) *fasciatus*, but also by a diet of nettles in some *Arion* (*C.*) *circumscriptus silvaticus*. Neither species produced the flush when fed a diet of carrot or paper.

10mm

Lateral bands relatively broad.

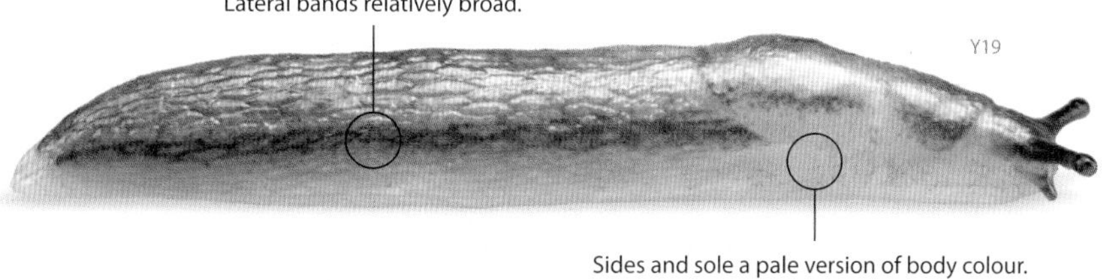

Sides and sole a pale version of body colour.

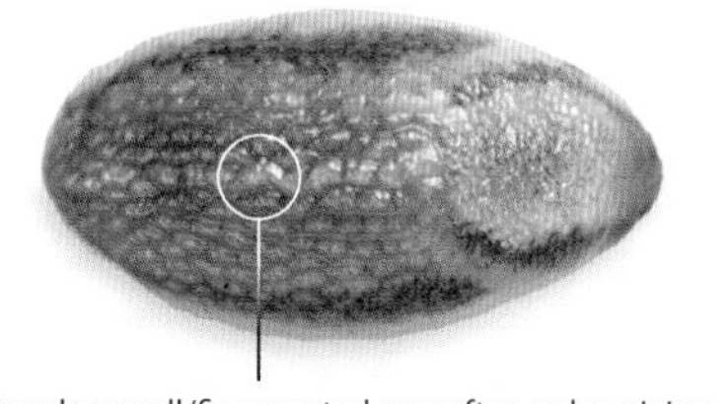

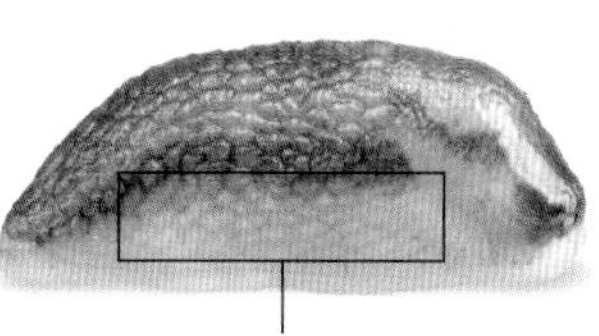

Tubercles small/fine; central row often paler, giving the impression of a keel (i.e. a "false keel").

[Orange or yellow pigment flush along sides below lateral band.]

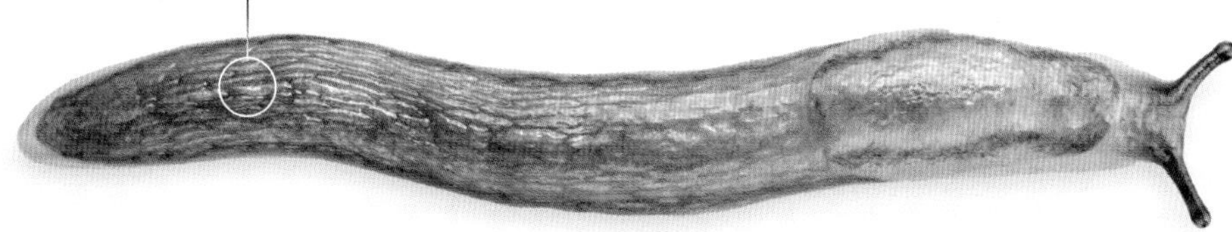

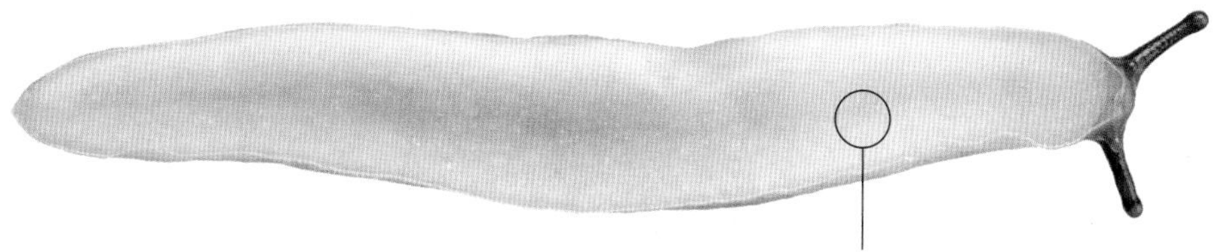

Sole pale grey to white, never dark.

Overall body colour yellow to brown. Much warmer than other *A.* (*Carinarion*) species.

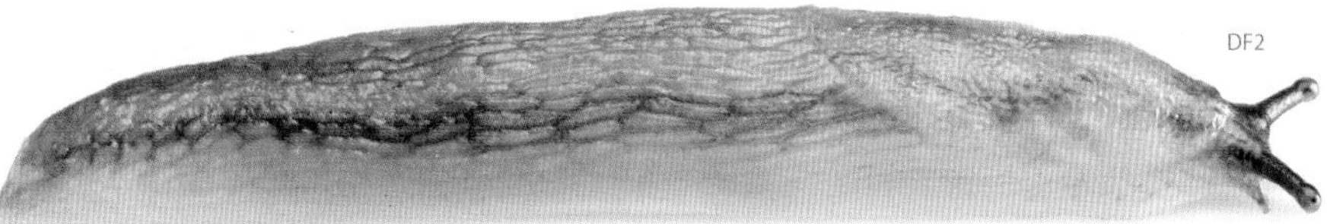

Arion (*Carinarion*) *fasciatus*

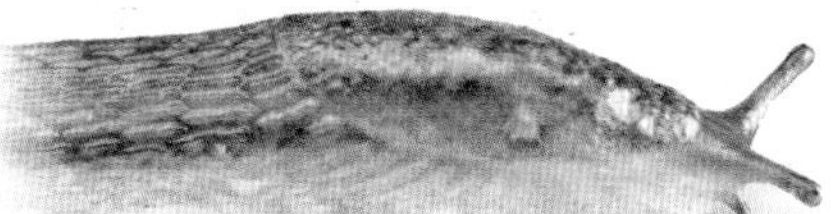

Arion (*Carinarion*) *circumscriptus circumscriptus* (for comparison)

Arion (*Carinarion*) *circumscriptus silvaticus* (for comparison)

Additional features

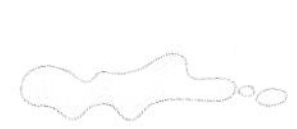

Mucus

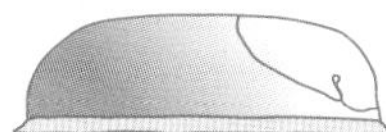

Contracted shape

Body colour

Adult size

Arion* (*Carinarion*) *circumscriptus circumscriptus Johnston, 1828

Spotted False-keeled Slug (Bourguignat's Slug, Forest Slug, Brown-banded Arion)

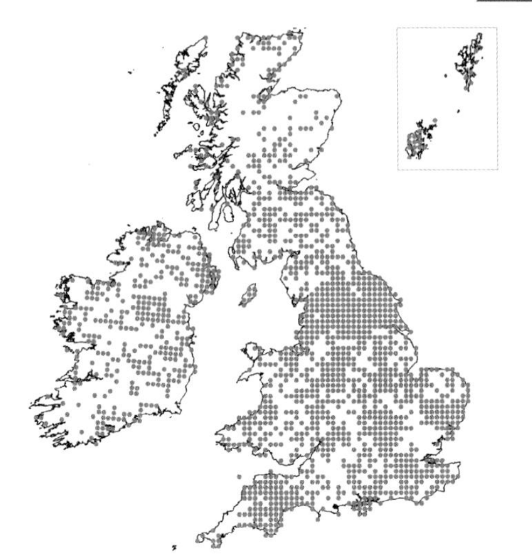

Identification. Up to 30-40 mm extended. A small, slightly flattened, slow-moving slug, bell-shaped in cross-section, with a "false keel" along the back, particularly when young. It contracts to a flattened dome, sometimes superficially resembling a woodlouse. The mucus is colourless. The back is grey to blue-grey, with relatively narrow dark lateral bands. Characteristically there are dark flecks or blotches on the mantle. The sole is a pale, opaque version of the body colour. Juveniles resemble adults.

Similar species. For distinction from other genera, see *A.* (*C.*) *fasciatus* (p. 44). Both subspecies of *A.* (*C.*) *circumscriptus* are usually smaller and less warmly-coloured than *A.* (*C.*) *fasciatus*. They can be distinguished by the dark mantle flecks and narrower lateral bands of *A.* (*C.*) *circumscriptus circumscriptus*, and the brighter white sole and broader lateral bands of *A.* (*C.*) *circumscriptus silvaticus*.

Dissection can allow the subspecies to be distinguished (p. 115) (Jordaens *et al.*, 2002).

Pest status. Not normally considered a pest (see *A.* (*C.*) *fasciatus*).

Range. Widespread throughout Britain and Ireland. It is likely that both subspecies of *A.* (*C.*) *circumscriptus* are native to Britain and Ireland. Both have been introduced to North America, (Grimm *et al.*, 2010).

Habitat. As for *A.* (*C.*) *fasciatus* but particularly common in woods, especially in the lowlands (Kerney, 1999). However this is not universally agreed; compare with *A.* (*C.*) *c. silvaticus*.

Biology. See *A.* (*C.*) *fasciatus*.

Arion* (*Carinarion*) *circumscriptus silvaticus Lohmander, 1937

Silver False-keeled Slug (Heath Slug, Forest Arion)

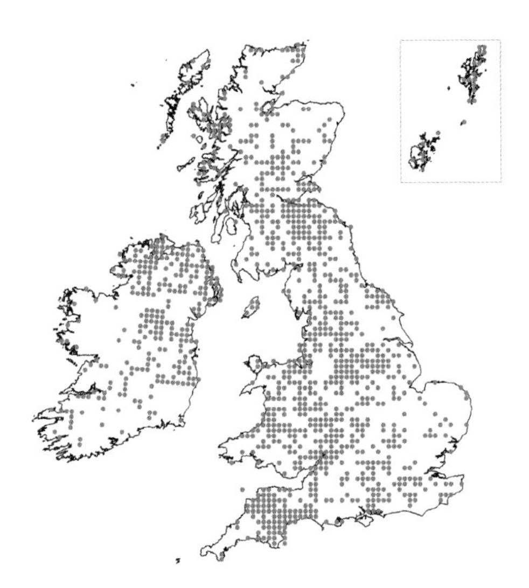

Identification. As for *A.* (*C.*) *circumscriptus circumscriptus* above, but without the dark mantle flecks, and usually with a brighter white sole and body sides, and broader lateral bands. Often has a "monochrome" black-and-white or silvery appearance, but can also be brownish.

Pest status. Not normally considered a pest, but does occur in arable land and pasture (see *A.* (*C.*) *fasciatus*).

Range. Widespread throughout Britain and Ireland except in eastern England where it may be rare (Killeen, 1992).

Habitat. As for the other subspecies, but extending further into treeless, acid or upland habitats (Kerney, 1999). Examples include pasture in Co. Antrim, floodplains in Speyside, and cliffs above 500 m in Snowdonia and the Yorkshire Dales. Some testers of this guide's identification charts, however, suggested that in their experience the subspecies seemed to show opposite preferences. If so then local differences in colonisation history may be to blame.

Biology. See *A.* (*C.*) *fasciatus*.

5mm

Arion (Carinarion) circumscriptus circumscriptus

Lateral bands relatively narrow.

12misc20

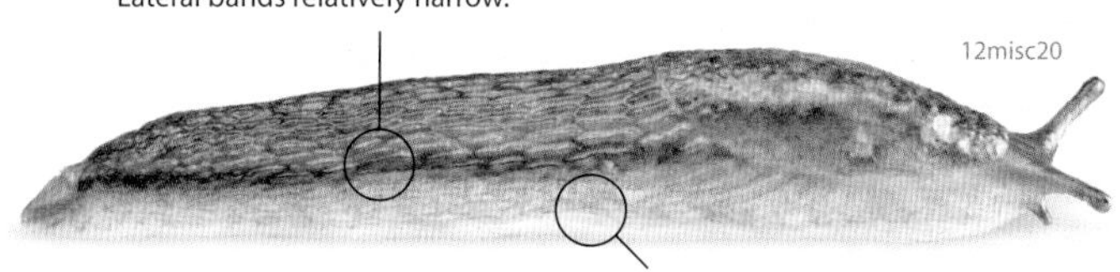

Sides and sole pale, often bright white.

Tubercles small/fine; central row often paler, giving the impression of a keel (i.e. a "false keel").

[Dark flecks or blotches usually present on mantle.]

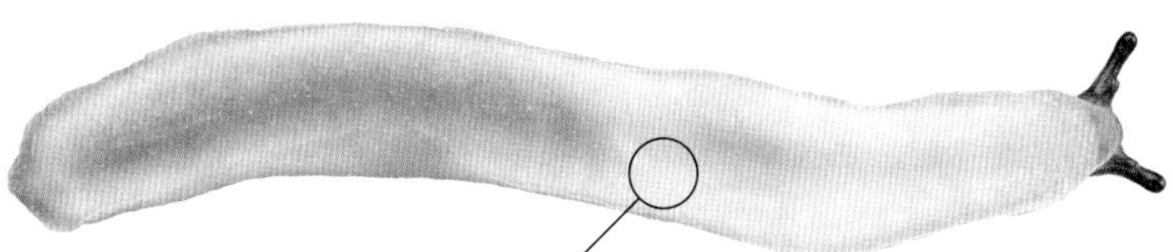

Sole pale grey to white, never dark.

Additional features

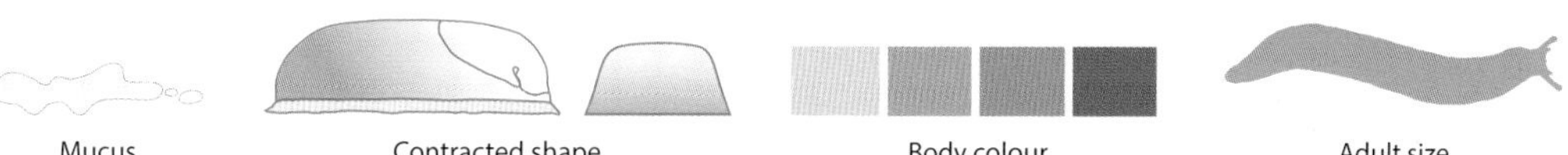

Mucus | Contracted shape | Body colour | Adult size

5mm

Arion (Carinarion) circumscriptus silvaticus

Lateral band relatively broad.

I99

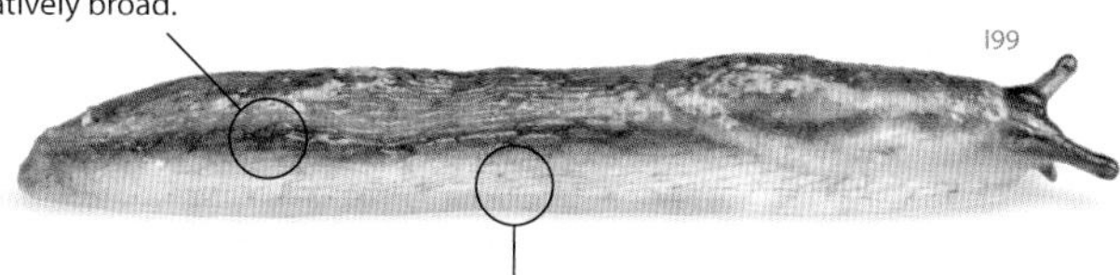

Sides and sole pale, often bright white.

Central area of mantle may be dark, but any pigment is diffuse, not in flecks.

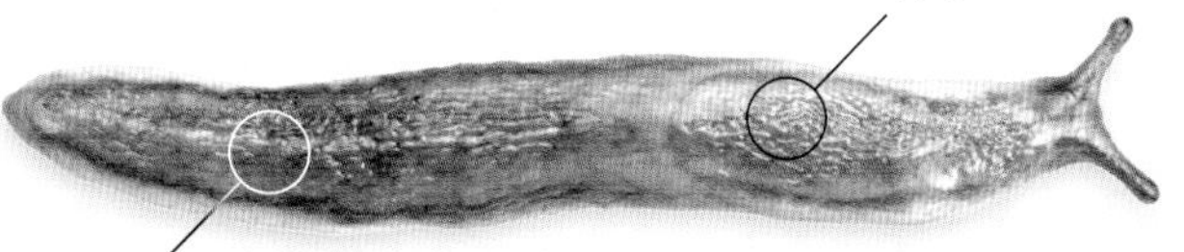

Tubercles small/fine; central row often paler, giving the impression of a keel (i.e. a "false keel").

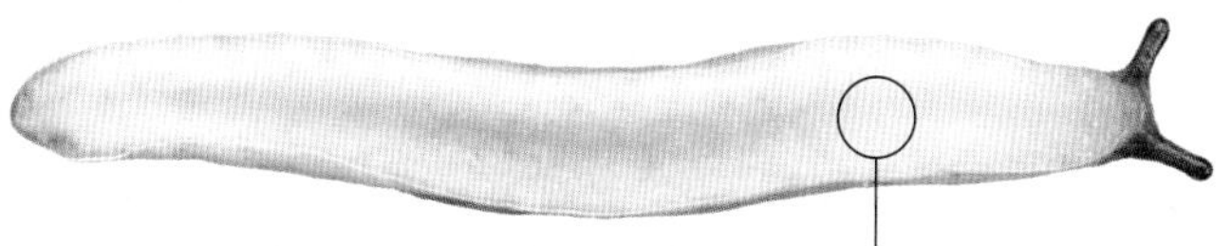

Sole pale grey to white, never dark.

Additional features

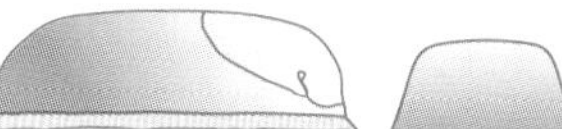

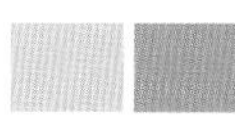

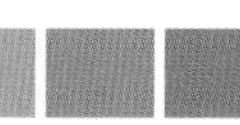

Mucus | Contracted shape | Body colour | Adult size

Arion (Kobeltia) distinctus Mabille, 1868

Brown Soil Slug (Common Garden Slug, Darkface Arion, Mabille's Orange-soled Slug, April Slug)

Identification. Up to 25-40 mm extended. A small, slightly flattened slug with fine tubercles. It is often slightly elongated and c-shaped at rest. The sole and sole mucus are yellow to orange. The back is usually dark brown-grey, suffused with a trace of yellow or putty-colour in pigment cells (chromatophores). The head and tentacles are black to cold blue-black. The dark lateral bands are usually broad and low on the body sides, almost reaching the foot-fringe, although this is somewhat variable. The foot fringe is orange but darker at the tail from the extension of the lateral bands. Juveniles resemble adults.

Similar species. Close examination of this and similar species is required. *Arion (K.) hortensis*, with which it is often confused, is blue-grey to blue-black in colour, even more noticeably so when young. Its body sides below the lateral bands are pale, with the last row of tubercles often strikingly white. It also tends to have higher lateral bands, a more orange-red sole and sole mucus and has subtly warmer or redder tentacles. The rarer *Arion (Kobeltia) occultus* (p. 54) and *A. (K.)* cf. *fagophilus* (p. 56) are also very similar.

Dissection is recommended in doubtful cases (p. 116).

Pest status. A garden, horticultural and agricultural pest (e.g. South, 1992; Glen & Moens, 2002) damaging plant shoots, roots and fruit near and below the soil surface.

Range. Common throughout Britain and Ireland except in high mountains. More widespread than *A. (K.) hortensis*, particularly in the north.

Probably native but readily spread by humans. Found across north and central Europe from southern Scandinavia (Holyoak & Seddon, 1983) to the Pyrenees (de Winter, 1984) but probably not in Iberia. Eastern limits uncertain.

Introduced to many other parts of the world including North America, New Zealand, South Africa and even tropical Sri Lanka (e.g. Herbert, 2010).

Many older records of *A. (K.) hortensis* are likely to refer in fact to *A. (K.) distinctus*. Details of the species' taxonomy can be found in Davies (1977; 1979), Backeljau & Van Beeck (1986), Barker (1999) and Anderson (2004).

For a time *A. (K.) distinctus* was known as "*A. hortensis* form A" (Davies, 1977; Kerney & Cameron, 1979).

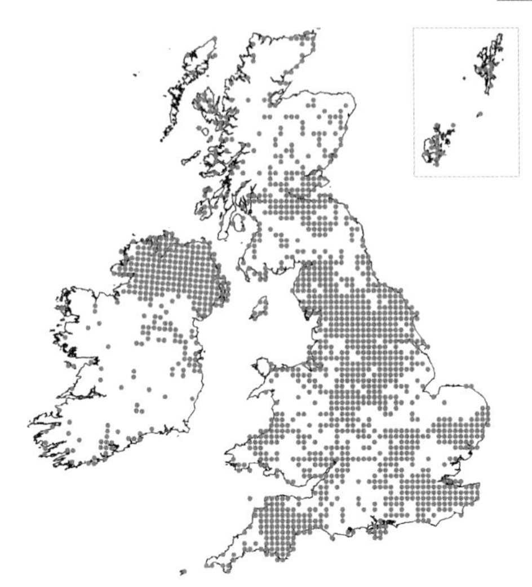

Habitat. *Arion* (K) *distinctus* occurs in moist disturbed habitats including agricultural land, gardens and waste ground. It also occurs in woodland and other semi-natural habitats, including all but the driest open areas and the harshest upland terrain. It has a slight preference for base-rich or heavy soils.

Biology. Often abundant on the soil surface in the shelter of debris or tussocks, and in soil cracks and cavities. In horticulture, it penetrates deeper into the soil than *Deroceras reticulatum* or the larger Arionidae (Quick, 1960; South, 1992). It is more tolerant of cold, moisture-saturated soils in northern areas than *A. (K.) hortensis* (Davies, 1977).

Arion (K.) distinctus is annual, usually adult and breeding in the spring and summer, although may breed all year if conditions allow. This contrasts with *A. (K.) hortensis* in which adults are normally found in autumn and winter.

It generally reproduces by outcrossing (Foltz *et al.*, 1982). In captivity, individuals laid eggs in around 10 clutches of 10-30 eggs each (Davies, 1977). Its appearance and impact in horticulture are thought to have inspired the nineteenth-century English name "April Slug" (Davies, 1979).

5mm

Lateral bands broad and low, almost reaching the foot fringe.

Lateral band usually runs level with, or below, the breathing pore.

Tubercles fine, not giving a warty appearance.

Back suffused with a trace of yellow or putty-colour in pigment cells.

Sole coloured yellow-orange by mucus.

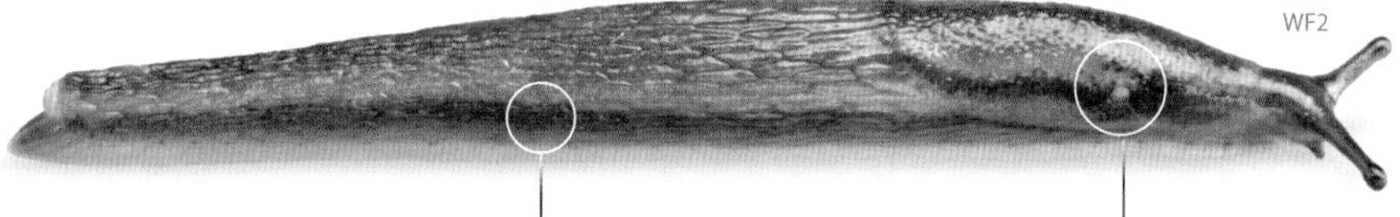

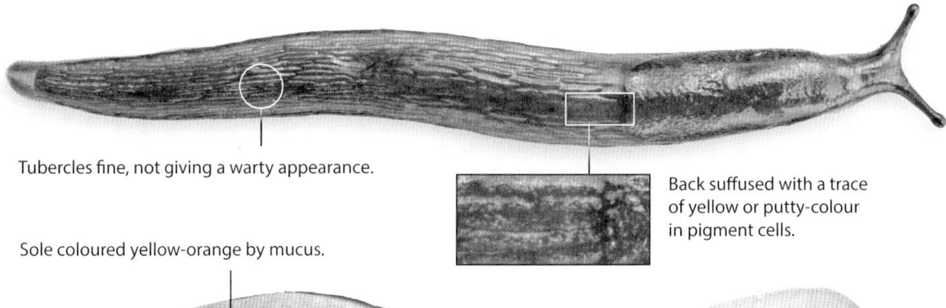

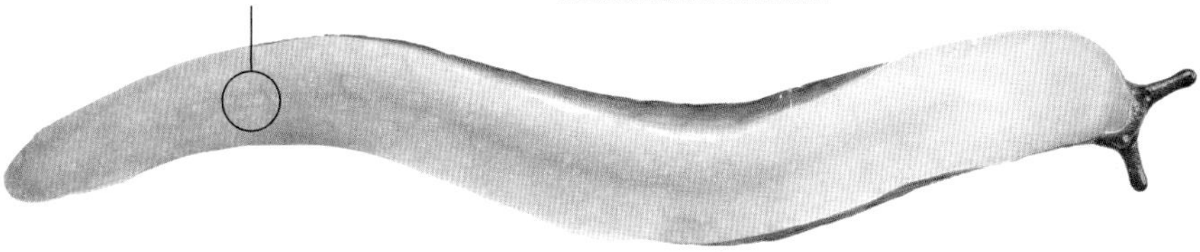

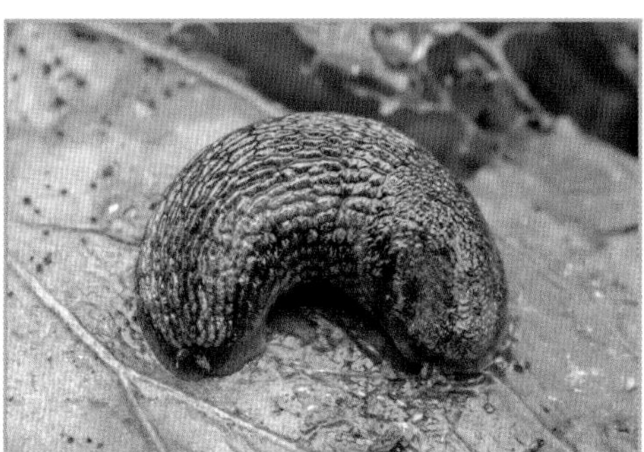

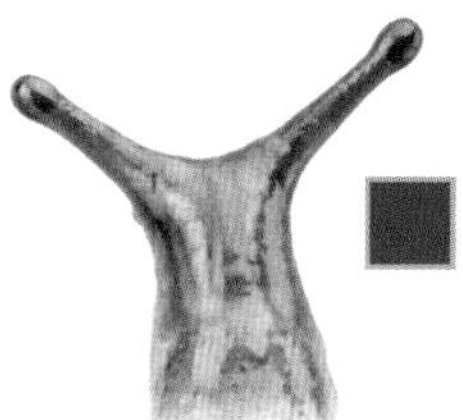

Head and tentacles black to cold blue-black in colour.

Subadults

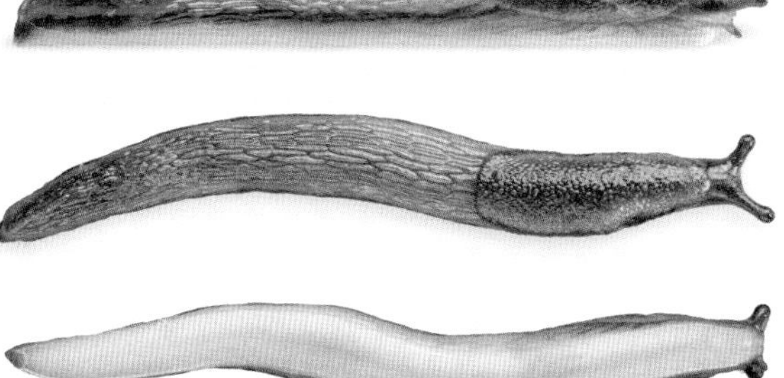

Variation

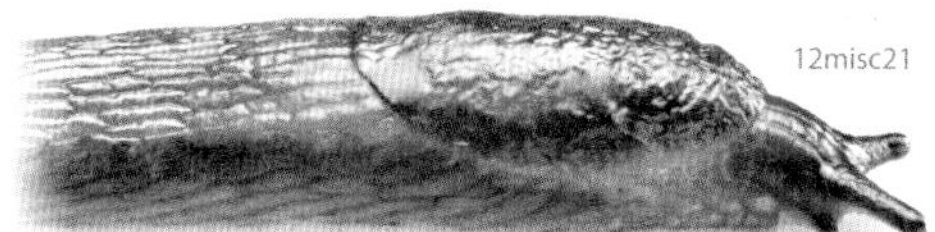

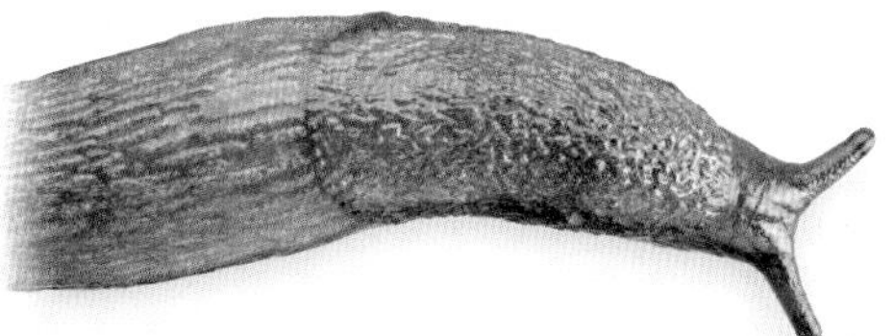

Additional features

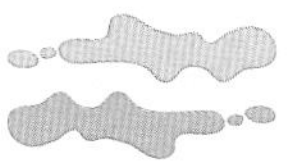

Sole mucus

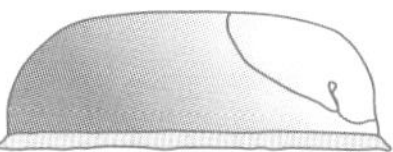

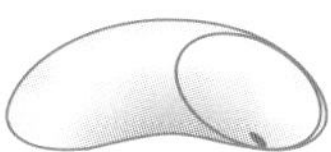

Contracted shape

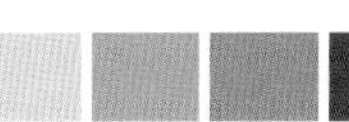

Body colour

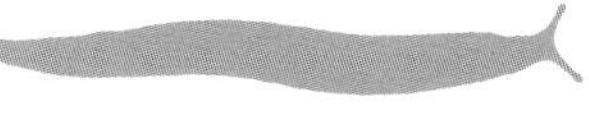

Adult size

Arion (Kobeltia) hortensis (A. Férussac, 1819)

Blue-black Soil Slug (Southern Garden Slug, Garden Arion, Férussac's Orange-soled Slug)

Identification. Up to 20-35 mm extended. A small, slightly flattened slug with fine tubercles. It is often slightly elongated and c-shaped at rest. The sole and sole mucus are deep orange to reddish-orange, and more intensely pigmented than in related species. The back is dark, almost black but often with a bluish element especially in juvenile stages. The head and tentacles are black to warm red-black. The dark lateral bands are usually broad and high on the body sides. The right band often passes over the breathing pore rather than through or under it. The foot fringe is orange and is often faintly lineolated. Juveniles resemble adults but are often distinctly bluer in colour.

Similar species. Close examination of this and similar species is required. In particular it has been confused with *A.* (*K.*) *distinctus*, which has yellowish pigment cells (chromatophores) on the back and lacks the blue pigment. It also tends to have a paler, yellower sole and sole mucus and colder, blue-black tentacles. The right lateral band often passes over the breathing pore in *A.* (*K.*) *hortensis*, but rarely does in *A.* (*K.*) *distinctus*. The rarer *Arion* (*Kobeltia*) *occultus* and *A.* (*K.*) cf. *fagophilus* are generally less similar to *A.* (*K.*) *hortensis* than they are to *A.* (*K.*) *distinctus* (see species accounts).

Dissection is recommended in doubtful cases (p. 116).

Pest status. A garden and horticultural pest (South, 1992), damaging plant shoots, roots and fruit near and below the soil surface.

Range. More restricted than *A.* (*K.*) *distinctus*. Widespread but often local in southern England, South Wales, and southern Ireland. Scarce in Ireland north of Dublin and in Britain north of the English midlands. In such areas it is restricted to coastal sites, gardens and sandy moraine, i.e. on better-drained and warmer soils. It may suddenly arrive in such areas as an introduction (A. Wardhaugh, pers. comm.).

Probably native but readily spread by humans. In continental Europe, more southerly in range than *A.* (*K.*) *distinctus*. Recorded from The Netherlands south to Iberia and east to the Alps. Common in Germany but perhaps mistaken for *A.* (*K.*) *distinctus* in some southern areas. Scarcely getting into southern Fennoscandia and not certainly recorded from the Balkans. Introduced to eastern and western North America (Grimm *et al.*, 2010) and New Zealand (Barker, 1999). Records from South Africa and potentially other places may in fact refer to *A.* (*K.*) *distinctus* (Herbert, 2010).

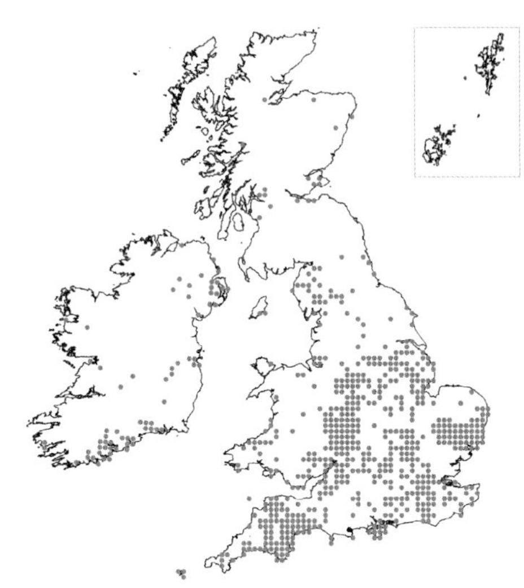

For a time *A.* (*K.*) *hortensis* was known as "*A. hortensis* form R", or "*A. hortensis* sensu stricto" (Davies, 1977; Kerney & Cameron, 1979).

Habitat. *Arion* (*K.*) *hortensis* occurs in similar habitats to that of *A.* (*K.*) *distinctus* and the two are often found together. Both occur in woodland and other semi-natural habitats, but *A.* (*K.*) *hortensis* has a greater preference for well-drained, base-rich or sandy soils. Davies (1979) considered that *A.* (*K.*) *hortensis* was more closely associated with gardens than *A.* (*K.*) *distinctus* but De Wilde (1983, 1986) found a lack of separation in Belgium. De Winter (1984) found *A.* (*K.*) *hortensis* much rarer than *A.* (*K.*) *distinctus* in The Netherlands.

Biology. Generally as for *A.* (*K.*) *distinctus* in terms of diet, habits, lifespan, clutch size, etc. However the studies of Davies (1977; 1979) revealed clear differences. In particular, *A.* (*K.*) *hortensis* matures mainly in the autumn and winter, meaning adults are generally found later in the year than those of *A.* (*K.*) *distinctus*. This seems to be generally true in Britain and Ireland although Welter-Schultes (2012) suggests garden populations can be found as adults all year.

The two are unlikely to interbreed often: the duration of mating in *A.* (*K.*) *hortensis* is over twice as long as in *A.* (*K.*) *distinctus*, and the two have different genitalia and spermatophores (Davies, 1977; 1979).

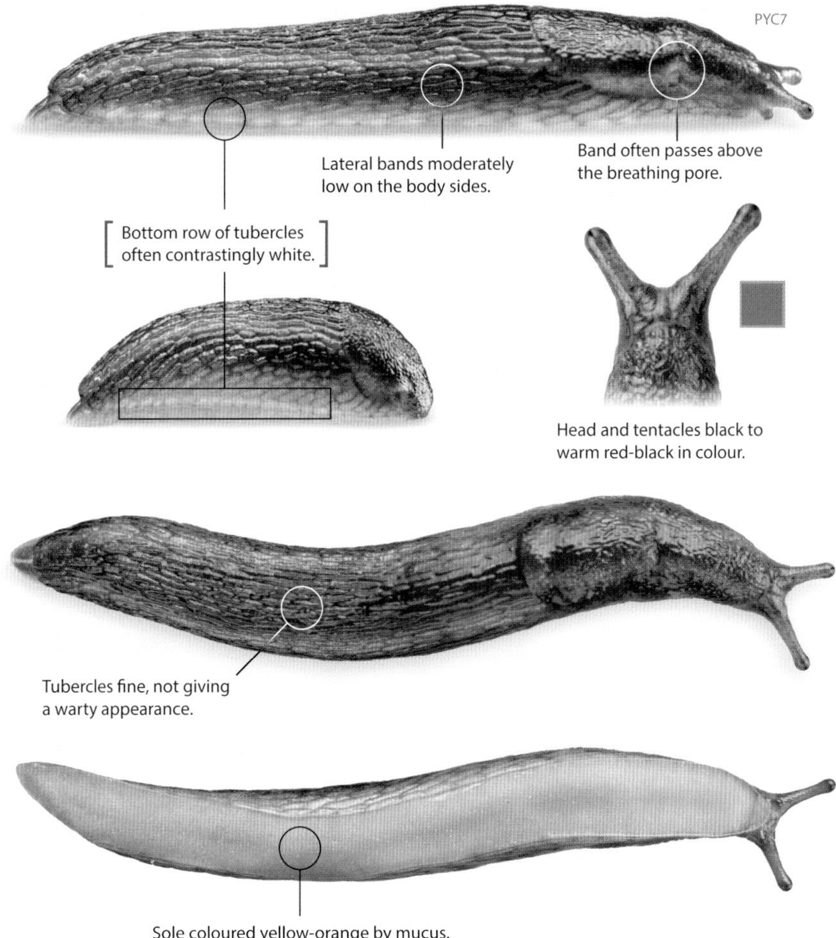

Juvenile

Variation

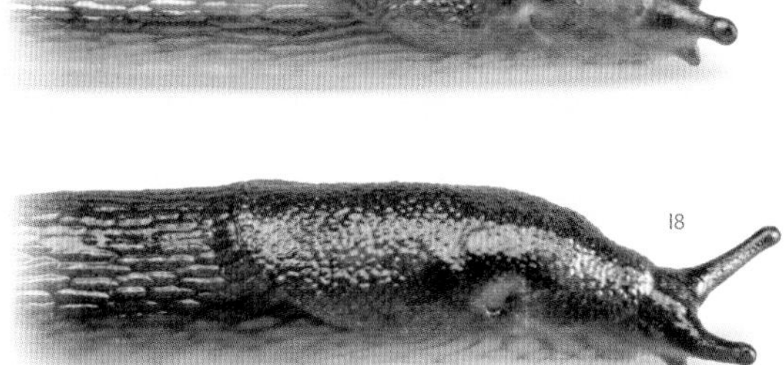

Additional features

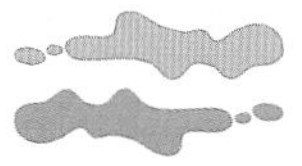

Sole mucus

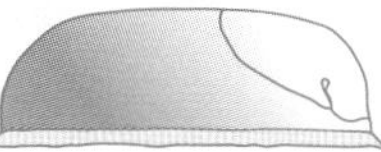
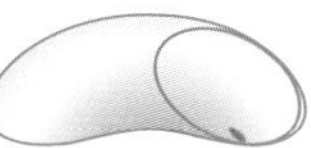

Contracted shape

Body colour

Adult size

Arion (Kobeltia) owenii Davies, 1979

Tawny Soil Slug (Inishowen Slug)

Identification. Up to 25-40 mm extended. A small, slightly flattened slug with coarse tubercles. It is often slightly elongated and c-shaped at rest. The sole and sole mucus are yellow to orange. The back is usually tawny yellow-brown to a rich warm brown. There is usually diffuse dark pigment along the centre of the back. The head and tentacles are black to purplish-brown or warm red-black. The dark lateral bands are usually high on the body sides, diffusing gradually and smokily down to the foot fringe. The foot fringe is uniformly orange or yellow, not dark towards the tail, and without lineolations. Juveniles resemble adults.

Similar species. This is probably the most distinctive *A. (Kobeltia)* species. Its warm tawny colour, coarse tubercles, diffuse lateral bands and purplish-brown tentacles set it apart from *A. (K.) distinctus*, *A. (K.) hortensis*, etc.. The exception is *A. (K.) intermedius*, some colour forms of which *A. (K.) owenii* resembles when juvenile. However, *Arion (K.) intermedius* matures at a smaller size, contracts to a more dome-like shape and may look prickly. It rarely has the purplish tint to the tentacles that is almost always seen in young *A. (K.) owenii*. *Arion (K.) owenii* is often abundant where it occurs, and adults can be found in any month of the year, so a wider search of the local area may help to confirm whether both species are present.

Dissection is recommended in doubtful cases (p. 116).

Pest status. This species has not been yet implicated as a pest. South (1992) considered it too uncommon to rival *A. (K.) hortensis* or *A. (K.) distinctus* in this respect. However, it can be abundant and research on this is recommended.

Range. Patchily recorded around three western foci: the north of Ireland, lowland Scotland, and Devon and Cornwall. The species is also frequent in South Wales and western Ireland. It appears local elsewhere, but may be spreading (Anderson, 1991).

This species was described from Inishowen in Co. Donegal (Davies, 1979). As noted by Kerney (1999), it was not located despite county mollusc recording projects in Cardigan, Bedfordshire or Suffolk. It was however very widespread in Devon and Cornwall (Turk *et al.*, 2001). A number of new vice-county records have recently appeared but fieldwork for this guide (2010-2013) suggests the species is indeed rare in many regions (eastern England, northern Scotland, North Wales, etc.).

Potentially originally endemic. The native range of this species beyond Britain and Ireland (if any) is not known. Kerney (1999) mentioned reports from Brittany and Norway. Those from Brittany (Kerney, 1999) are unconfirmed according to Falkner *et al.* (2002). The species is known at a few, wet garden or disturbed sites in Hungary (Pintér & Suara, 2004; G. Majoros, pers. comm.). Given its distinctive appearance, the possibility that this species is of Irish or British origin remains difficult to discount.

For a time *A. (K.) owenii* was known as "*A. hortensis* form B" (Davies, 1977; Kerney & Cameron, 1979).

Habitat. In Ireland, primarily in old, moist or wet semi-natural woodland and scrub. In western Ireland, Cornwall and South Wales it may also abound on roadsides, in gardens and allotments, and even in sheep pasture. In the east the few, isolated records are from mature disturbed habitats, as at Highgate Cemetery, London and a disused chalk quarry at Boxford, Berkshire (Davies, 1977). It was said to co-occur with *A. (K.) distinctus* and *A. (K.) hortensis* at these sites. Elsewhere it can be abundant in patches in which other *Kobeltia* species are rare or absent.

Biology. Similar to *A. (K.) distinctus* and *A. (K.) hortensis*. Outcrossing occurs (Foltz *et al.*, 1982) with an intermediate duration of copulation (Davies, 1977; 1979). Occasional post-reproductive giants, over 40 mm long, are known in gardens as well as in captivity.

5mm

[Lateral bands broad, usually diffusing down to the foot fringe.]

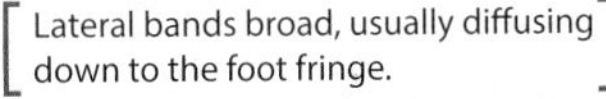

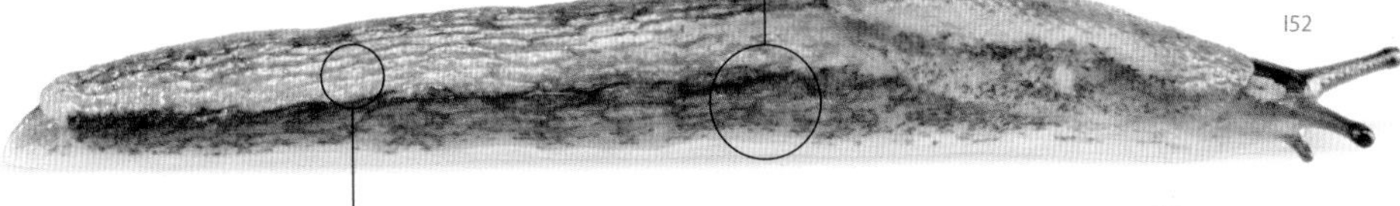

Tubercles coarse, giving a rough or warty appearance, especially in drier conditions.

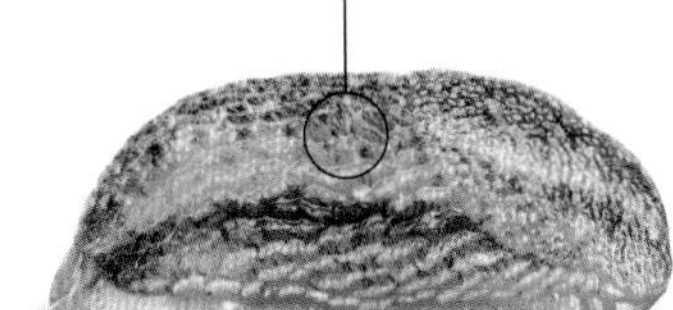

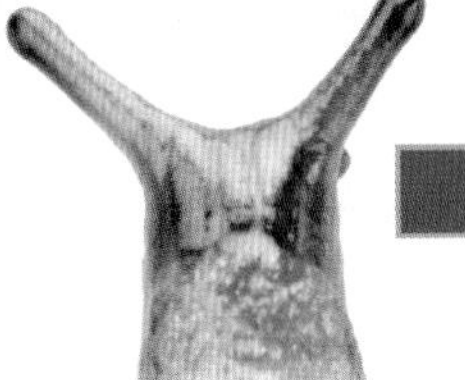

Head and tentacles black to purplish-brown in colour.

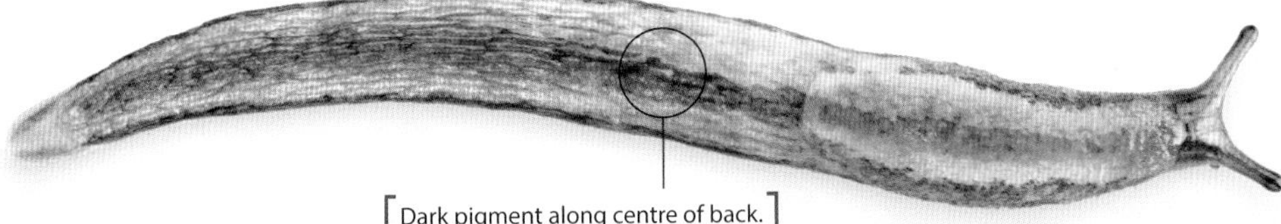

[Dark pigment along centre of back.]

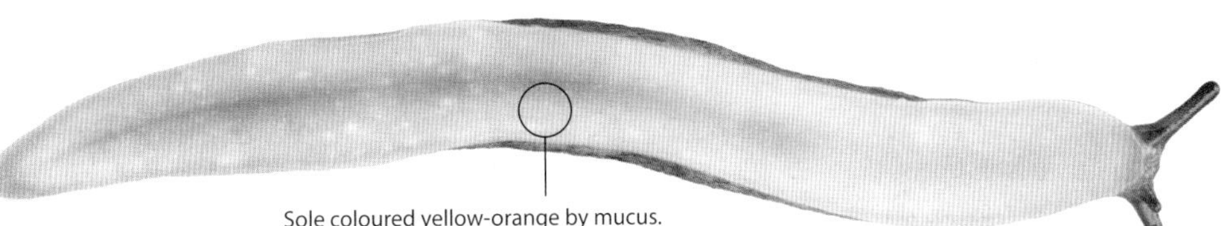

Sole coloured yellow-orange by mucus.

Variation

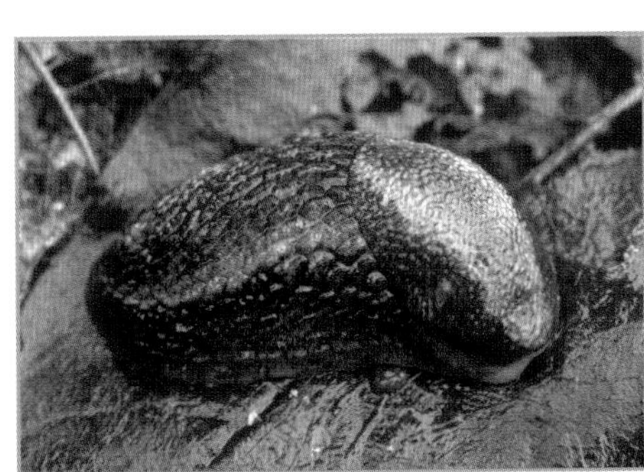

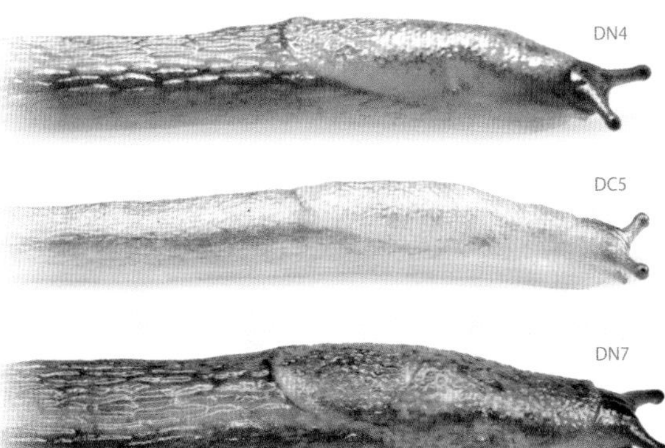

Additional features

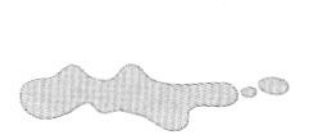

Sole mucus

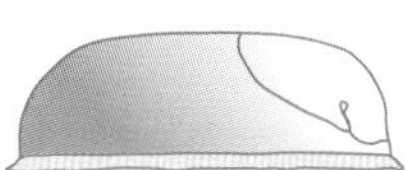

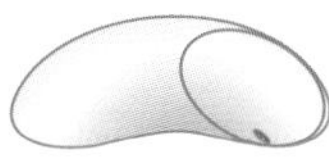

Contracted shape

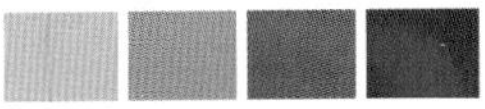

Body colour

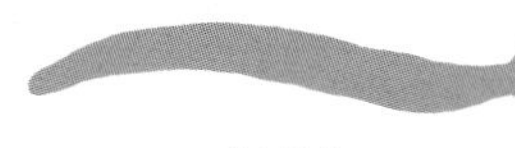

Adult size

Arion (Kobeltia) occultus Anderson, 2004

Disappearing Soil Slug (Disappearing Slug, Cryptic Garden Slug)

Identification. Up to 35-40 mm extended. A small, flattened and rather parallel-sided slug with coarse tubercles. It contracts to a flattened dome, looking strap-like, although can assume a bell-shaped profile in humid, cool conditions. The sole and sole mucus are pale yellow to orange. Rough handling rapidly removes the sole mucus leaving the sole whitish. The back has an underlying dark-brown colour, but is strongly suffused with yellow-brown to yellow-grey pigment cells (chromatophores). The head and tentacles are black to cold blue-grey. The mid- to dark grey lateral bands are broad and high on the body sides. The body sides beneath the bands are paler, white to yellowish, sometimes pale grey. The foot fringe is broad and uniformly orange or yellow, not dark towards the tail, and without lineolations. Juveniles resemble adults.

Similar species. Close examination of this and similar species is required. It is particularly close to *A. (K.) distinctus* and even more similar to *A. (K.)* cf. *fagophilus*, with which it will key out using Chart 4 (p. 15). Both species have coarser tubercles and higher lateral bands than *A. (K.) distinctus*, and are generally paler. The sole mucus is slightly but consistently paler than in *A. (K.) distinctus*.

It differs from *A. (K.)* cf. *fagophilus* in its often larger size, in being generally more yellow on the back with coarser tubercules and darker, broader lateral bands. There is overlap between the two in some characters and populations discovered in future might vary from what is currently considered normal.

Dissection is recommended in doubtful cases (p. 116).

Pest status. Unknown. Not considered a pest at present, but probably feeds on plant roots in the soil, so could become a horticultural pest.

Range. Known only from the vicinity of Ballywalter on the Ards peninsula of Co. Down (Anderson, 2004). Certainly introduced at this locality. It has recently been recorded from a garden centre 10 miles away and may spread more widely into gardens. A report for Inishmore, Aran Islands, Co. Galway (Beckmann, 2007a) has not been confirmed.

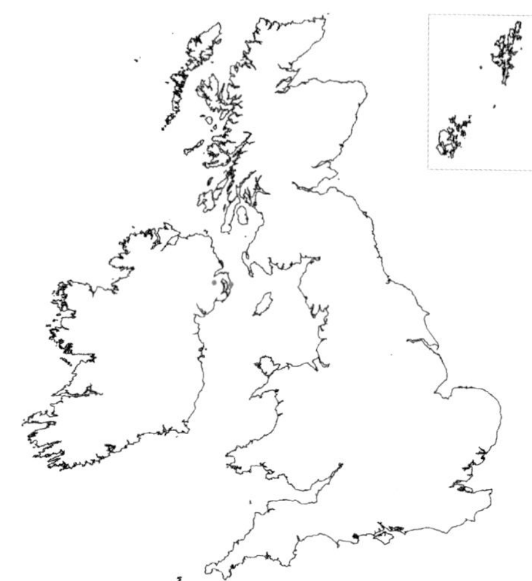

Possibly under-recorded through confusion with *A. (K.) distinctus*, but it seems genuinely rare. Its country of origin is unknown but it is probably from south-western Europe (see also *A. (K.)* cf. *fagophilus*, p. 56).

The habitat and a tendency for it to both aestivate and hibernate suggest that it originates from mountainous terrain subject to climatic extremes including winter cold and summer drought.

Habitat. A woodland, hedgerow and garden-inhabiting species within its very limited range in Ireland. It occurs in sandy sycamore woods at Ballywalter beach at densities of 20-40 per square metre. Older but wetter woodland inland supports a small population but here individuals are smaller and less abundant.

Biology. Adults are present in most months. The species hibernates in soil from November to March. At other times of year it is even more inclined to 'disappear' into soil in dry or cold weather than *A. (K.) distinctus* and *A. (K.) hortensis*. Mucus-lined cells for this are readily constructed in captivity, a habit shared with *A. (K.) intermedius*.

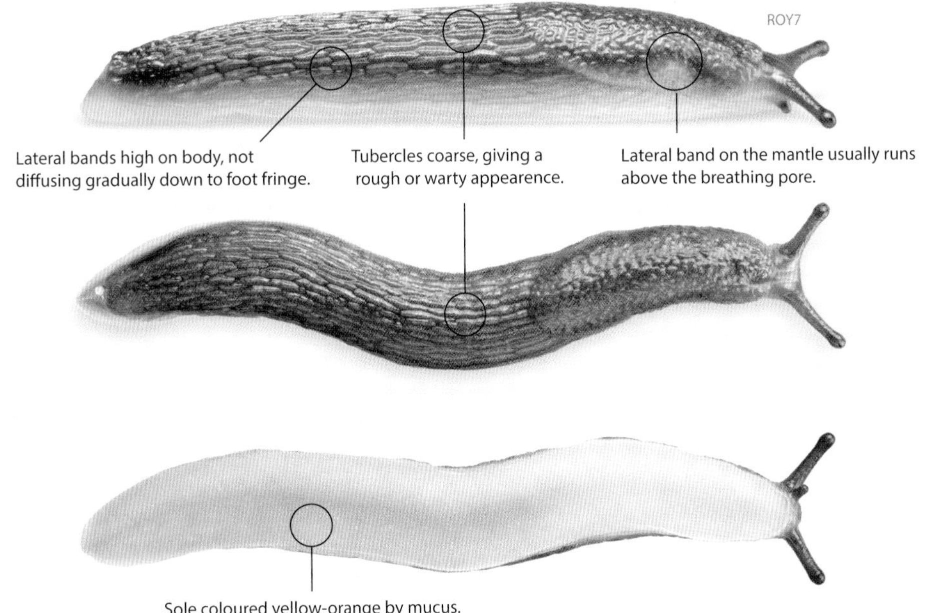

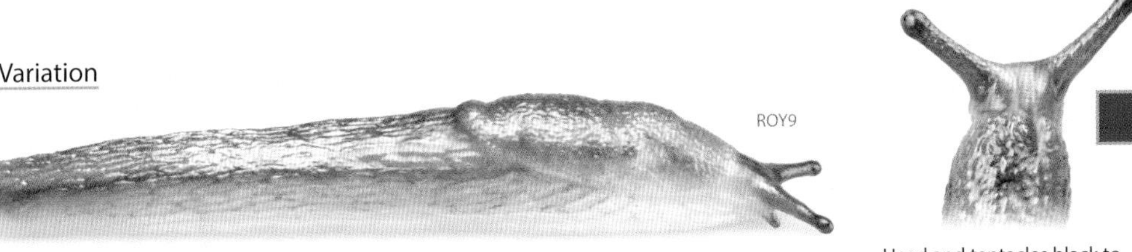

Sole coloured yellow-orange by mucus.

Variation

Head and tentacles black to blue-black in colour.

Additional features

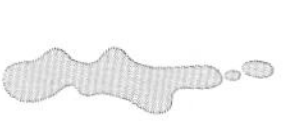

Sole mucus

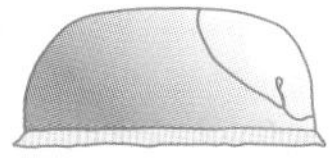

Contracted shape

Body colour

Adult size

Arion (*Kobeltia*) cf. *fagophilus* de Winter, 1986

Silurian Soil Slug

Identification. Up to 35-40 mm extended. A small, slightly flattened slug with coarse tubercles. It contracts to a flattened dome. The sole and sole mucus are pale yellow to orange. The back has an underlying grey-brown colour or blue-grey colour, but is suffused with yellow-brown to yellow-grey pigment cells (chromatophores). The head and tentacles are black to cold blue-grey. The mid- to dark grey lateral bands are high on the body sides. The body sides beneath the bands are pale grey. The foot fringe is broad and uniformly orange or yellow, not dark towards the tail, and without lineolations. Juveniles resemble adults but may have a distinctly blue tinge.

Similar species. Close examination of this and similar species is required. It is particularly close to *A.* (*K.*) *distinctus* and even more similar to *A.* (*K.*) *occultus*, with which it will key out using Chart 4 (p. 15). Both species have coarser tubercles and higher lateral bands than *A.* (*K.*) *distinctus*, and are generally paler. The sole mucus is slightly but consistently paler than in *A.* (*K.*) *distinctus*.

It differs from *A.* (*K.*) *occultus* in its often smaller size, in being generally less yellow on the back, in having slightly less coarse tubercules and in having fainter, narrower lateral bands. There is overlap between the two in some characters and populations discovered in future could vary from what is currently considered normal.

The blue-grey colouration of *A.* (*K.*) cf. *fagophilus*, especially in juveniles, can also cause confusion with *A.* (*K.*) *hortensis*. However, *A.* (*K.*) cf. *fagophilus* has much coarser tubercles, a paler back and a paler sole than *A.* (*K.*) *hortensis*, and lacks the warm tinge to the tentacles seen in that species.

Dissection is recommended in doubtful cases (p. 116).

Pest status. Unknown. Not considered a pest at present, but probably feeds on plant roots in the soil, so could become a horticultural pest.

Range. Known only from a few sites in the lower Taff and Ely river valleys, Glamorgan. It is likely to have been introduced although native status cannot be ruled out. Possibly under-recorded through confusion with *A.* (*K.*) *distinctus*, although it seems genuinely scarce. It is likely to be present at other, similar sites in South Wales. Its closest relatives, other than *A.* (*K.*) *occultus*, appear to be in the Pyrenees.

Habitat. River banks or wet woodlands of alder, ash and other native trees, albeit not far from Himalayan balsam, Japanese knotweed and other invasive plants that spread passively along rivers.

Biology. Adults are present from summer to autumn but only juveniles have as yet been found in winter and spring.

This species is genetically distinct from *A.* (*K.*) *occultus*. DNA sequences from the Welsh populations are a close match to those from "*Arion hortensis*" from the eastern Pyrenees (which is clearly not true *A.* (*K.*) *hortensis*), but not to *A.* (*K.*) *occultus* or to *A.* (*K.*) *fagophilus* de Winter, 1986 (Quinteiro *et al.*, 2005; Rowson *et al.*, 2014). *Arion* (*K.*) *fagophilus* is a species described from the western Pyrenees that differs from the Welsh population and *A.* (*K.*) *occultus* in having tentacles which are clearly red-tinged (de Winter, 1986). Tentacle colour was a feature which Davies (1979) considered reliable in separating *Kobeltia* species.

5mm

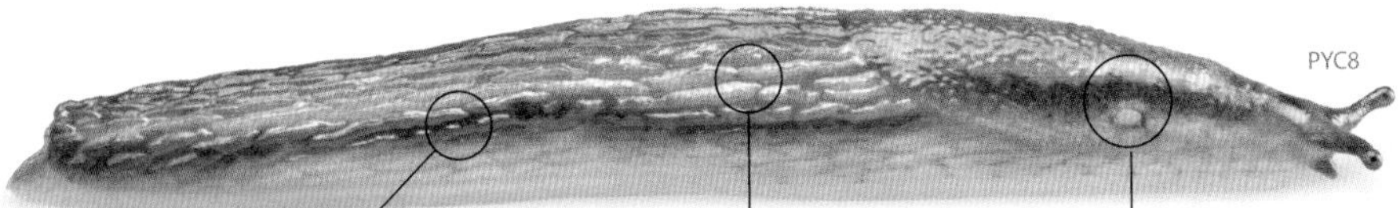

PYC8

Lateral bands high on body, not diffusing gradually down to foot fringe.

Tubercles coarse, giving a rough or warty appearence.

Lateral band on the mantle usually runs above the breathing pore.

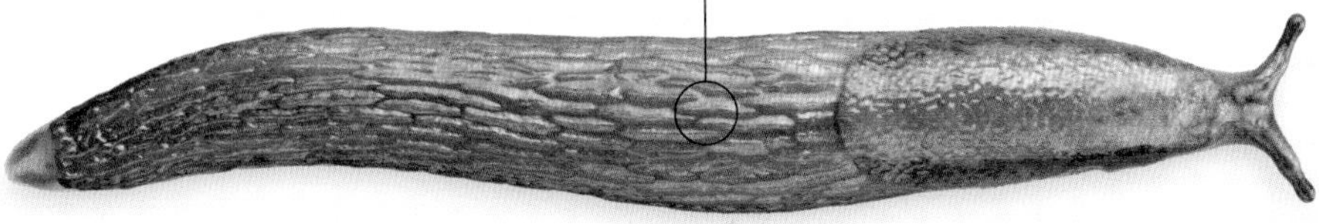

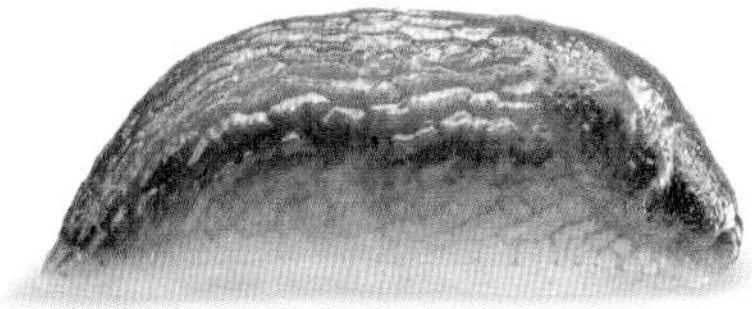

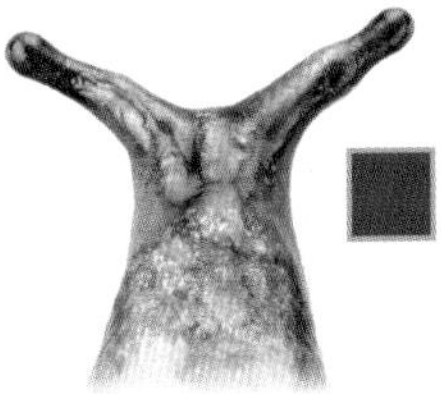

Head and tentacles black to blue-black in colour.

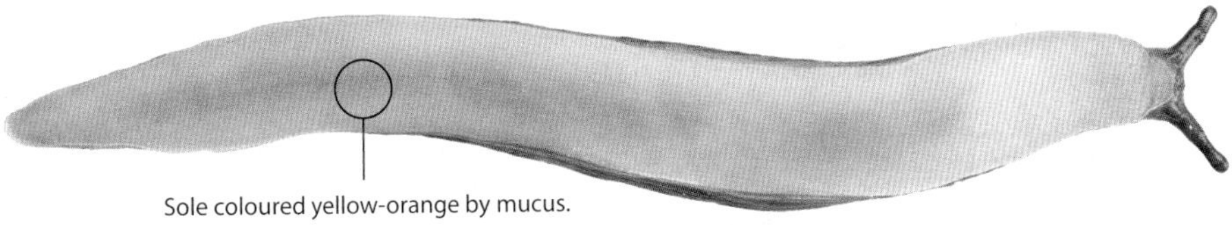

Sole coloured yellow-orange by mucus.

Juveniles and subadults

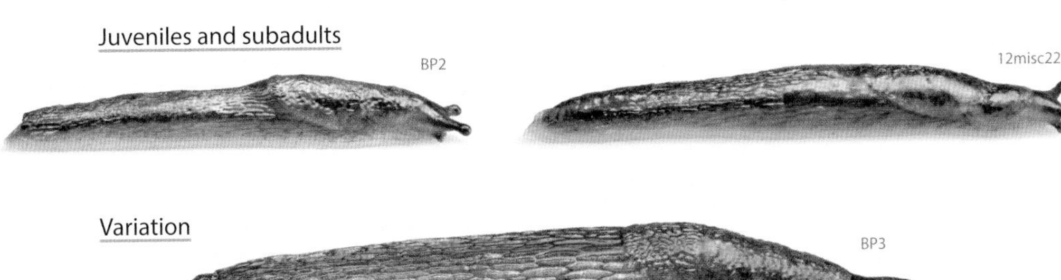

Variation

BP3

Additional features

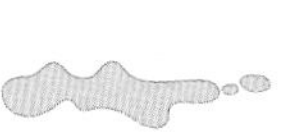

Sole mucus

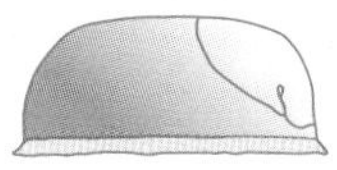

Contracted shape

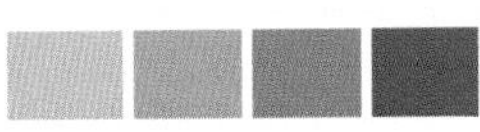

Body colour

Adult size

Arion (Kobeltia) intermedius Normand, 1852

Hedgehog Slug (Hedgehog Arion, Glade Slug)

Identification. Up to 15-20 mm extended. A very small slug with coarse tubercles, each of which is often drawn to a point or multiply pointed (serrated) ridge when contracted (hence "hedgehog slug"). This seems most noticeable in dry or cold conditions (or alternatively, in subadult specimens; Welter-Schultes, 2012). The body contracts to a proportionately taller dome than other *A.* (*Kobeltia*) species. The sole and sole mucus are pale yellow to orange. The back is often a dull yellow-grey, but can vary from white, tawny orange, to brown or blue-grey. The head and tentacles are dark, though seldom black. Dark lateral bands are often absent; if present, they are faint and high on the body sides. Juveniles resemble adults.

Similar species. This species may resemble the juveniles of other species. *Arion* (*K.*) *intermedius* contracts to a more compact dome than other *A.* (*Kobeltia*) species and may appear 'prickly' because of the serrated tubercles. In wooded habitats a brown form with lateral bands is common and can be very similar to small *A.* (*K.*) *owenii*, which have purplish rather than dark tentacles. On peaty ground a particularly dark, blue-gray form occurs which could be confused with juvenile *A.* (*K.*) *hortensis* or *A.* (*K.*) *distinctus*.

Very young juveniles of the *A.* (*Mesarion*) species have yellow to orange body mucus and a pale sole. Those of the *A.* (*Carinarion*) species tend to have the keel particularly well-marked when young. Finally, very young juveniles of the large, *A.* (*Arion*) species have coarser tubercles for their size. All these groups lack the yellow to orange sole mucus of *A.* (*K.*) *intermedius* and other *A.* (*Kobeltia*) species.

Dissection is not generally required. The other *A.* (*Kobeltia*) species may be ruled out by their internal features (p. 116). In the wild, however, they always mature at a larger size than *A.* (*K.*) *intermedius* (Davies, 1977).

Pest status. Not always considered a pest, although occurs in large numbers in winter wheat and other arable fields (e.g. South, 1992). Beyond Europe it may cause some of the problems of invasive species.

Range. Widespread throughout Britain and Ireland, being seemingly absent only from rich lowland soils.

Throughout western and northern Europe. Introduced to all continents except Antarctica and present even in the tropics. It has a tendency to invade native forest outside Europe (Barker, 1999; Grimm *et al.*, 2010; Herbert, 2010; Stanisic *et al.*, 2010).

Habitat. *Arion* (*Kobeltia*) *intermedius* occurs in almost any semi-natural habitat including wetlands and on sandy soils (e.g. Killeen, 1992). It is tolerant of acidic conditions and can occur in conifer plantations and on mountain summits. A scarcity in gardens and on rich soils has often been noted (Scharff, 1891; Taylor, 1902-7; Boycott, 1934; South, 1992; Kerney, 1999).

Biology. The diet includes dead leaves and fungi (Davies, 1977; Quick, 1960). It can survive dry or cold weather by resting (aestivating) curled up in mucus-lined cells in moss or soil for several weeks. It has a greater tendency to do this than most *A.* (*Kobeltia*) species (Davies, 1977; South, 1992; Barker, 1999), though this is observed in *A.* (*K.*) *occultus* (Anderson, 2004).

Genetic studies suggest that *A.* (*K.*) *intermedius* reproduces mainly by self-fertilisation (Backeljau & de Bruyn, 1990; Foltz *et al.*, 1982). However, evidence for mating and the transfer of spermatophores also exists (Garrido *et al.*, 1995; Barker, 1999; Reise *et al.*, 2001). The species lives for up to a year, but in captivity is able to produce up to three generations in a year (Davies, 1977).

5mm

Lateral bands often absent; if present, faint and high on body.

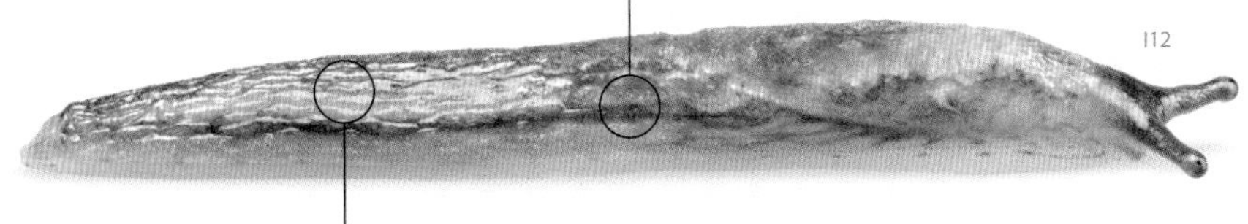

[Tubercles coarse, giving a "prickly" appearance in dry or cold conditions.]

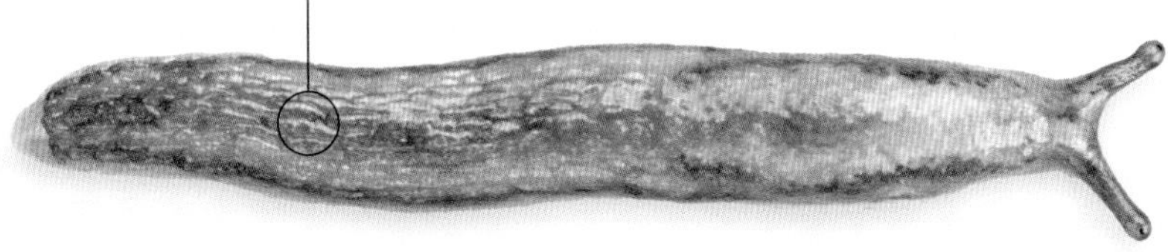

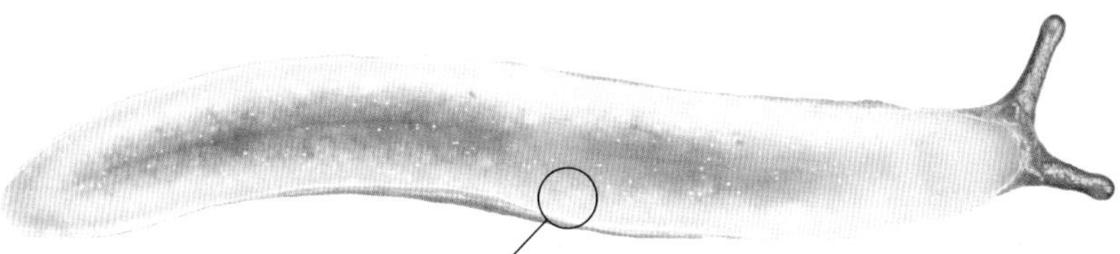

Sole coloured pale yellow to yellow-orange by mucus.

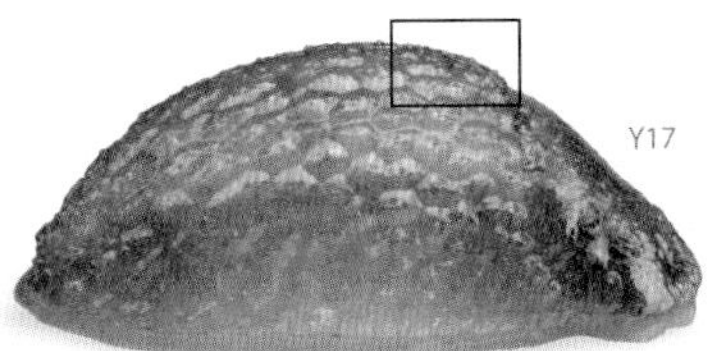

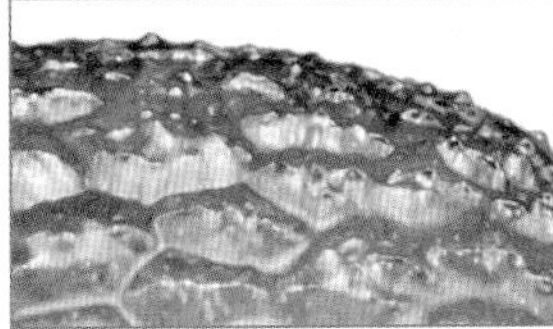

[Ridge of each tubercle drawn to points giving a "prickly" appearance.]

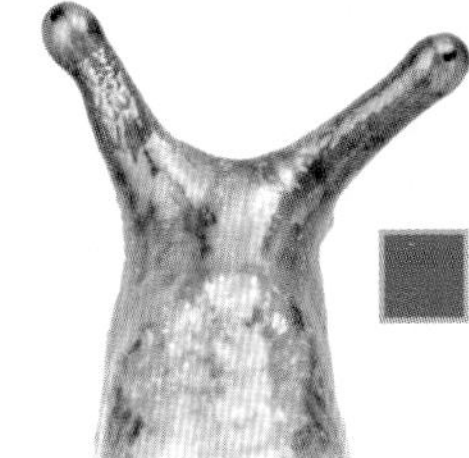

Head and tentacles variable in colour, seldom black.

Variation

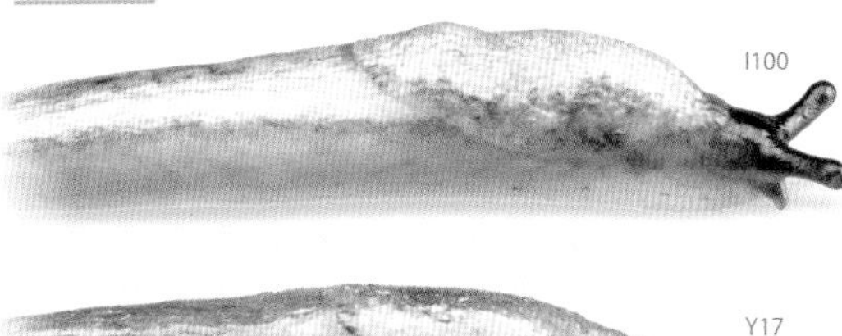

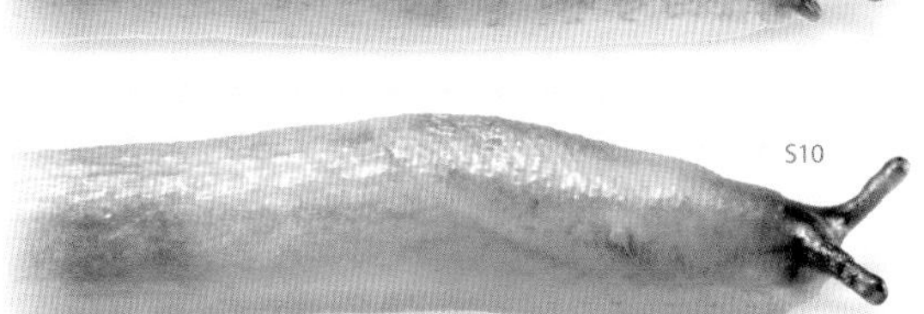

Additional features

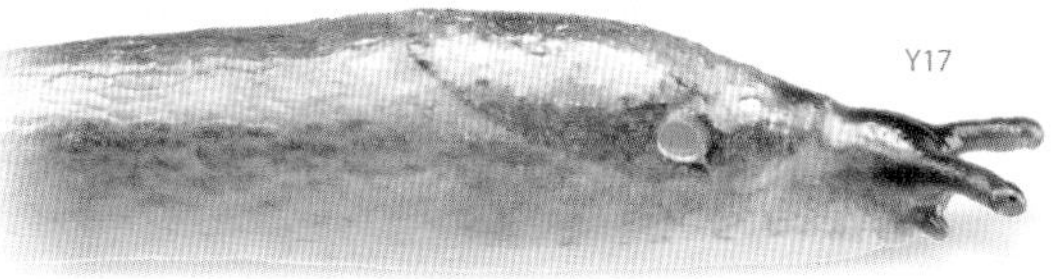

Sole mucus

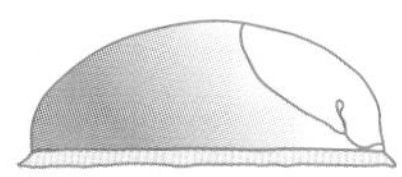

Contracted shape

Body colour

Adult size

Geomalacus maculosus Allman, 1843

Kerry Slug (Spotted Slug)

Identification. Up to 60-90 mm extended. A medium sized, flattened slug, the back characteristically covered in pale spots. When disturbed characteristically releases its hold on the ground, rolling into a ball and curling the tail around and against the head.

There appear to be two distinct colour forms. A dark grey to black form with underlying bluish tones and white spots is found in open habitats. In shady places a distinct form occurs with hazel-brown to ginger-brown body colour, faint lateral bands, yellow-gold body spots and yellowish mucus. A form in which the darker areas are crimson has been bred from Irish stock (Oldham, 1942). The forms can occur together and the apparent distinction between woodland and open ground forms can be substantially blurred where open heath borders wooded areas. It is, nevertheless, true to say that large areas of open heath and bog will support only the dark gray to black, white-spotted form.

Juveniles resemble the yellow-spotted, brown adult form but have more obvious lateral bands.

Similar species. There are no similar species in Ireland or in Britain. The distinct spotting of the upper surface and unique defence posture should serve to distinguish it from everything else.

Pest status. Not a pest. The species feeds on a wide range of lichens, mosses, liverworts, fungi and algae (Taylor, 1902-7; Boycott & Oldham, 1930; Platts & Speight, 1988) but may be induced to eat lettuce in captivity. Godan (1983) claimed that it eats seedlings of sugar beet in Europe but this has not been substantiated.

Range. *Geomalacus maculosus* was, until recently, confined in Ireland to the Old Red Sandstone areas of western Cork and Kerry. In 2010 it was discovered in Sitka spruce plantations at Lettercraffroe, West Galway (Kearney, 2010). Platts and Speight (1988) describe how commercial afforestation has reduced its range in Iberia, but in Ireland the opposite appears to apply. It frequently occurs near planted conifers within its main Kerry/Cork range where it is usually detectable along heathy fire breaks.

Outside Ireland this species is restricted to north-west Iberia (Platts & Speight, 1988; Castillejo, 1998). Its occurrence there and in Ireland, but not Britain or France, has been much debated.

The term 'Lusitanian' has been applied to indicate survival throughout the last glaciation on now-submerged land south of Ireland, a putative refugium called Lusitania. However, it now appears likely that *Geomalacus* is an early introduction to Ireland. DNA studies of the snail *Cepaea nemoralis* in Ireland suggest an origin in the eastern Pyrenees (Grindon & Davidson, 2013). This has been attributed to the movement of Mesolithic (Stone Age) peoples from Iberia, bringing the edible snail with them. They may also have brought, deliberately or accidentally, 'Lusitanian' species like *G. maculosus*.

Habitat. Mainly blanket peat and bog at elevations up to 300 m. An aversion to limestone is noted by Platts & Speight (1988). Within its range in Ireland it inhabits virtually every habitat from dense native scrub to open heath and bog, although requiring boulders or trees to support the growth of its food. According to Platts & Speight (1988) it does not occur under invasive rhododendron (*Rhododendron ponticum*) even where this has been removed to restore native oak woods, as at Killarney.

Biology. By day this species shelters under stones, boulders and tree bark except in wet weather.

It is an outcrossing species mating in autumn. The spermatophore (sperm-transferring structure) is very long and coiled, with a single low, serrated ridge following along one side for almost the full length. The characteristic eggs (p. 122) hatch in six to eight weeks.

This is our only legally protected slug species. It is protected against collection and disturbance by European and national laws in Ireland, Spain and Portugal. Its presence has been used a selection feature for a number of protected areas.

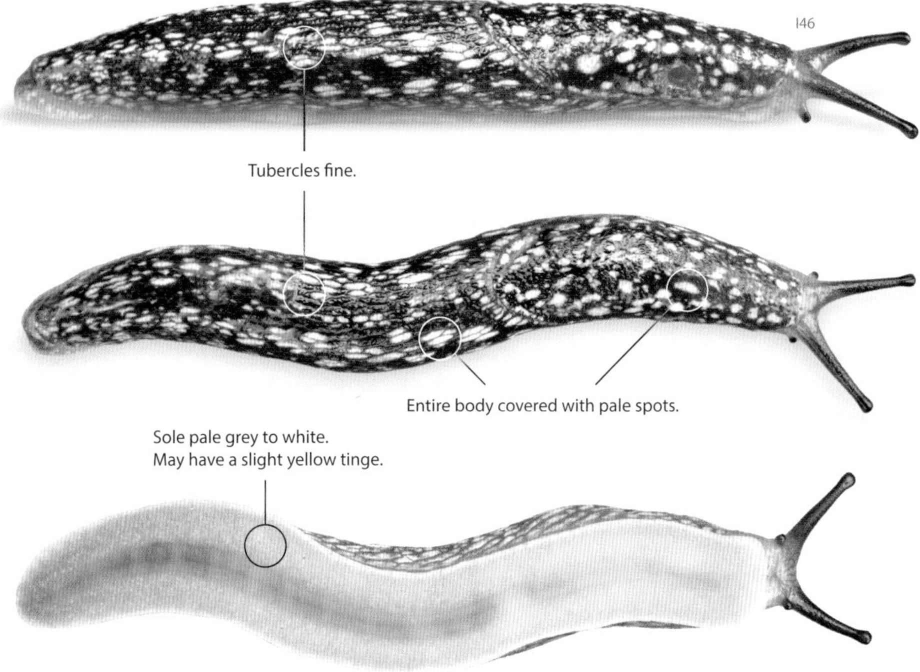

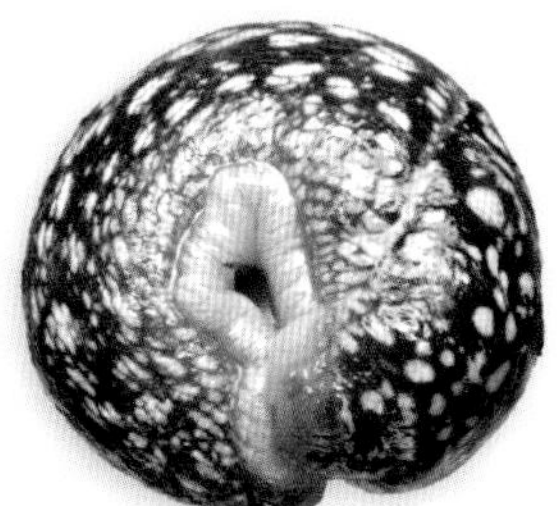

When disturbed, contracts to a ball formed by bending the sole in half.

Juveniles and subadults

Additional features

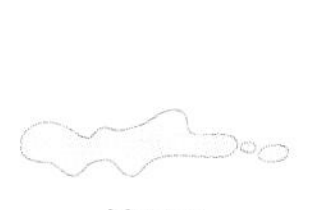

Mucus

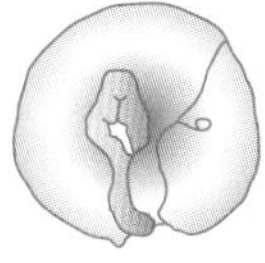

Contracted shape

Body colour

Adult size

Limax maximus Linnaeus, 1758

Leopard Slug (Tiger Slug, Great Grey Slug, Giant Garden Slug, Spotted Garden Slug, Cellar Slug)

Identification. Up to 100-150 mm extended, perhaps longer. A very large, usually strikingly patterned, robust and active slug with a short but strong keel. When contracted the body is often plump with the keel standing out and wrinkled. The mucus is colourless and sticky. The body is often gunmetal grey but ranges from pale ochre to nearly black. Both mantle and tail are usually heavily marked with dark markings. The mantle may be spotted or marbled, but never banded. The tail often has broad dark bands which may be broken into blotches or spots. The keel is sometimes slightly paler than the tail. The head and tentacles are usually reddish-brown, without dark speckles. The sole is always uniformly pale. Juveniles are similarly coloured, any mantle bands soon being broken up into spots.

Similar species. Dark woodland forms of *L. maximus* may resemble pale-soled *Limax cinereoniger*, but that species has coarser tubercles and a longer keel, and usually has dark-spotted, rather than reddish, tentacles. Rare, virtually unmarked variants of *L. maximus* still retain the plump body and reddish tentacles. Half-grown *L. maximus* may closely resemble *Lehmannia marginata*, but differ in their relatively longer, usually redder tentacles and stickier mucus. Species of *Ambigolimax* tend to be pinkish all over, rather than just on the tentacles, and reach a smaller size. *Limax maximus* rarely has the green or yellow colouring seen in the species of *Limacus*. Juveniles of *L. cinereoniger* and other species that are banded on the mantle can be ruled out as *L. maximus*.

Dissection is required only in the most difficult of these cases (p. 117).

Pest status. This species is seldom implicated as a plant pest (South, 1992). An omnivore, it strongly prefers fungi and dead plant and animal matter to live plants, although these are sometimes attacked (Cook & Radford, 1988). It is however attracted to pet food and stored products and is occasionally recorded indoors.

Range. Throughout Britain and Ireland except in the highlands. Probably native to much of western Europe but widely spread by man. Established on all continents except Antarctica (e.g. Barker, 1999; Grimm *et al.*, 2010; Herbert, 2010).

Habitat. Broadleaved woodland of all types is the preferred habitat along with scrub, hedgerows, parks and gardens. It often occurs near buildings (occasionally indoors) and in areas with colder winters it is more strictly associated with man. It has been recorded near the high water mark of Irish sea shores (Scharff, 1891), on sea cliffs in Pembrokeshire, and, remarkably, even on beaches in Chile (Landler & Nuñez, 2012), perhaps reflecting some salt tolerance.

Biology. *Limax maximus* is strongly nocturnal and is a vigorous climber. It covers long distances in search of food and returns to refuges that it may defend against other slugs. Ellis (1969) claimed that it was attracted to light when hungry. Individuals are active all year round in suitable weather. Eggs may be laid throughout the milder months, and are sensitive to low, rather than high, temperatures. The species lives for several years, maturing in its first autumn (Cook & Radford, 1988).

This species is well known for its spectacular mating behaviour (p. 3). Two partners circle on an overhanging or vertical surface, lashing their tails. They secrete a tough mucus 'rope' about 150 mm long, entwine and slip down the rope to copulate at the bottom. The enormous, bluish genitalia hang below the bodies, pulsing in a globe-like configuration as sperm are exchanged. One partner often climbs up and may eat the mucus rope, although the rope's dried remains are sometimes found in the morning.

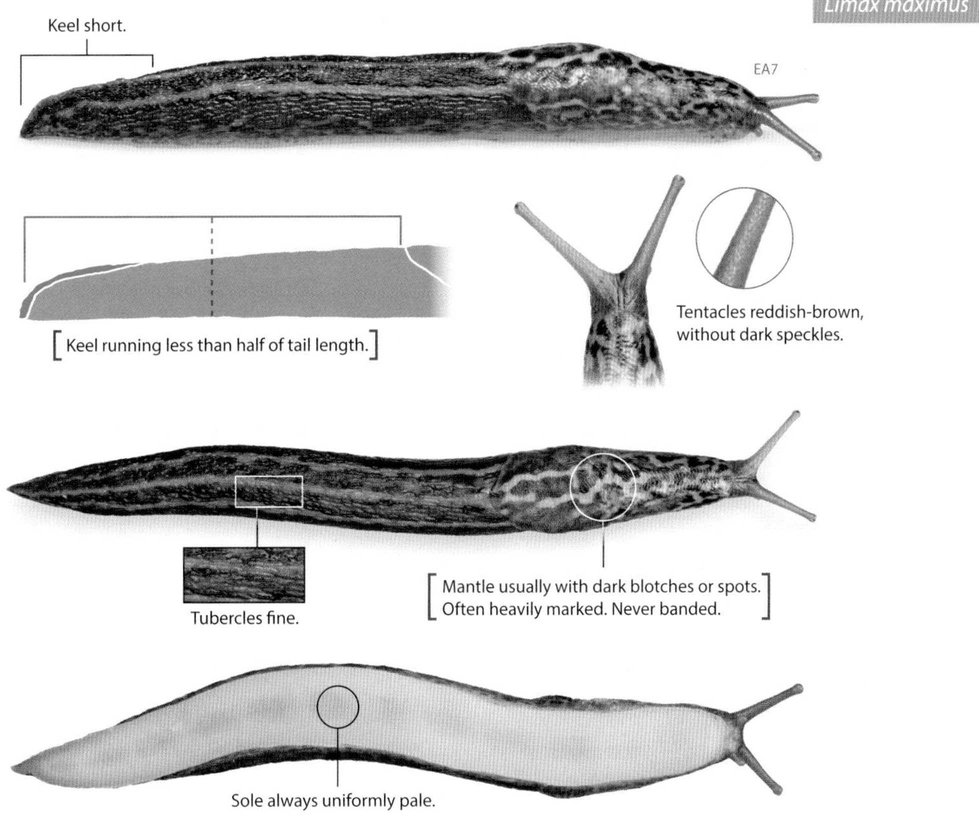

Juveniles and subadults

Variation

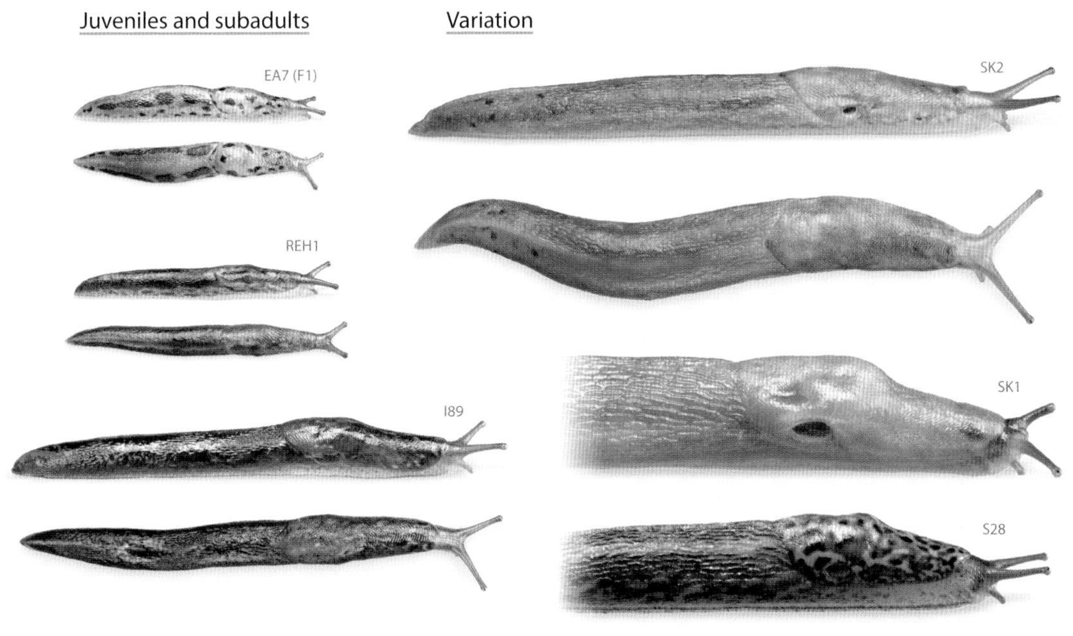

Additional features

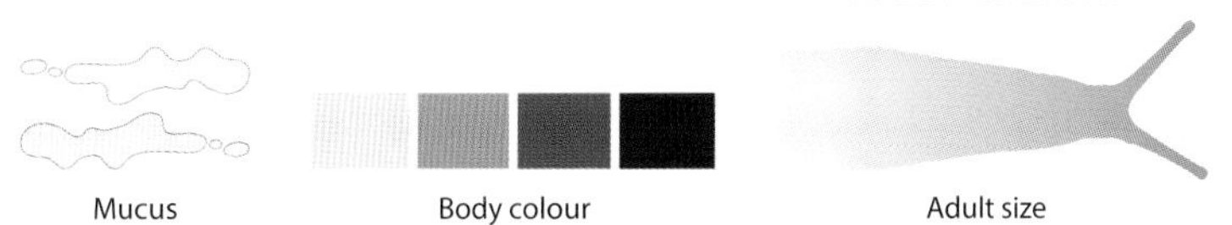

Limax cinereoniger Wolf, 1803

Ash-Black Slug (Ashy-grey Slug)

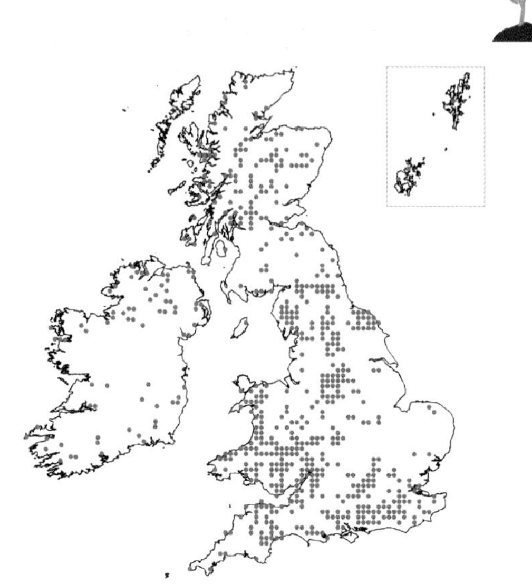

Identification. Up to 100-150 mm extended, perhaps longer (said to reach 300 mm, but rarely; Kerney & Cameron, 1979). A very large slug with a long, conspicuous keel running about half the length of the tail. The tubercles are coarse. The mucus is colourless and sticky. The body is commonly ash-black in colour but can also be pale ochre, brown, or grey. The mantle always lacks markings. The tail may have obscure lateral bands or spots, and the keel is often contrastingly pale. The head and tentacles are grey to brown, usually with minute dark speckles (Quick, 1960). The sole may be uniformly pale, especially in juveniles, but is often characteristically dark at the edges with a pale central stripe. Juveniles are paler than adults, frequently a rich toffee colour. When very young they may have broken lateral bands extending onto the mantle.

Similar species. Pale-soled individuals may be mistaken for *L. maximus*, which has a shorter keel, a plumper body, finer tubercles and reddish tentacles. *Limax maximus* is also often marked on the mantle, even when the whole slug is dark. Juvenile *L. cinereoniger* are best distinguished from *L. maximus* and other genera by their long, conspicuous keel and coarser tubercles.

Limax cf. *dacampi* is a very large, pale species known only from one area in Yorkshire. It has even coarser tubercles than *L. cinereoniger*, pale tentacles, and bluish edges to the sole.

Dissection is only required when identity is uncertain due to atypical markings or unusually large size (p. 117).

Pest status. Not a pest (a woodland species feeding mainly on fungi; Taylor, 1902-7).

Range. Widespread but local throughout Britain, becoming rare in the lowlands of southeast England. Widespread but even more local in Ireland, though much less so in the north. A native forest species through most of Europe, replaced by related species in the south. Unlike several other British limacids, it does not appear to have been introduced beyond Europe (a report from Canada is probably erroneous; Grimm *et al.*, 2010).

Habitat. *Limax cinereoniger* was declared "our noblest slug, and a wonderful judge of scenery" by Boycott (1936). It is famous as an indicator of old or ancient woodland, including Scots pine woodland. It tolerates traditional woodland management and a degree of replanting but generally requires a woodland ecosystem. In eastern England, it is restricted to ancient woods (e.g. Killeen, 1992). Exceptions to this are few. It has been recorded from sea cliffs in western Ireland and peat bog around forestry plantations in Co. Galway and in other areas. In Pembrokeshire (Quick, 1960) and the Welsh mountains it seems it can sometimes persist in formerly wooded but now open areas up to the theoretical treeline. It has been recorded from a large garden adjoining woodland in the New Forest, but generally is not found in gardens or other disturbed habitats. Most of its sites are in moist woodlands on acid soils (Walden, 1981; Tattersfield, 1990) although it is not averse to chalk or limestone (Kerney, 1999).

Biology. This nocturnal species is an active climber and able to find fungi or moisture from some distance away (Taylor, 1902-7; A. Norris, pers. comm.). Its high mobility seems to let it exploit deep refuges and it can be almost impossible to find by day during dry weather.

It is able to live for around five years, maturing after two. It can self-fertilise, or mate suspended from overhanging branches. The genitalia hang down as long as the body but *L. cinereoniger* does not produce the mucus 'rope' seen in *L. maximus* (Quick, 1960).

Limax cinereoniger and *L. maximus* are seldom found together in the same area of woodland, potentially reflecting some antagonism as well as differing habitat preferences.

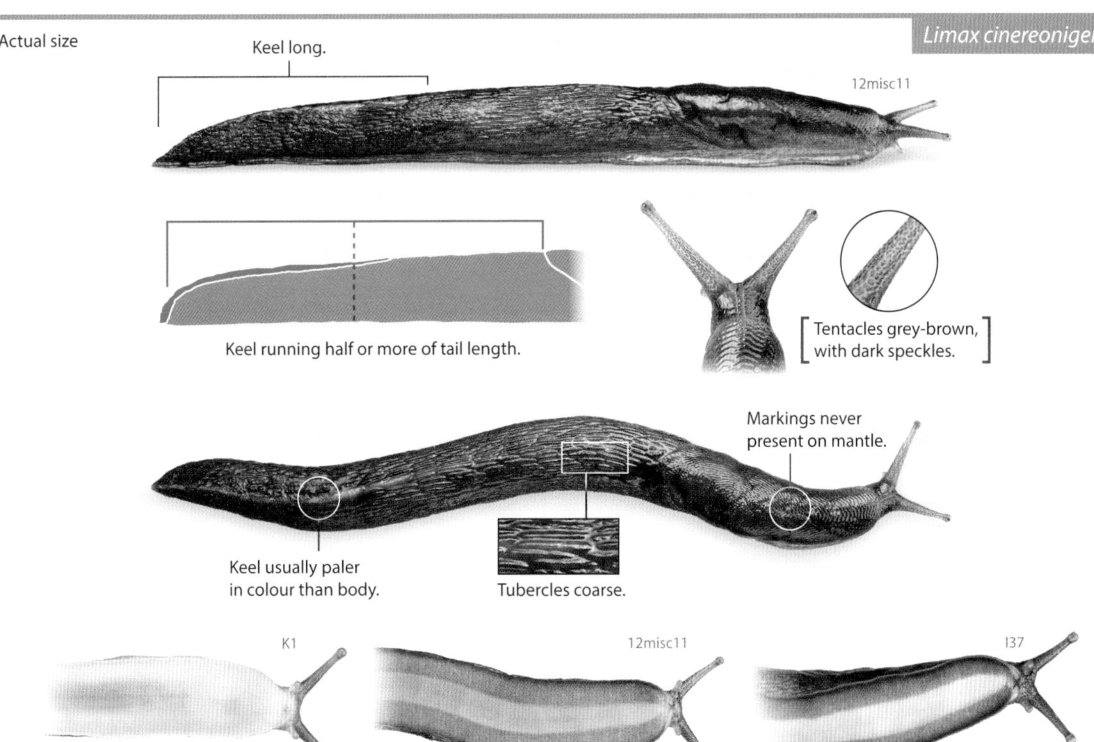

Sole often with dark stripes at sides with a pale central strip, or uniformly pale.

Juveniles and subadults

Variation

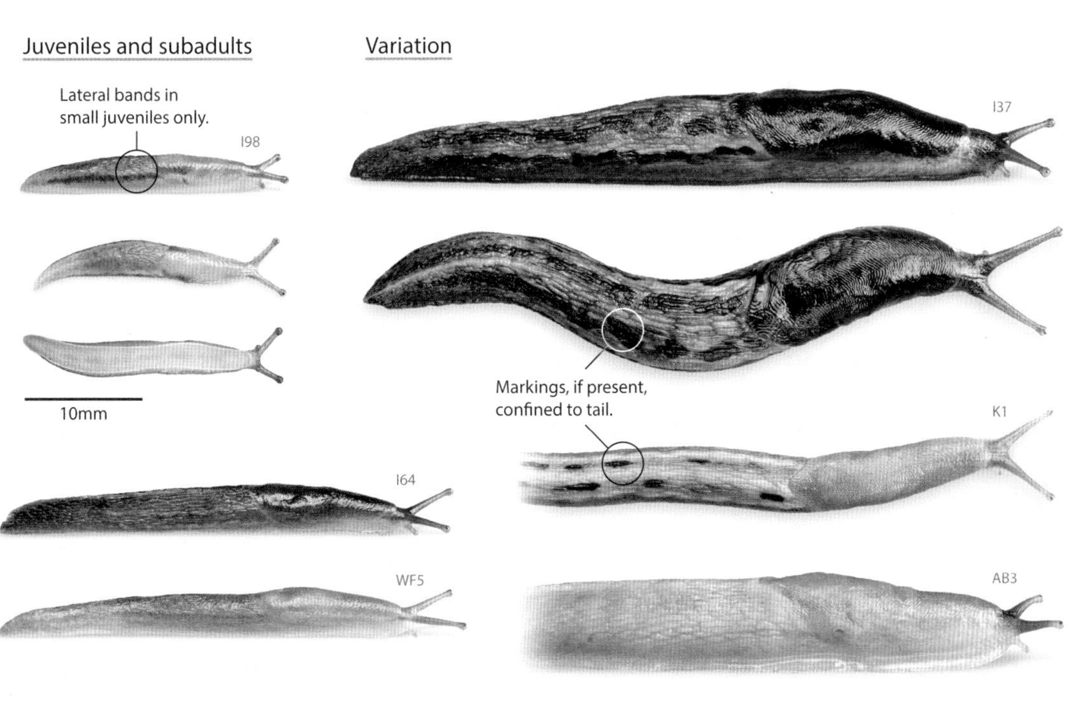

Additional features

Mucus

Body colour

Adult size

Limax cf. *dacampi* Menegazzi, 1854

Fylingthorpe Slug

Identification. Up to 130-150 mm extended. A very large, heavily built slug with a long, conspicuous keel running about half the length of the tail. The tubercles are even coarser than those of *L. cinereoniger*. The mucus is pale yellow and sticky. The body is pale ochre in colour. The mantle always lacks markings. The tail may have obvious black spots, and the keel is contrastingly pale. A pale stripe along the keel may continue as far as the mantle. The head and tentacles are pale, lacking the dark speckles seen in *Limax cinereoniger*. The sole is blue-grey at the edges with a pale central stripe. The edges may become darker towards the tail tip. When disturbed, the animal may lurch back and forth repeatedly, recalling a stalling car.

Only one population is yet known in Britain so this species may be more variable than this suggests.

Similar species. In Britain (or Ireland) this species is likely to be confused only with *L. cinereoniger* (it differs from *L. maximus* in the same ways as does *L. cinereoniger*). *Limax* cf. *dacampi* has even coarser tubercles than *L. cinereoniger*, has paler tentacles without dark speckles, and has bluish edges to the sole. It is even larger and more heavily-built when adult and has yellower mucus than typical *L. cinereoniger*. The lurching behaviour does not seem to have been recorded in that species.

Dissection is recommended to confirm the identify of suspect individuals (p. 117).

Pest status. Unkown

Range. So far known only from one locality near Robin Hood's Bay in north-east Yorkshire. The slugs of Yorkshire (although a very large area) have been relatively well-studied so it is unlikely that this very conspicuous species has been widely overlooked in the region.

Limax cf. *dacampi.* is almost certainly an accidental introduction from the Apennine mountains of Tuscany, central Italy, where genetically similar individuals have been collected.

Habitat. The Yorkshire site is an ornamental mixed woodland with an understorey of cherry laurel, in the grounds of a boarding school. The slugs have also been seen around the school buildings.

Biology. Little published information is available. The species is genetically and anatomically very distinct from *L. cinereoniger* and *L. maximus* (Rowson *et al.*, 2014). There is a great evolutionary diversity of *Limax* species in the Apennines, the Mediterranean, the Balkans and Alps with several species endemic to relatively small areas (Nitz *et al.*, 2009; 2010).

These continental taxa include *L. punctulatus* Sordelli, 1871, *L. redii* Gerhardt, 1933, and others notable for their extraordinarily long penises. During mating these hang entwined like those of *L. maximus* (p. 62) although exchange sperm in a different way (Nitz *et al.*, 2010). The penis of Yorkshire specimens is of this form, and is longer than the animal's body even when retracted (p. 117). When extended it is likely to be twice this length or more. Eggs laid in captivity were similar in appearance to those of *L. maximus* but failed to hatch.

This species was discovered by M. J. Perry, a teacher at the school. While on fieldwork in east Yorkshire we were shown the site by T. Crawford and A. Norris who had been sent photographs of the species.

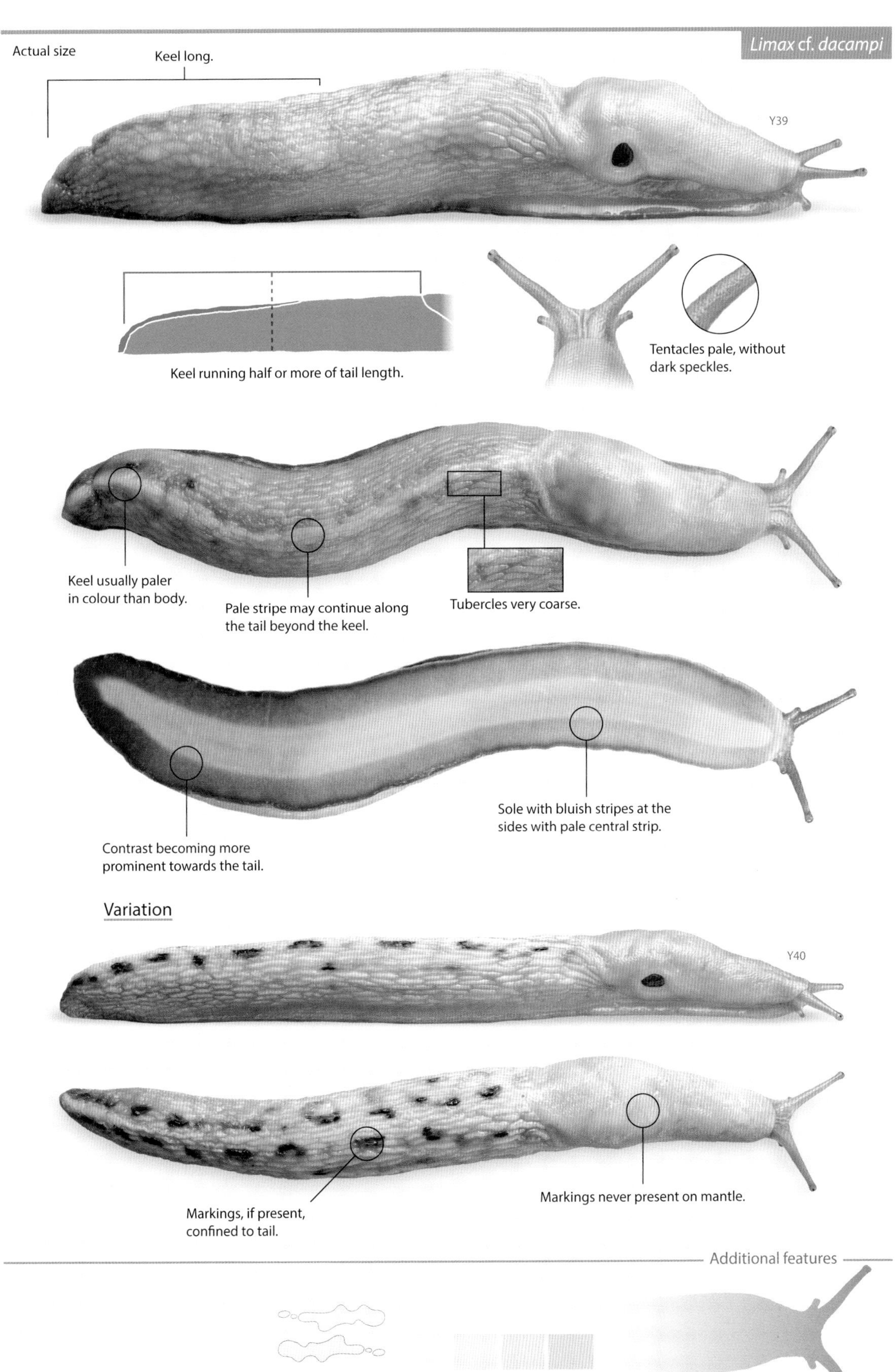
Actual size
Keel long.
Y39
Keel running half or more of tail length.
Tentacles pale, without dark speckles.
Keel usually paler in colour than body.
Pale stripe may continue along the tail beyond the keel.
Tubercles very coarse.
Contrast becoming more prominent towards the tail.
Sole with bluish stripes at the sides with pale central strip.
Variation
Y40
Markings, if present, confined to tail.
Markings never present on mantle.
Additional features
Mucus
Body colour
Adult size

Limacus flavus (Linnaeus, 1758)

Yellow Cellar Slug (Yellow Slug, Yellow Garden Slug, House Slug, Cellar Slug)

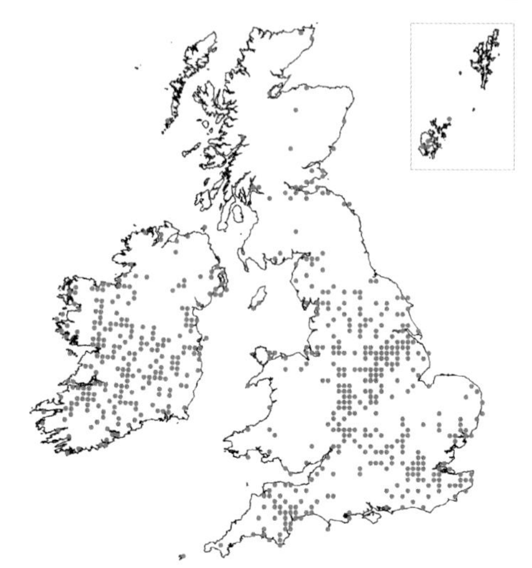

Identification. Up to 80-130 mm extended. A medium-sized to large slug with a short, indistinct keel. The body and tail are often slender (relative to *L. maculatus*), tapering gradually towards the tail tip. The tubercles are relatively fine. Body colour varies from yellow-green through orange to yellow-brown. The body is marked with yellow-brown or yellow-green blotches or spots. Characteristically a central yellow stripe extends along the back to the tail tip. Bands are never present. The tentacles are steely blue. The sole is pale. The mucus is colourless or tinged yellow to orange, mainly around the head. Juveniles are darker and greener than adults.

Similar species. Juveniles may resemble *Lehmannia marginata* or *Limax maximus*. However, both adults and juveniles usually have a green tinge not present in other genera, and have blue or bluish tentacles not seen in *L. marginata* or *L. maximus*.

Dissection is not required except to distinguish *L. flavus* from *L. maculatus* if uncertainty exists (p. 117).

Pest status. Probably not a pest of live plants, though may attack stored products (Godan, 1983). An effective feeder on mould and algae, and often found in compost heaps. It may be responsible for slug trails left on indoor carpets and will steal or foul pet food. It has been thought to damage flowers when confined in conservatories.

Range. Widespread throughout Britain and Ireland, but apparently increasingly even more local than the map suggests. *Limacus flavus* is either declining, or is over-recorded due to confusion with *L. maculatus* (p. 70). For this guide, typical examples could be obtained only from Devon and South Wales.

Originally probably a Mediterranean species that has long been transported by humans. Wiktor *et al.* (2000) said it was a forest species originating in south-east Europe and Asia Minor. It occurs throughout northern Europe and has been introduced to all continents except Antarctica, including in tropical regions (e.g. Quick, 1960). Some of these populations may in fact belong to *L. maculatus*.

Habitat. Almost always closely associated with buildings, often feeding and possibly even breeding indoors. Until recently, a common garden and urban species. Records from woodlands (e.g. Quick, 1960), unless from old ruins, are somewhat suspect (see *L. maculatus*).

Biology. *Limacus flavus* often passes unnoticed despite its large size. It is strictly nocturnal, emerging well after dark to graze on algae, fungi and detritus. According to Taylor (1902-7) it is attracted to leftover food and even to sugar or soap. It is a strong climber. It thrives best where deep refuges in ventilators, cracks or drains are available and will appear to home, returning to the same ones daily. Individuals may shelter together though are seldom found in such large aggregations as *L. maculatus*. As in many slugs and snails, one eye tentacle may be left half extended as a lookout (Taylor, 1902-7).

The species lives for several years, maturing in the first autumn, as does *L. maculatus* (Cook & Radford, 1988). Mating is said to be rapid (Quick, 1960; Barker, 1999) as it is in *L. maculatus*, but the species can self-fertilise (Evans, 1983). The characteristically lemon-shaped eggs are sensitive to low, rather than high temperatures in *L. flavus* but sensitive to both extremes in *L. maculatus* (Cook & Radford, 1988). The eggs can however survive underwater (Welter-Schultes, 2012).

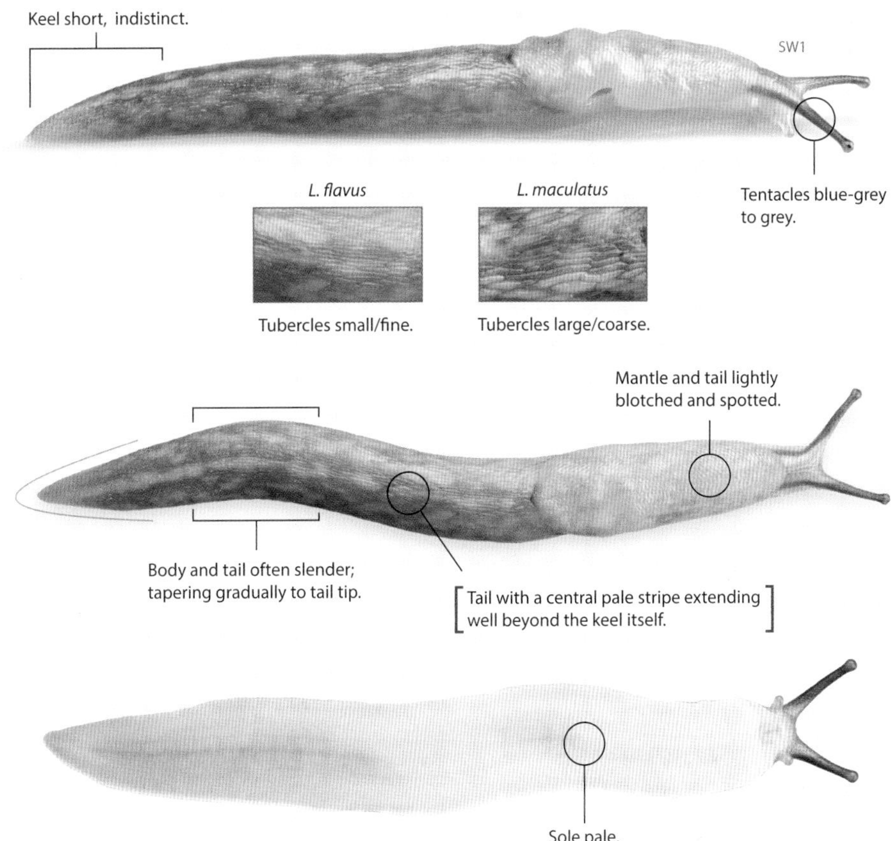

Juveniles and subadults

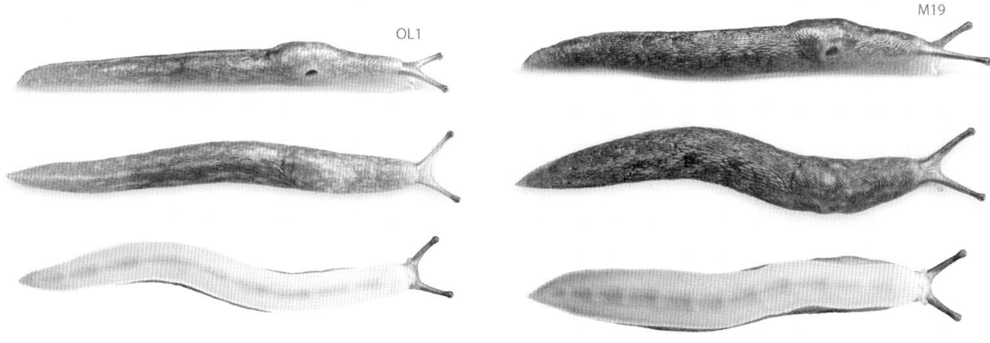

Additional features

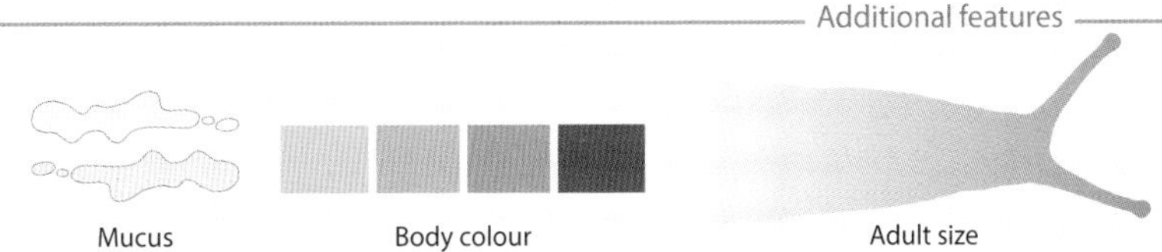

Limacus maculatus (Kaleniczenko, 1851)

Green Cellar Slug (Irish Yellow Slug)

Identification. Up to 80-130 mm extended. A medium-sized to large slug with a short, indistinct keel. The body and tail are often plump and cylindrical (compared to *L. flavus*), tapering abrubtly towards the tail tip. The tubercles are relatively coarse. Body colour varies from pale ochre, through yellow-green to grey (rarely) and blackish. The body is marked with deep green-grey or green-black blotches or spots. Any pale stripe on the keel does not extend onto the tail, at least in adults. Bands are never present. The tentacles are grey-blue. The sole is pale. The mucus is colourless or tinged yellow to orange, mainly around the head. Juveniles are often very dark green, sometimes nearly black.

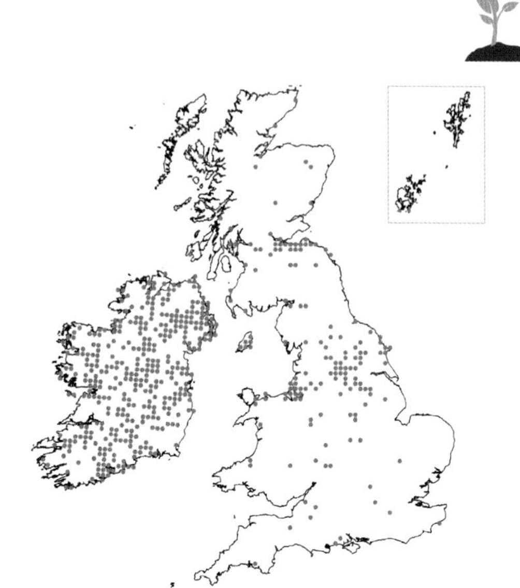

Similar species. Adults of *Limacus* species are generally unmistakeable as such, given their size, colour and markings. Juveniles may resemble *Lehmannia marginata* or *Limax maximus*. However, both adults and juveniles usually have a green tinge not present in other genera, and have blue or bluish tentacles not seen in *L. marginata* or *L. maximus*.

It has been said that the markings of *L. maculatus* usually extend right to the foot fringe while stopping higher on the body sides in *L. flavus*, and that *L. maculatus* matures at a smaller size (Wiktor & Norris, 1982). These differences do not seem to be reliable in British and Irish specimens.

Dissection is not required except to distinguish *L. maculatus* and *L. flavus* with certainty (p. 117). This is recommended if the presence of *L. flavus* is to be ruled out.

Pest status. As for *L. flavus*, which has a similar diet (Cook & Radford, 1988). It has been recorded in Ireland eating damp wallpaper off walls in outbuildings, and devouring pet food during the night. It also has an ability to thrive away from buildings which may be a cause for concern although it generally does not eat green crops and has been present in Irish woods for a long time without significant damage being recorded.

Range. Widespread throughout Britain and particularly Ireland, apparently much more so than the map suggests. This species is certainly increasing its range and abundance in Britain but has been common in Ireland for many years.

Limacus maculatus was first reported as *Limax grossui* Lupu, 1970 (Chatfield, 1976) and later described as a new species, *Limax pseudoflavus*, from Co. Roscommon (Evans, 1978a,b). All three names apply to the same species (Wiktor & Norris, 1982). *Limax ecarinatus* Boettger, 1881 is sometimes used for this species (Wiktor, 2001; Welter-Schultes, 2012) but is only applicable when the constituent genus is *Limax*, rather than *Limacus*.

The species was described from the Crimea, Ukraine (Kaleniczenko, 1851). It is native to the forests of the Caucasus and Black Sea coasts (Wiktor & Norris, 1982). It is scattered throughout northern Europe and Russia. On other continents it has often been discussed but rarely recorded (e.g. Barker, 1999; Wiktor *et al.*, 2000; McDonnell *et al.*, 2009).

Habitat. As for *L. flavus* but also increasingly common in woods, forestry and farmland. In Ireland and western Britain it can occur wherever the shelter of logs or debris is available, sometimes in groups of several dozen animals.

Biology. In the last 100 years, or even the last 50 years, *L. maculatus* has become very common. This seems to have been at the expense of *L. flavus*, at least in the well-monitored areas of Belfast and Leeds (NMNI, 2010; A. Norris, pers. comm.). Taylor's (1902-7) and Quick's (1960) descriptions and figures show they were familiar mainly with *L. flavus*. Nevertheless they both mentioned records from woods, a habitat where now only *L. maculatus* is common (although comprehensive night surveys have not been done).

Possibly *L. maculatus* competes better in our landscape and climate than *L. flavus* and is replacing it. Perhaps it is simply better at concealment in more open habitats. Welter-Schultes (2012) assigns an apparent decline of *L. flavus* in central Europe to the restoration of old buildings. There is also genetic evidence for unequal hybridisation between the two species (Rowson *et al.*, 2014).

Actual size

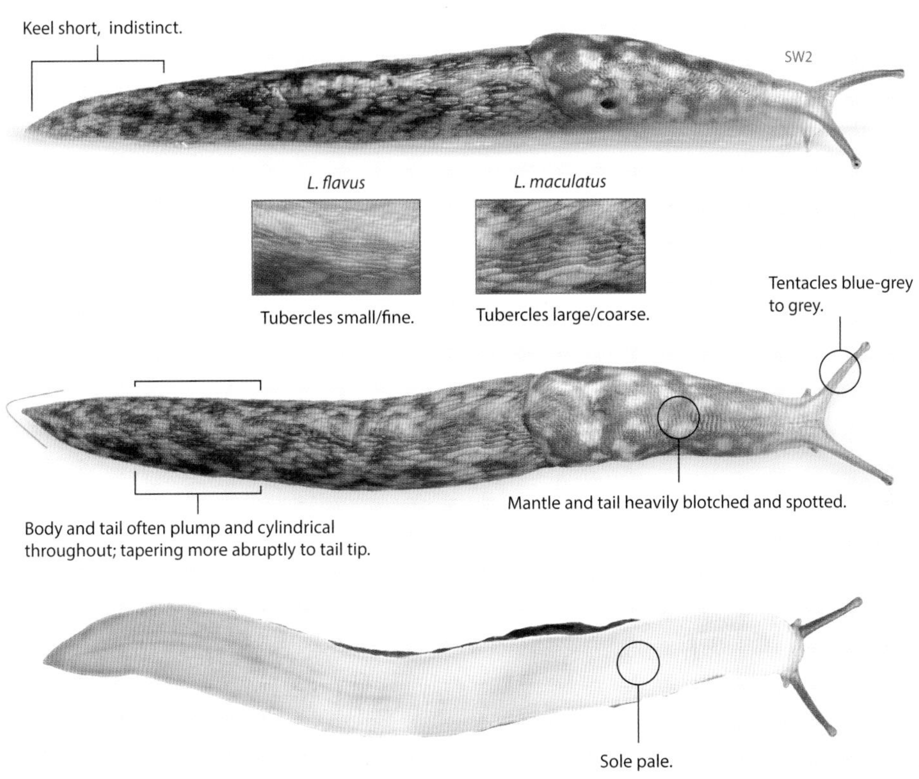

Juveniles and subadults

Variation

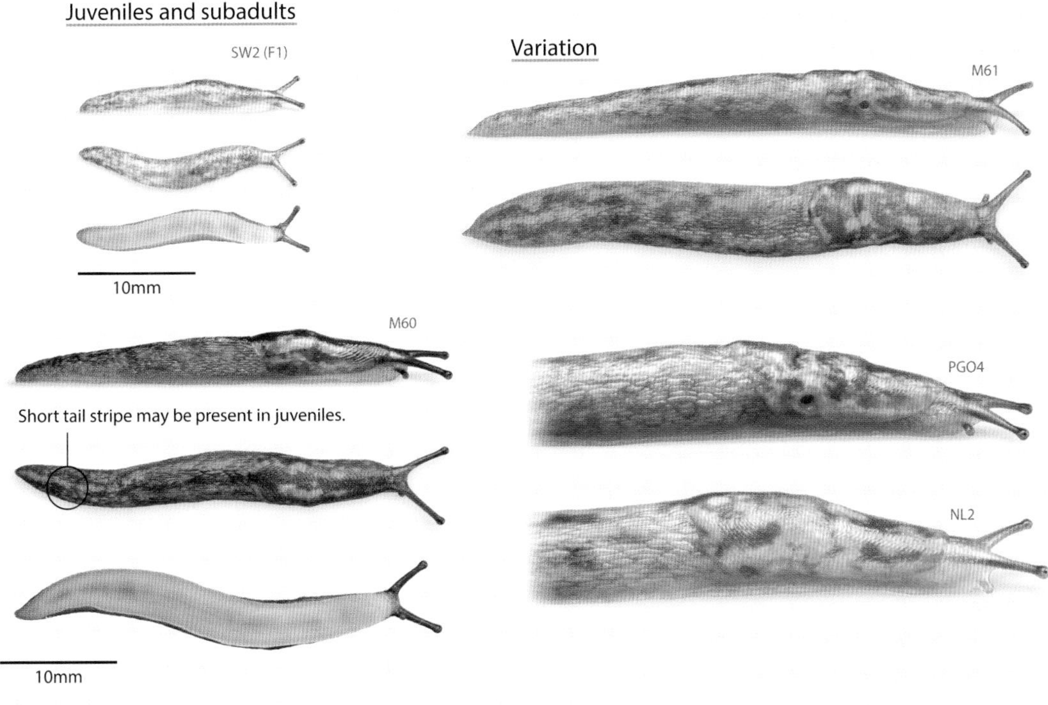

Additional features

Mucus

Body colour

Adult size

Malacolimax tenellus (O. F. Müller, 1774)

Lemon Slug (Tender Slug, Slender Slug)

Identification. Up to 35-50 mm extended. A small, fast-moving slug with a short keel. The body texture is noticeably soft and flaccid. Characteristically the body is usually unmarked, slightly translucent lemon-yellow, although individuals range between light brown and orange. The tentacles are dark brown, black or violet. Very indistinct brown bands are occasionally present on the mantle. The mucus is lightly tinged yellow or orange. Juveniles are paler than adults or colourless.

Similar species. Juveniles of *Limax*, *Limacus* and *Lehmannia* are usually heavily marked and darker. If unmarked, they can be distinguished by their coarser tubercles. *Deroceras* species have a more prominent keel and an asymmetrical pattern of mantle grooves.

Pest status. Not considered a pest (feeds on woodland fungi).

Range. Patchy and local across Britain. Not recorded from Ireland.

This species may be underrecorded although it is enthusiastically reported when found. Apparent gaps in its British distribution may be bridged by future records. However it is certainly rarer in southern and western Scotland and south-west England than elsewhere (the last records for Devon and north-west Scotland are pre-1950). In southern England it has been recently reconfirmed as present in Epping Forest but apparently not yet in the New Forest. A 19th century report from Shetland given by Taylor (1902-7) is highly doubtful.

The habitat and distribution of *M. tenellus* suggest it is native to Britain (it seems not to have colonised Ireland, or to have become extinct there). It otherwise occurs throughout northern and central Europe except northern Scandinavia and Iceland. It is uncommon in many north-west European countries.

Habitat. In Britain *M. tenellus* is found only in long-established woodlands, both broad-leaved and coniferous, on a variety of soils. There are a few records from ancient wood-pasture or ancient trees standing in secondary woodland (Alexander, 2010). It is unknown from modern plantations, except where adjacent to or part of older woods. It appears dependent on continuous tree cover, even in woods much modified by coppicing, pollarding or replanting. Its ability to disperse across unwooded habitats seems to be limited. It is thus considered a very good indicator of ancient woodland (i.e. woodland dating back to at least 1600 in England and Wales, or 1750 in Scotland). Other slugs usually present in the same habitats include *Limax cinereoniger* and *Lehmannia marginata*. Although sometimes abundant, *M. tenellus* is easily the least widespread of these.

Biology. The species is only easily found during the fruiting season of fungi (mushrooms and toadstools) on which it feeds. A wide range of fungus species is attacked although damage to *Russula* and *Boletus* species is often noted. It is also said to graze lichens and algae (Welter-Schultes, 2012). Although active mainly at night, in moist weather *M. tenellus* can be found on fungi or in nearby litter, pine needles, or dead wood. It climbs trees only weakly. The species is annual, laying eggs in the autumn after mating, although self-fertilisation is possible (Foltz *et al.*, 1984; Welter-Schultes, 2012). The juveniles feed underground on the mycelia (root-like networks) of fungi so are rarely seen.

Malacolimax tenellus is clearly vulnerable to the destruction of ancient woodland and as such seems likely to have declined. Sensitive afforestation could perhaps favour its spread.

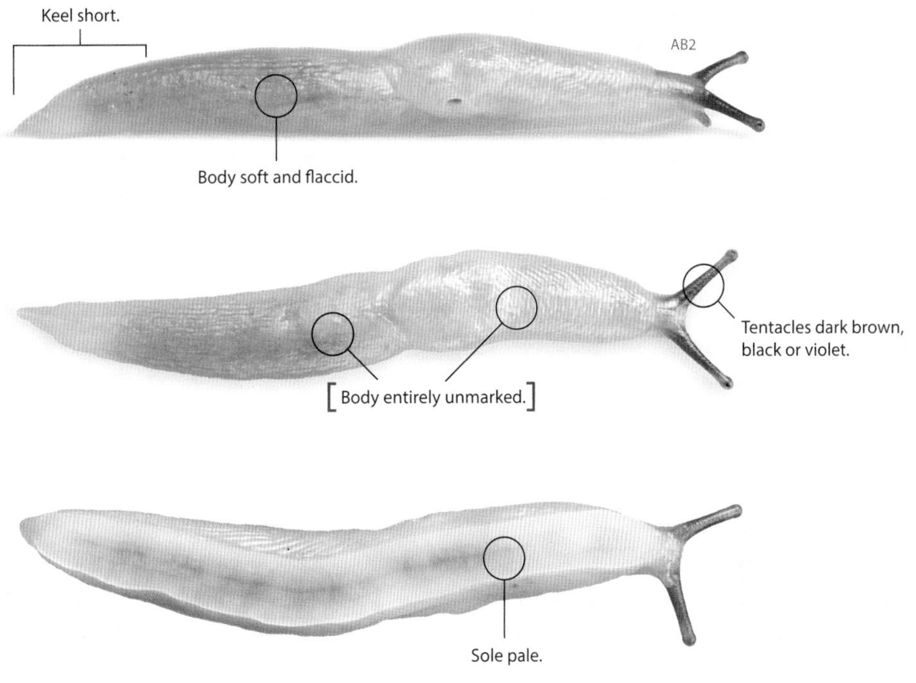

Variation

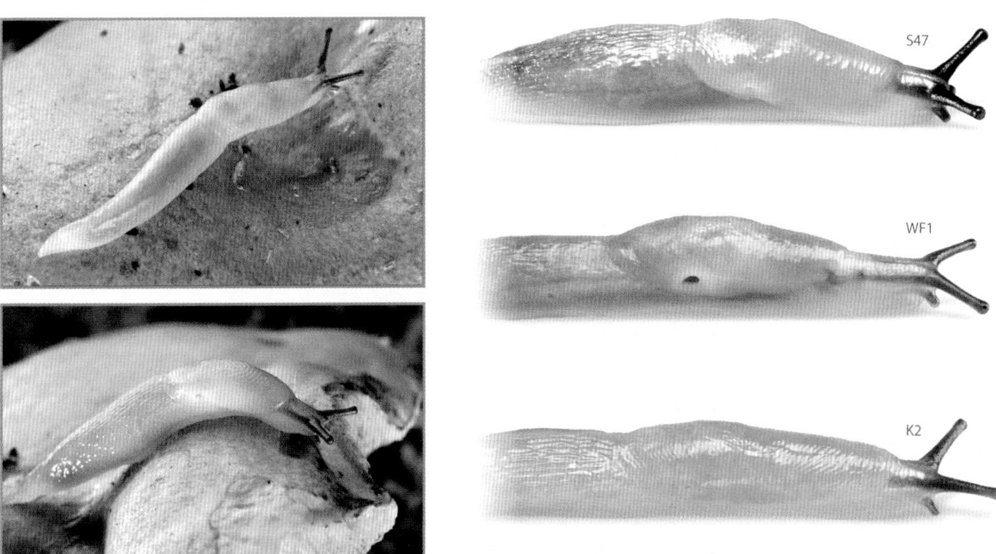

Additional features

Mucus

Body colour

Adult size

Lehmannia marginata (O. F. Müller, 1774)

Tree Slug

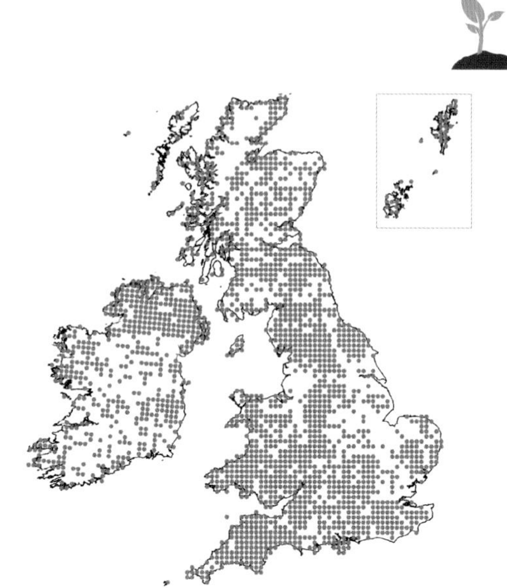

Identification. Up to 60-90 mm extended. A medium-sized slug with a short keel. The body contracts to a hump or is bent into a C-shape. Body colour varies (although seldom much within a population) from pale grey to ochre or brown. A pinkish tinge is usually absent. In wet conditions, the body is translucent against strong light. The body usually has diffuse dark markings, including blotches, spots, or faint lateral bands. Occasionally, the whole body is spotted with neat black spots, or is almost covered with black pigment. A pale central stripe often runs from the keel onto the tail, longer than the keel itself. The sole is pale. The mucus is colourless, watery and copious, causing the slug to slip around and out of the hand. Juveniles resemble adults, although the lateral bands may show a little more strongly.

Similar species. *Lehmannia marginata* is generally darker than the *Ambigolimax* species, lacks the pinkish tinge, and has more watery mucus. The juveniles of *Ambigolimax* species are more distinctly (and thinly) banded than those of *L. marginata*.

It can be more difficult to distinguish *L. marginata* from half-grown *Limax maximus*, or even *L. cinereoniger*. The *Limax* species are firmer-bodied, often fatter, and have longer tentacles for their size. In *L. maximus* the tentacles are often reddish. The distinct, heavy blotches of the common forms of *L. maximus* are less common in *L. marginata* whose pattern tends to be more diffuse. On handling the *Limax* species have stickier, less watery mucus.

Dissection not required.

Pest status. Not a pest (has a specialised diet and does not attack plants).

Range. Widespread across Britain and Ireland, although more local in the industrial Midlands, London, eastern England and the far north.

This native species occurs almost throughout Europe, although it gives way to close relatives in the south. It has been reported as introduced into Australia and New Zealand (Taylor, 1902-7; Quick, 1960; South, 1992), but the latter populations were either misidentified or short-lived according to Barker (1999). It is established in Newfoundland, Canada but was misidentified elsewhere in North America (Grimm *et al.*, 2010).

Habitat. This is the archetypal slug of tree trunks, particularly in western woods. It can also exist in treeless rocky places, from mortared stone walls and ruins to sea cliffs and mountain summits over 1000 m, where dark forms predominate. It has been suggested these may form a seperate species, *L. rupicola* Lessona & Pollonera, 1882 (Bank *et al.*, 2007), but this does not seem justified in Britain or Ireland (Rowson *et al.*, 2014). As Kerney (1999) notes, the availability of hard grazing surfaces is often critical. Their absence in lowlands and the lack of lichens in urban areas probably limits the species' distribution. It is seldom common in gardens in Britain (for an exception see Killeen, 1992) but is more so in Ireland.

Biology. *Lehmannia marginata* grazes on lichens, fungi and algae on bark and rocks using its specialised radula. In captivity it will often refuse to eat plant material and starve (e.g. Scharff, 1891). Like other woodland species it shelters, sometimes gregariously, under bark and debris by day. On mild nights it may climb several dozen metres to the canopy of tall trees, often building up mucus trackways on trunks. It was said by Taylor (1902-7) to have an unusual capacity to absorb water and to be able to remain in cavities in the crooks of the branches if it does not reach the ground. Like other slugs it has some ability to descend from branches on a mucus thread.

Mating has rarely been observed but is said to occur in the autumn and winter (Quick, 1960). It is an outcrosser (Foltz *et al.*, 1984) and may be annual, unlike larger limacids, or live as long as three years (Welter-Schultes, 2012). The eggs are vulnerable to high, rather than low, temperatures (Quick, 1960; Cook & Radford, 1988).

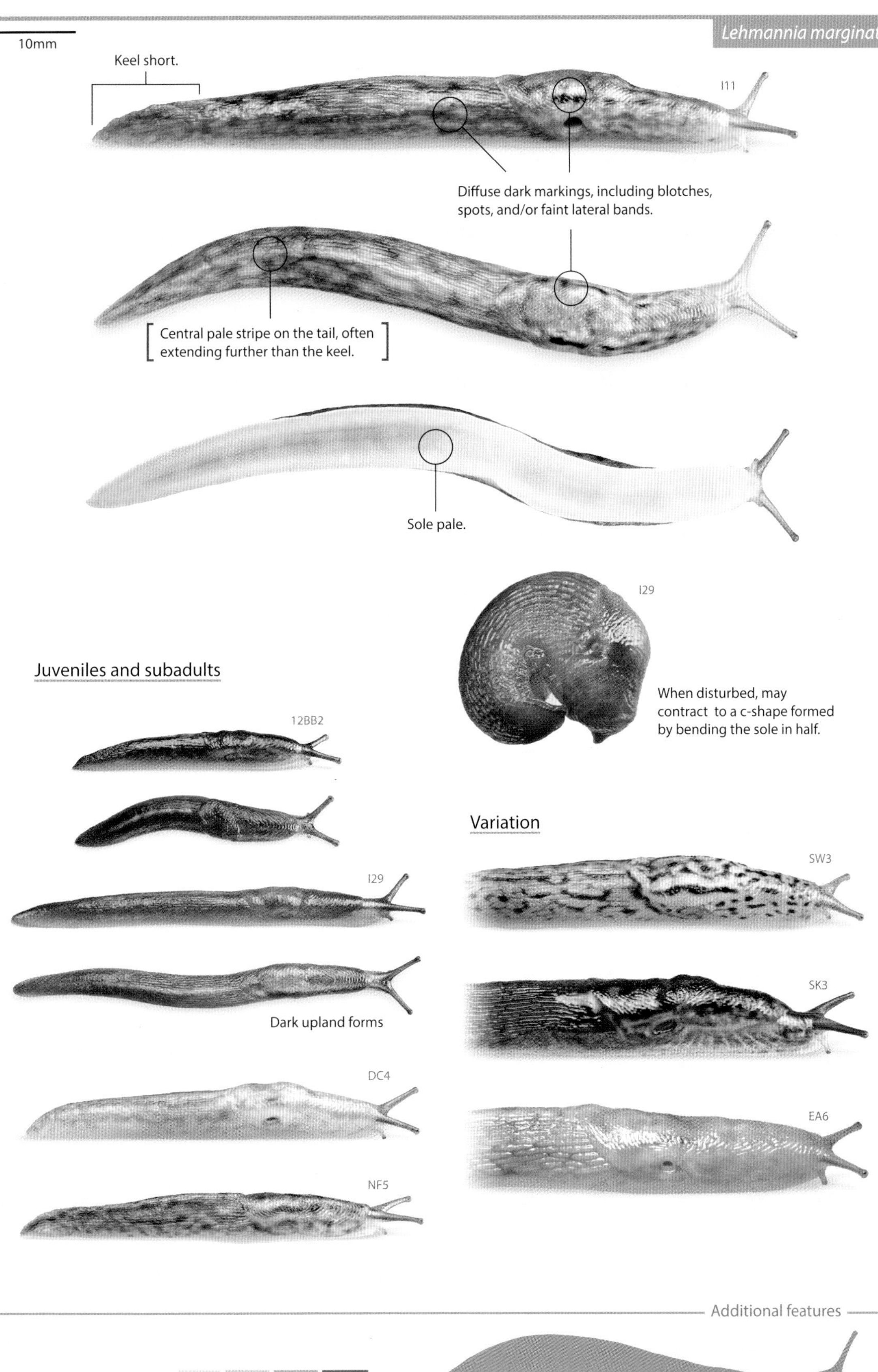
10mm
Keel short.
I11
Diffuse dark markings, including blotches, spots, and/or faint lateral bands.
Central pale stripe on the tail, often extending further than the keel.
Sole pale.
I29
When disturbed, may contract to a c-shape formed by bending the sole in half.
Juveniles and subadults
12BB2
I29
Dark upland forms
DC4
NF5
Variation
SW3
SK3
EA6
Additional features
Mucus
Body colour
Adult size

Ambigolimax valentianus (A. Férussac, 1821)

Iberian Threeband Slug (Greenhouse Slug, Threeband Garden Slug, Valencia Slug, Spanish Slug)

Identification. Up to 50-80 mm extended. A medium-sized slug with a short, inconspicuous keel. The body contracts to a hump or is bent into a C-shape when disturbed. Body colour varies from pale grey, through yellow-grey or yellow-violet to brown but usually with a distinct pinkish tinge. It may look translucent against strong light. The body is generally recognisable from distinct but thin and dark mantle bands, other markings often being faint, including blotches, spots, and faint lateral bands along the tail. The latter are high on the body and run as tramlines down to the tail tip. A third, central band is sometimes present but is more diffuse than the other two. The keel is not marked by a pale stripe. The sole is pale. The mucus is colourless. Juveniles resemble adults, although the lateral and central bands are often more distinct.

Similar species. *Ambigolimax* species are generally paler and pinker than *Lehmannia marginata* and lack the copious watery mucus. Their juveniles are particularly strongly banded. They might also be confused with young *Limax maximus*, which is firmer-bodied, often fatter, and has longer tentacles for its size.

The markings of *A. valentianus* are often more diffuse and less densely pigmented than those of *A. nyctelius*, although this is variable. In general *A. nyctelius* may vary more within a population than *A. valentianus*. The two may occur together, however. Dissection is required to distinguish them with confidence (p. 118).

Pest status. Potentially an emerging pest of horticulture (as it is on the continent; Godan, 1983). Unlike *Lehmannia marginata*, this species is omnivorous and will attack living plants. In greenhouses it can be a serious pest of orchids and other flowers (South, 1992).

Range. Under-recorded, but widespread though patchy across southern and western Britain and Ireland. Perhaps more local in the north.

The earliest British and Irish records are from public greenhouses in Swansea in 1936 and Belfast in 1948 (Quick, 1960). It was established outdoors by 1981 (Kerney, 1999) and between then and now has spread explosively (NMNI, 2010). Most urban areas probably have populations. Some confusion with *A. nyctelius* has probably occurred.

A native of Iberia (described from Valencia, eastern Spain), *A. valentianus* is spreading throughout northern Europe, outdoors as well as indoors in greenhouses. It was formally known by the name *Lehmannia poirieri* (Mabille) (Quick, 1960).

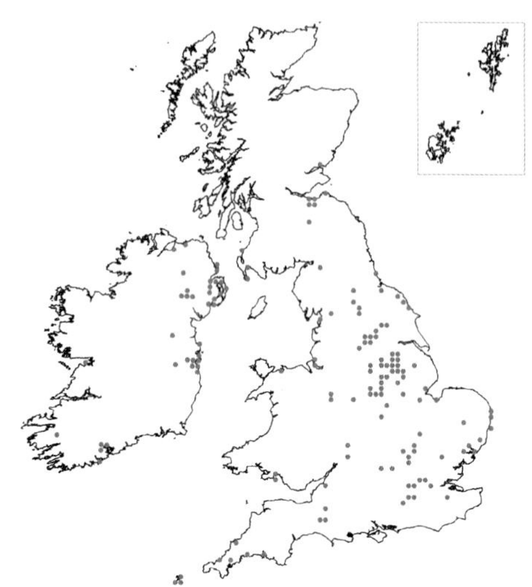

Low temperatures may limit its distribution but the species has withstood recent cold winters in Britain and Ireland. It is well established in North and South America, South Africa and Australasia and is likely to spread further through Asia (e.g. established In China, Wiktor *et al.*, 2000).

Habitat. Around buildings, in gardens and allotments, and disturbed ground generally (see also *Deroceras invadens*). It often shelters in compost bins and under plant pots in both gardens and garden centres. It is increasingly found in woodlands where it may partially displace *Lehmannia marginata* under bark on old logs, although it is still rare in more open habitats such as unsheltered grassland and fields.

Biology. *Ambigolimax valentianus* climbs trees less readily than *Lehmannia marginata*, but note the propensity to occur under bark on dead wood on the ground. It has sometimes been said never to climb (Quick, 1960; Barker, 1999; McDonnell *et al.*, 2009; Herbert, 2010 etc.), in contrast to *A. nyctelius* (Wiktor, 1996), but we have found it doing so weakly.

This species is an annual outcrosser (McCracken & Selander, 1980). *Ambigolimax nyctelius* is probably similar in this respect. Both species appear to be gregarious when at rest. The two were formerly treated in the genus *Lehmannia* along with *L. marginata* but *A. valentianus* has begun to be treated in *Ambigolimax* by some authors (e.g. Gargominy *et al.*, 2011). It seems likely given their genetic similarity (Rowson *et al.*, 2014) that the British *A. nyctelius* also belongs to this genus.

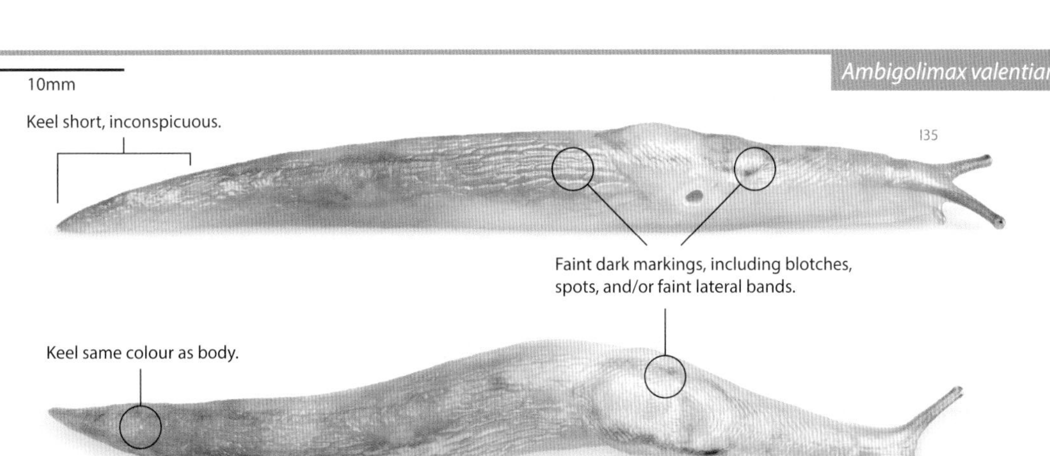

Variation

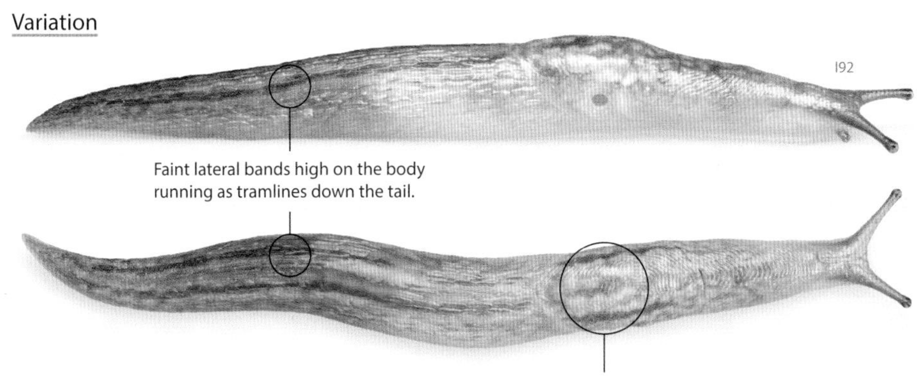

Juveniles and subadults

Additional features

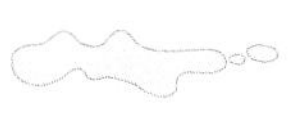
Mucus

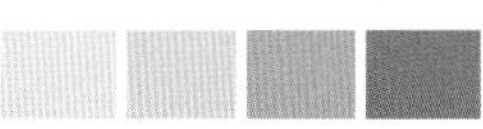
Body colour

Adult size

Ambigolimax nyctelius (Bourguignat, 1861)

Balkan Threeband Slug (Vine Slug, Bourguignat's Slug, Striped Garden Slug, Striped Field Slug)

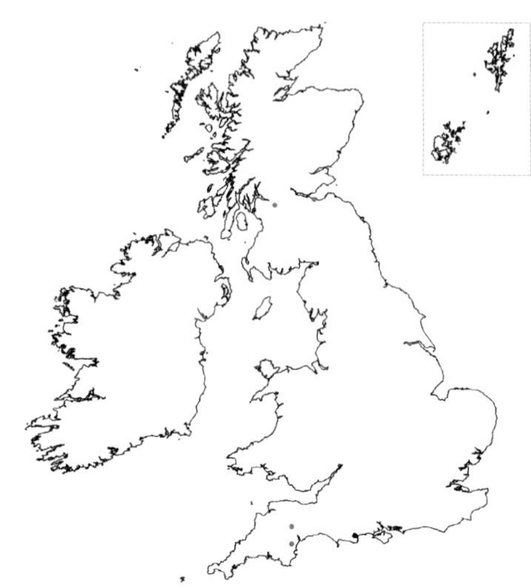

Identification. Up to 50-80 mm extended. A small to medium-sized slug with a short, inconspicuous keel close to the tail. The body contracts to a hump or is bent into a C-shape when disturbed. Body colour varies from pale grey, through yellow-grey or yellow-violet to brown but usually with a distinct pinkish tinge. It may look translucent against strong light. The body usually has prominent dark markings including blotches, spots, or faint lateral bands. These bands are often high on the body and run as tramlines down to the tail. A third, central band may be present but is more diffuse than the other two. The keel is not marked by a pale stripe. The sole is pale. The mucus is colourless. Juveniles resemble adults, although the lateral and central bands are often more distinct.

Similar species. *Ambigolimax* species are generally paler and pinker than *Lehmannia marginata* and lack the copious watery mucus. Their juveniles are particularly strongly banded. They might also be confused with young *Limax maximus*, which is firmer-bodied, often fatter, and has longer tentacles for its size.

This species is often smaller than *A. valentianus*, but the size ranges overlap. The markings are often less diffuse and darker than those of *A. valentianus*, although this is not consistent. It has been suggested that *A. nyctelius* varies more within a population than *A. valentianus*. The two may occur together, however. Dissection is required to distinguish them with confidence (p. 118).

Wiktor (1983, 1996) records that *A. nyctelius* is a tree-climber in its native habitat, in contrast to *A. valentianus*. Specimens found climbing are thus especially worth investigating.

Pest status. Potentially an emerging pest of horticulture. Like *A. valentianus*, this species attacks living plants. According to Barker (1999) it can inflict significant damage on some cultivated plants in New Zealand.

Range. Very underrecorded, but probably widespread in southwest England. Also established outdoors in South Wales and at least in greenhouses in Scotland and Northern Ireland.

The earliest British record dates from the 1930s from greenhouses at the botanical gardens in Edinburgh and Glasgow; "garden frames" in Britain were also mentioned by Quick (1960).

Despite appearing in the guide by Kerney & Cameron (1979), the species has been little recorded. It was collected outdoors in Pakefield, Suffolk in 1987 (Killeen, 1992) and at Crediton and Newton Abbot, Devon in 2000 (Anderson, 2008). Its similarity to *A. valentianus* has probably led to the species being overlooked. It might thus occur in other suitable areas although it still seems rarer than *A. valentianus* outside the southwest.

Ambigolimax nyctelius was described from North Africa by Bourguignat (1861). It is probably native to southeast Europe (the Balkans, Bulgaria etc.; Wiktor, 1983; 1996). It is spreading in northern Europe and is established in South Africa, around the Indian Ocean, in North America and in New Zealand (Quick, 1960; Barker, 1999; Griffiths & Florens, 2006; Herbert, 2010). It is common in relatively natural habitats in Australia (South, 1992).

Habitat. As for *A. valentianus*. It is not restricted to greenhouses, at least in the southwest.

Biology. The identity of this species remains problematic. British specimens (including those from Glasgow Botanical Gardens) have a much shorter penis than previously illustrated for *A. nyctelius* (Connolly, 1939; Quick, 1960; Wiktor, 1983; etc.). Other Balkan species, e.g. *Lehmannia szigethyae* Wiktor, 1975 may merit further investigation.

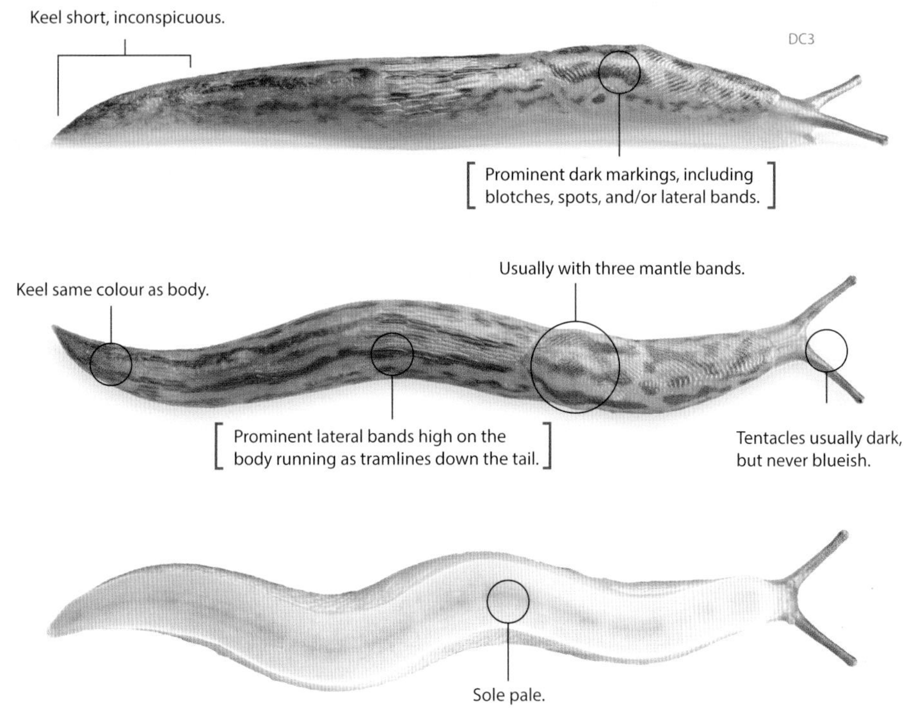

Juveniles and subadults

Variation

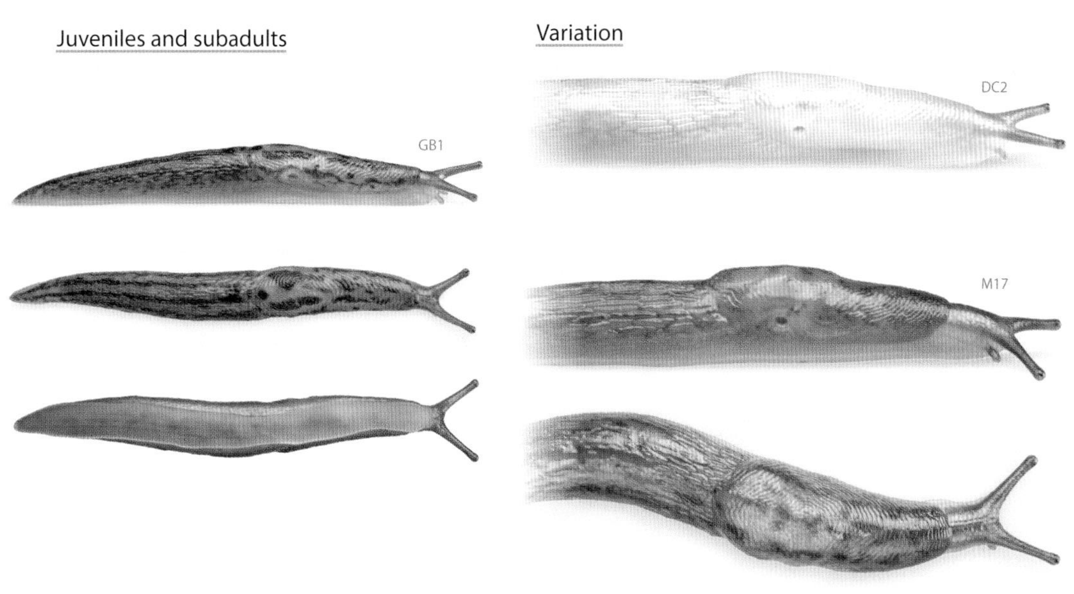

Additional features

Mucus

Body colour

Adult size

Deroceras reticulatum (O. F. Müller, 1774)

Netted Field Slug (Gray/Grey Field Slug, Field Slug, Grey Garden Slug, Reticulate Slug, Milky Slug)

Identification. Up to 35-50 mm extended. A small, active slug with a short, distinct keel, usually producing milky mucus when handled. The tail is usually longer than the mantle. The body contracts to a swollen hump. Colour is variable, even within a population, ranging from bright white to grey to deep purple-brown, but pale buff is most common. Individuals are said to darken towards winter (Quick, 1960). The rim of the breathing pore is seldom contrastingly paler than the body sides except when crawling, when it may appear paler. The head and tentacles are usually dark. The body is usually flecked with dark pigment and an irregular reticulate (fishnet) pattern between the tubercles, or larger blotches. The markings never form bands. The sole is pale but dark gut contents usually show through the central strip. The mucus is usually milky when the slugs are roughly handled, although may be released more reluctantly in dry conditions or on acidic soils. Juveniles resemble adults.

Similar species. This abundant species should soon become so familiar that confusion with other *Deroceras* is unlikely. Very dark individuals may be distinguished from other *Deroceras* species by their milky mucus. Separation from *D. agreste* is more difficult (see the account for that species).

Dissection is not required except to distinguish this species from *D. agreste*.

Pest status. By far the most commonly cited pest slug species. One of the most serious plant pests of Europe, and perhaps elsewhere. A wide range of plants are attacked including cereals, grasses and their seeds, above and below ground. The slugs shelter in soil cracks as well as on and in crop plants themselves, completely penetrating arable fields and pasture. It can also attack stored produce.

Range. Widespread and common throughout Britain and Ireland although more local in the highlands and the far north.

The native range is unclear but probably includes all of Britain and Ireland (Kerney, 1999). In eastern and northern Europe *D. reticulatum* is restricted to disturbed areas and in the south is replaced by other species in natural habitats (Wiktor, 2000). It is well-established in the temperate parts of all continents (Barker, 1999; Wiktor, 2000; Grimm *et al.*, 2010; Herbert, 2010; etc.).

Habitat. All open habitats except uplands, extensive wetlands, and some dune systems. Seldom found in closed-canopy woodland although often present at the margins.

Biology. As a pest *D. reticulatum* has been intensively studied. In its favour, it has become a laboratory organism useful in many fields of research.

The species is an annual outcrosser (Foltz *et al.*, 1984) but can breed at any time of year in Britain and Ireland, laying up to 700 eggs in total. It often produces two or more generations a year (Hunter, 1968). In favourable years the survivors can become abundant. The number of individuals can exceed 50 per square metre in gardens (Quick, 1960; South, 1992; Wiktor, 2000) and exceed 250 per square metre in cereal crops (Symondson *et al.*, 1996).

The milky coloured mucus, caused by calcareous granules (Quick, 1960), can deter predators including some carabid beetles (Mair & Port, 2002). However, other carabids can help control its populations. *D. reticulatum* is also a favoured prey of slow worms.

An increase in *D. reticulatum* shells in archaeological strata is often an indicator of the development of arable agriculture (Evans, 1972). Its effects as a pest were bemoaned in the 18th century by Thomas Pennant and Gilbert White (Ellis, 1969). Taylor (1902-7) records the species' use as a treatment for respiratory problems (eaten boiled in milk to treat consumption) as recently as the 1900s.

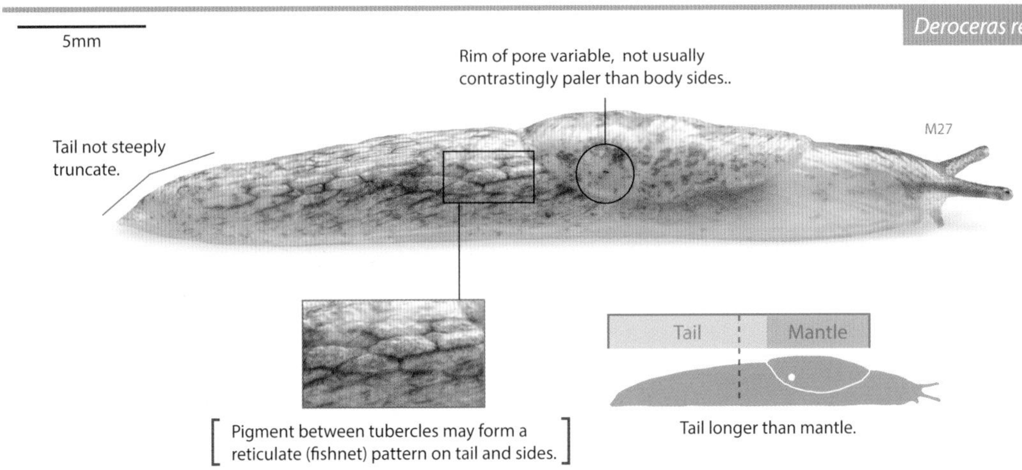

5mm
Rim of pore variable, not usually contrastingly paler than body sides..
M27
Tail not steeply truncate.
Tail
Mantle
[Pigment between tubercles may form a reticulate (fishnet) pattern on tail and sides.]
Tail longer than mantle.

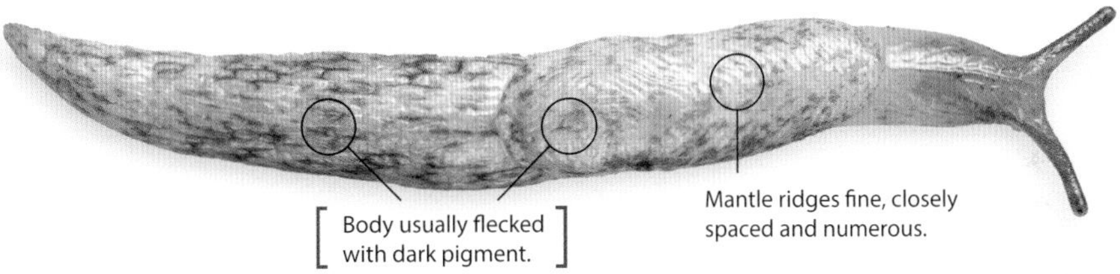

[Body usually flecked with dark pigment.]
Mantle ridges fine, closely spaced and numerous.

Sole pale.

Variation

M29

I10

12misc1

Additional features

Opaque/milky

Mucus	Body colour	Adult size

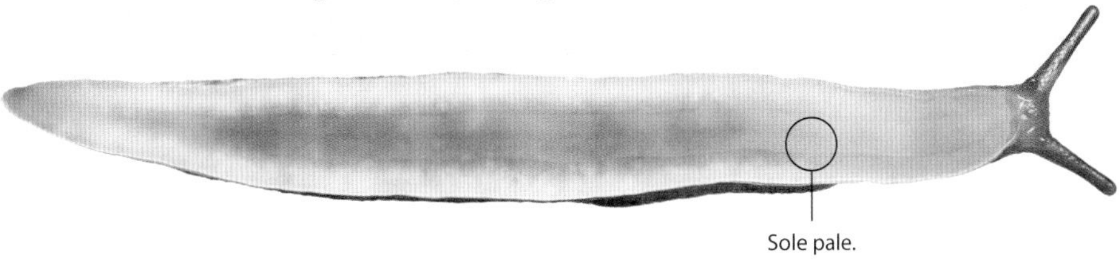

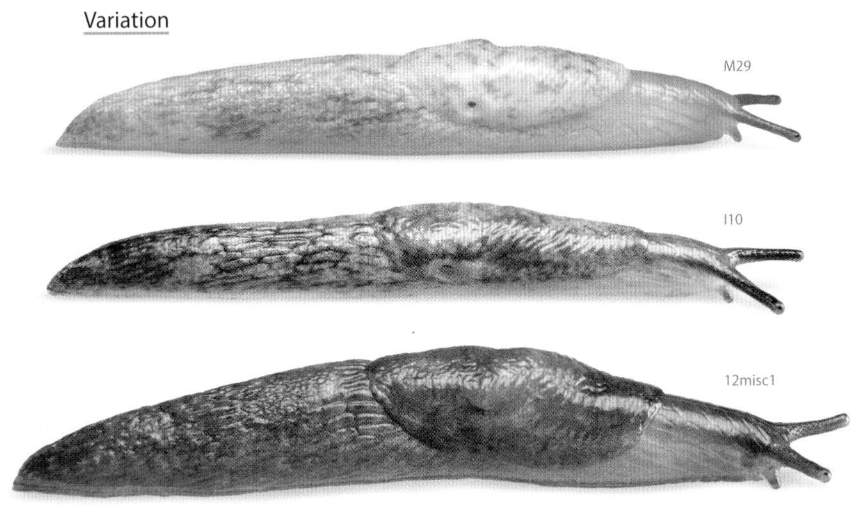

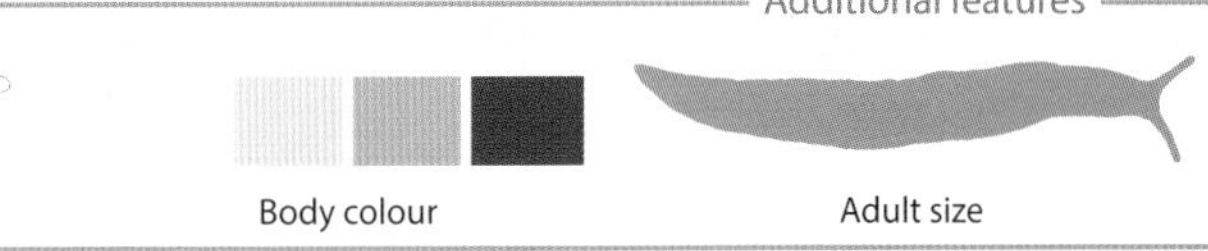

Deroceras agreste (Linnaeus, 1758)

Arctic Field Slug (Northern Field Slug, Field Slug)

Identification. Up to 25-45 mm extended. A small, soft, active slug with a short distinct keel at the tail, and usually producing milky mucus when handled. The tail is usually longer than the mantle. The body contracts to a swollen hump. Colour varies, but less so than in *D. reticulatum*, ranging from pale magnolia to buff or oatmeal. This species is always devoid of markings and often has a warm tone that has been likened to a sun-tan or freshly baked bread. The rim of the breathing pore is not contrastingly paler than the body sides when at rest but may appear pale when crawling. The head and tentacles are dark. The sole is pale but dark gut contents usually show through the central strip. The mucus is usually milky when handled, although may be released more reluctantly in dry conditions or on acidic soils. Juveniles resemble adults.

Similar species. Unlikely to be confused with any species with which it might co-occur except for *D. reticulatum*, which is far commoner throughout Britain and Ireland. It seems that any specimen with a trace of dark markings will prove to belong to that species. (Quick [1960] suggested that occasional dark markings were present but these cases must be exceedingly rare). Unfortunately, *D. reticulatum* quite often lacks markings, making it externally indistinguishable from *D. agreste* in such cases. With experience of a particular area, the two can be distinguished by any locally-consistent differences in size or colour. Kerney & Cameron (1979) described the tubercles of *D. agreste* as being finer than those of *D. reticulatum*.

Dissection (p. 119) is generally essential to confirm the identity of *D. agreste*.

Pest status. Not a pest in Britain and Ireland, in contrast to *D. reticulatum*. Although a herbivore with a broad diet it does not occur in large enough numbers in disturbed habitats to constitute a threat (Wiktor, 2000).

Range. A northern species, widespread in Scotland and northern England yet even there more local than *D. reticulatum*, with only scattered outliers further south than this.

Some records, especially south of Yorskhire, are suspect. This species was not distinguished from *D. reticulatum* until 1915 and continues to be mistaken for it. However, outlying populations are known in the Norfolk Broads (Ellis, 1941), Co. Wicklow (Anderson, 2006) and the north face of the Brecon Beacons (Rowson *et al.*, 2014).

Probably native to northern and central Europe including Britain and Ireland, north to Scandinavia and the Kola peninsula of arctic Russia and east into Siberia (Kerney, 1999; Wiktor, 2000). It is also recorded from Iberia (Castillejo, 1998). Wiktor (2000) records it as being spread by humans. If so, the species has been less successful than other British and Irish *Deroceras*.

Habitat. Found in relatively undisturbed, open habitats. Many records, including those in the Pennines and Brecon Beacons, are from upland pasture, above 400 m, under stones. In Scotland it also occurs around tall roadside herbs, in coastal dunes (as at the sole Irish site), and near streams. In the Broads it inhabits permanently wet reed swamp and fen carr. Like *D. reticulatum* this species avoids woodlands (Wiktor, 2000) although Kerney (1999) says that it has been recorded from birch woods.

Biology. The restriction to semi-natural open habitats suggests the southern sites are relicts of a wider Late-glacial range as proposed by Kerney (1999). They are also places in which *D. reticulatum* is uncommon or absent. Genetic evidence for unequal hybridisation between the two, in which *D. reticulatum* sperm is transferred to *D. agreste* but not vice versa, could partly explain the rarity of *D. agreste* (Rowson *et al.*, 2014). Usually it is self-fertilising (Foltz *et al.*, 1984). The species seems likely to become even more restricted in future.

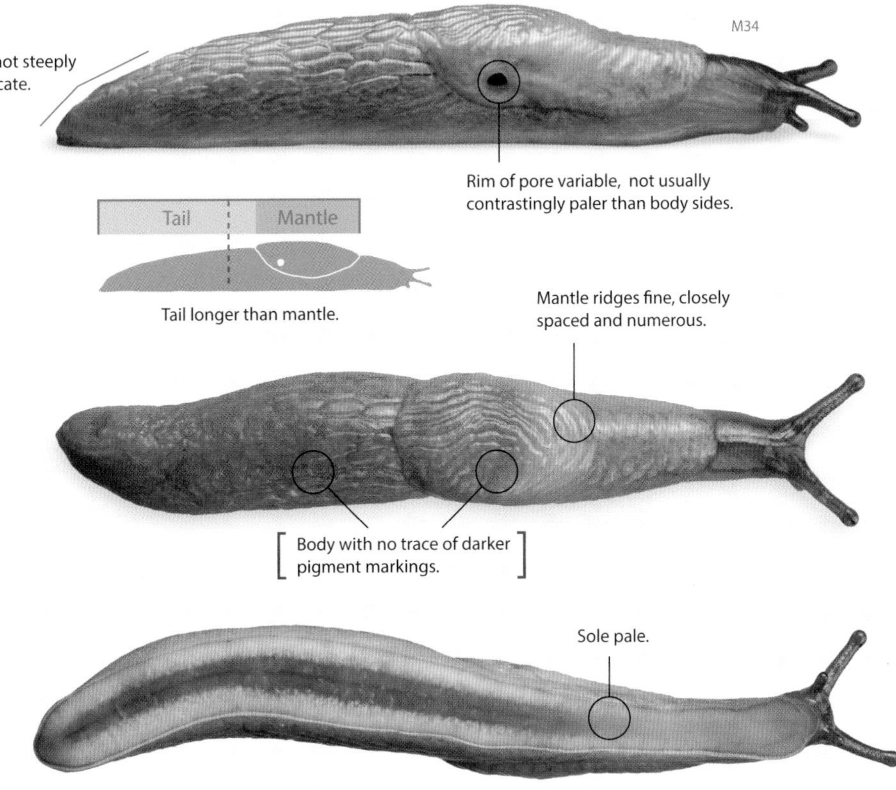

Variation

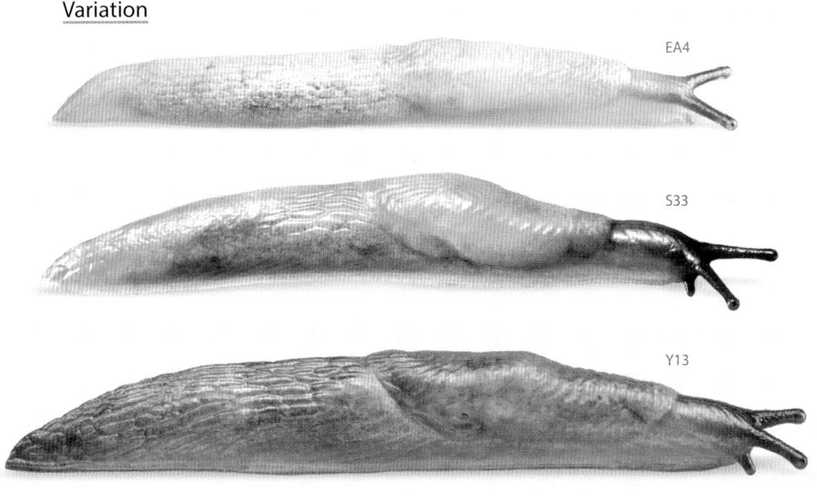

Additional features

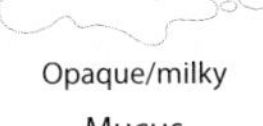

Mucus

Body colour

Adult size

Deroceras invadens Reise, Hutchinson, Schunack & Schlitt, 2011

Tramp Slug (Longneck Field Slug, Brown Field Slug, Caruana's Slug, Sicilian Slug)

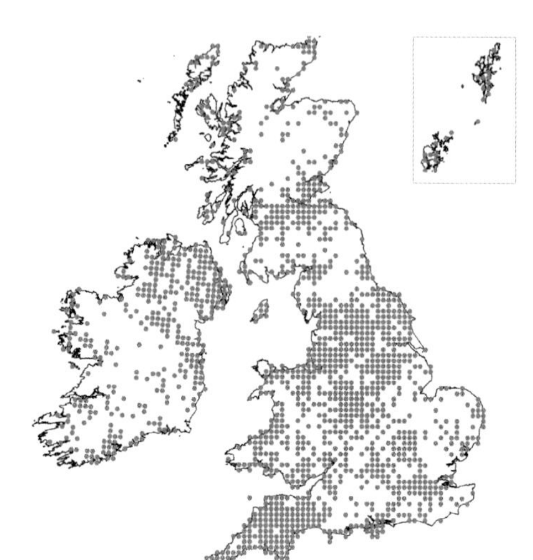

Identification. Up to 25-35 mm extended. A small, soft, very fast-moving slug with a short keel. The keel is steeply truncate or squared-off at the tail tip, often more strongly than in *D. laeve*. The tail is usually longer than the mantle. The body contracts to a swollen hump. Colour ranges from pale chestnut or mid-grey to blackish-brown, often with paler organs and the shell showing through the centre of the mantle, giving a two-toned appearance. The rim of the breathing pore is usually contrastingly paler than the body sides both when at rest and when crawling. The body is usually flecked with black, although the markings are easily overlooked. The sole is a little paler than the body. The mucus is colourless and watery. The animal is often very active and will snap at other slugs in a container or attempt copulation with them. It vigorously lashes its tail when disturbed or bitten by other slugs. The neck has also been described as being longer than in other species. Juveniles resemble adults.

Similar species. This species is usually darker and smaller than *D. reticulatum*, with which it is often found. Unlike that species it never produces milky mucus. A contrastingly pale rim to the breathing pore when at rest usually rules out both *D. reticulatum* and *D. laeve*. However, both *D. reticulatum* and *D. agreste* show a pale border to the breathing pore when crawling. Adults of *D. invadens* are almost always larger than *D. laeve*, often have a less steeply truncate keel (de Winter, 1988), and seldom occur in the same microhabitat. In addition, the tail is shorter than the mantle in *D. laeve* but not in *D. invadens*. The dark markings of *D. invadens* often become more apparent in preservation, rather than less apparent as in *D. laeve*. See the account for *D. panormitanum* (p. 86) for details on distinguishing that species.

Dissection not required, unless *D. panormitanum* is suspected (p. 119).

Pest status. Has been cited as a pest in Britain although with limited detail (South, 1992; Kerney, 1999). It is considered an important pest of crops and gardens in New Zealand (Barker, 1999) but appears not to have been mentioned as a significant pest of cereals or root crops (Reise *et al.*, 2006). It may cause other problems associated with invasive species.

Range. Probably widespread throughout Britain and Ireland except in the highlands, more so than the patchy recording suggests.

First detected in Cornwall in 1930 and Co. Cork in 1958 (Quick, 1960; Kerney, 1999), this species was unknown to Taylor (1902-7) so may initially have been introduced between 1900-1930. According to Kerney (1999) it spread rapidly between 1974 and 1999. Hayward (1954) assigned Holocene fossil shells from Romney Marsh in southeast England to *D. invadens*. This seems doubtful. After their revision, Reise *et al.* (2011) concluded *D. invadens* was probably of Italian (rather than Sicilian or Maltese) origin. It now occurs throughout much of Europe and on all continents other than Antarctica (Reise *et al*, 2011).

Habitat. Initially after introduction associated with disturbed, urban and roadside habitats, including gardens and farms, but increasingly found elsewhere in the lowlands. Readily found under debris and rubbish wherever this has been dumped. Like other small slugs it adheres readily to vehicles, animals and clothing which may aid its dispersal.

Biology. An annual species, able to breed at any time of year in Britain and Ireland and to self-fertilise (Quick, 1960) but predominantly outcrossing (Foltz *et al.*, 1984). Reise *et al.* (2006) consider that Quick's (1960) report of Californian individuals lacking a penis was due to confusion with *D. laeve*.

Deroceras invadens was until recently widely known as *D. panormitanum* (now a separate species, p. 86) or *D. caruanae* (see Reise *et al.*, 2011 for details).

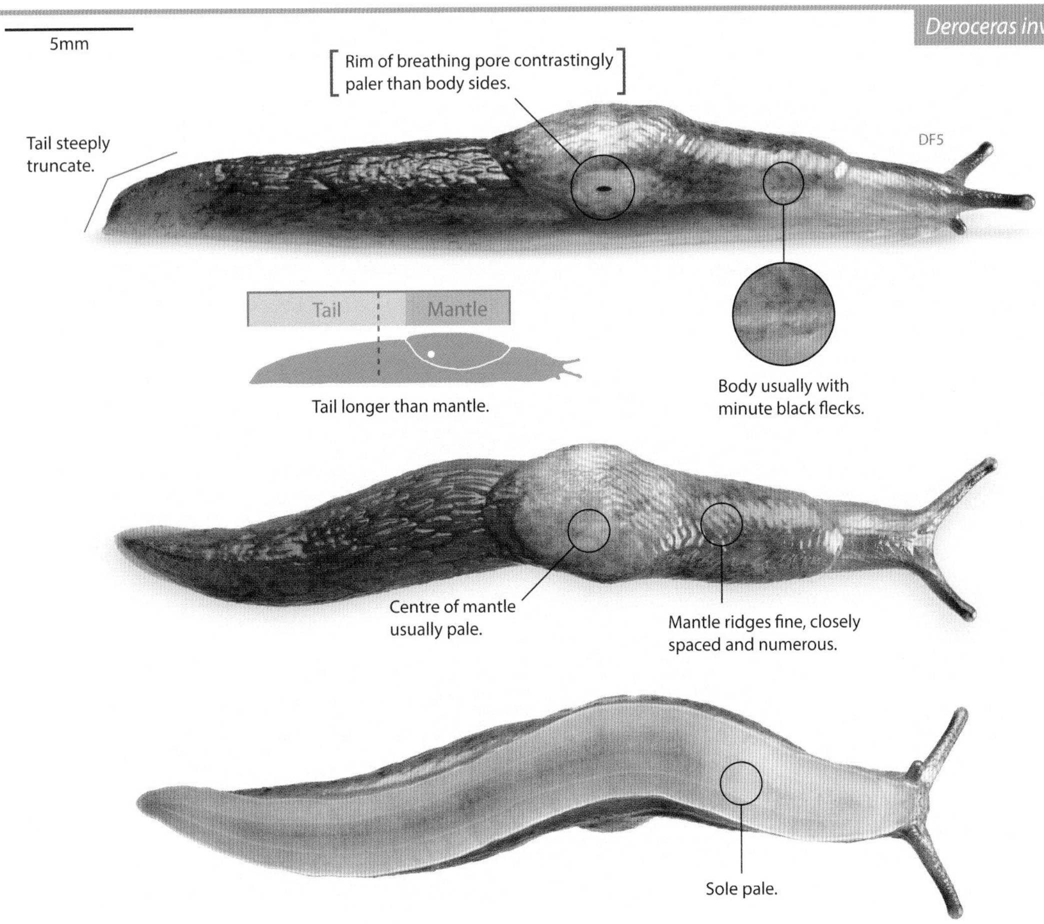

5mm

Rim of breathing pore contrastingly paler than body sides.

Tail steeply truncate.

DF5

Tail | Mantle

Tail longer than mantle.

Body usually with minute black flecks.

Centre of mantle usually pale.

Mantle ridges fine, closely spaced and numerous.

Sole pale.

Variation

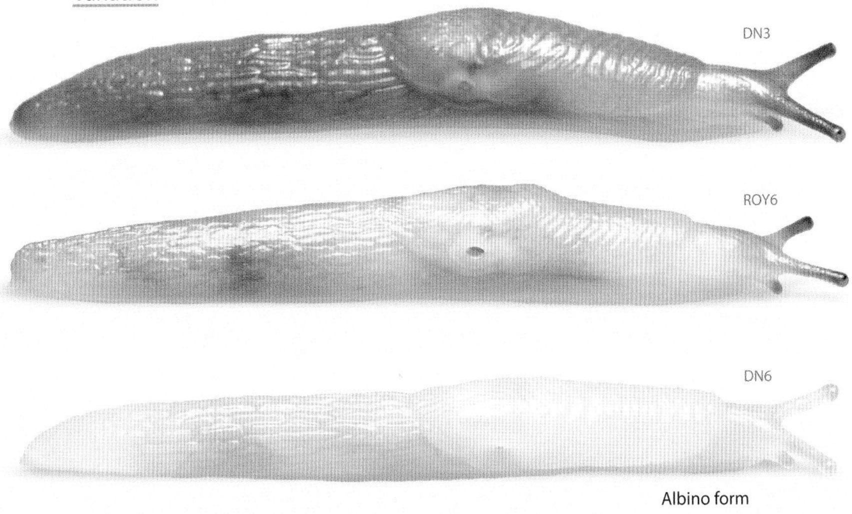

DN3

ROY6

DN6

Albino form

Additional features

Mucus

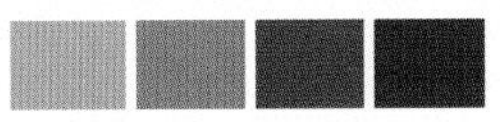

Body colour

Adult size

Deroceras panormitanum (Lessona & Pollonera, 1882)

Sicilian Slug

Identification. Up to 25-35 mm extended. A small, soft, very fast-moving slug with a short keel. The keel is steeply truncate or squared-off at the tail tip, often more strongly so than in *D. laeve*. The tail is usually longer than the mantle. The body contracts to a swollen hump. Colour ranges from pinkish-cream to very dark blackish-brown, often with paler organs and the shell showing through the mantle. The rim of the breathing pore is usually contrastingly paler than the body sides. The body is usually flecked with black, although these markings are easily overlooked. The sole is a little paler than the body. The mucus is colourless and watery. The animal behaves like *D. invadens*, crawling actively and lashing its tail vigorously when disturbed.

Similar species. Comments under *D. invadens* (p. 84) about distinguishing *D. invadens* from *D. laeve* and *D. reticulatum* likewise apply to *D. panormitanum*.

Deroceras panormitanum and *D. invadens* are said not to be reliably distinguishable externally (Reise *et al.*, 2011). Only one British population is at present known, in which the animals are all dark. However, some first generation offspring produced in captivity are pale to mid brown. This variability may serve to disguise the species in other locations. All specimens so far examined are uniformly coloured on the mantle with quite dense pigment. In contarst, in many populations of *D. invadens* the central mantle appears noticeably paler and more translucent than the tail. This may aid future identification.

Dissection is required to confirm the occurrence of this species (p. 119). Alternatively, highly detailed observations of mating behaviour with reference to Reise *et al.*'s paper (2011) and videos could suffice.

Pest status. Unknown.

Range. Known only from one site in Britain: a city centre garden in Cardiff, opposite a fruit and fish market, where it was abundant in 2012 and early 2013. The introduced snail *Helix lucorum*, almost certainly a recent arrival, was first found at the same locality a year earlier. *Helix lucorum* has been found to be common in the London area only in recent years and it is plausible that *D. panormitanum*, too, may be a recent introduction that is already widely distributed.

Reise *et al.* (2011) consider *D. panormitanum* native to Sicily and Malta.

Habitat. If *D. panormitanum* occurs elsewhere in Britain or Ireland, it is likely to be in disturbed habitats, perhaps exotically planted. Its distribution on Malta and Sicily includes disturbed areas (Reise *et al.*, 2011).

Biology. This species was detected in Britain only as a result of Reise *et al*'s (2011) revision. The Cardiff population matches *D. panormitanum*, rather than *D. invadens*, in its genitalia and DNA sequence. Little is known about *D. panormitanum* beyond the details in their paper because it has long been confused with *D. invadens*.

The taxonomic name changes caused by the revision may cause confusion for the less experienced when consulting earlier works. The species referred to as *D. panormitanum* in this guide was not previously recognised in Britain or Ireland. The worldwide tramp species, previously known as *D. panormitanum* in Britain and Ireland and elsewhere, has been renamed *D. invadens*. The name *D. caruanae* (Pollonera, 1891), as used in guides by Kerney & Cameron (1979), Cameron *et al.* (1983) and Kerney (1999) relates to *D. panormitanum* and not *D. invadens*. However, the English name "Caruana's slug", which is still in verbal use, was generally used for what is now *D. invadens*.

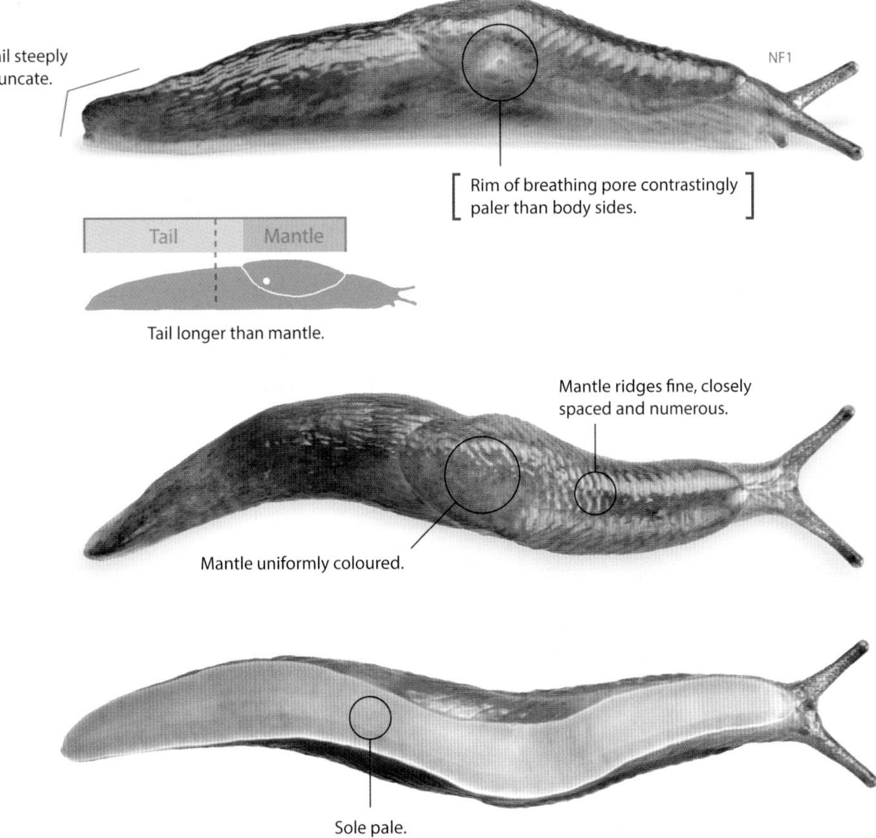

Variation

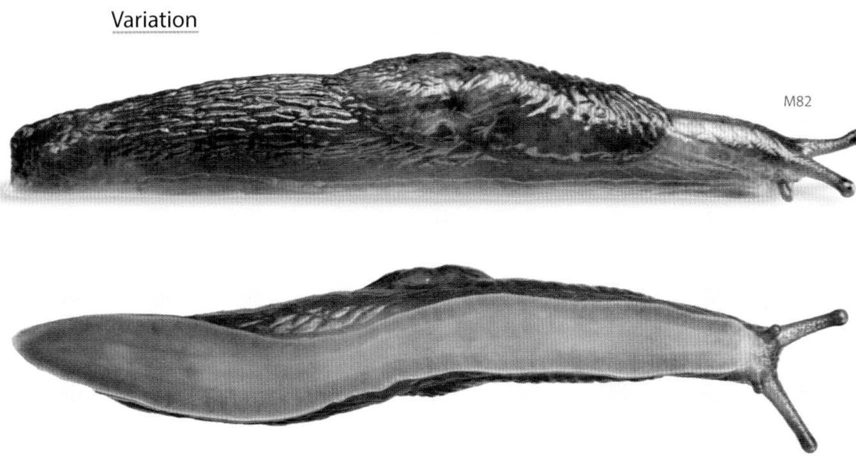

Additional features

Mucus

Body colour

Adult size

Deroceras laeve (O. F. Müller, 1774)

Marsh Slug (Meadow Slug, Brown Slug, Smooth Slug)

Identification. Up to 15-25 mm extended. A very small, soft, fast-moving slug with a short keel. The keel is steeply truncate or squared-off at the tail tip. The tail is the same length as the mantle or shorter. The ridges on the mantle are usually fewer, coarser and appear more widely-spaced than those of larger species. The head and tentacles may appear relatively large, giving a "juvenile" appearance. The body contracts to a swollen hump. Colour ranges from amber or pale chestnut to a rich deep brown, sometimes with paler organs showing through the skin. The rim of the breathing pore is not contrastingly paler than the body sides even when crawling. The body is usually flecked with black, although these markings are difficult to see (and often disappear in preservation). The sole tends to be the same colour as the body (and distinctly darker than that of *D. invadens*). The mucus is colourless. Juveniles resemble adults.

Similar species. Juveniles of other *Deroceras* and limacid species are seldom as dark as *D. laeve*, but if so, often have some trace of heavier markings such as blotches or bands.

Dark brown forms of *D. invadens* can strongly resemble *D. laeve*. However, these have a pale rim to the breathing pore, more and finer ridges on the mantle, and reach a larger size. The mantle is also relatively longer, compared to the tail, in *D. laeve*. Both may co-occur in wet habitats (e.g. valley bottoms) but only *D. laeve* is likely in genuine wetlands and at the very edges of large bodies of water.

Dissection not required, but can be used to distinguish *D. laeve* from other species (p. 119).

Pest status. South (1992) did not include *D. laeve* in his list of British pest species although noted it had been reported as a pest in France, and as a pest of forage crops in North America. Barker (1999) noted that most pest reports concerned floriculture. It is often abundant in greenhouses, heated and unheated, where it might damage fruit and tender parts of plants (South, 1992; Wiktor, 2000). However, it may also provide a service by eating mealybugs (Quick, 1960).

Range. Widespread throughout Britain and Ireland.

This is the worlds' most widely distributed slug. It is presumed native throughout Europe into the Arctic, and may also be native in Asia and North America (Wiktor, 2000; Grimm *et al.*, 2010).

Elsewhere it occurs on all continents except Antarctica and is widely established in the tropics, occurring up to 3500 m altitude (Barker, 1999; Wiktor, 2000; Herbert, 2010; Stanisic *et al.*, 2010; etc.). It is presumably readily dispersed by floods, storms, and animals as well as humans.

Habitat. Any suitably moist habitat, from wet woodland and damp pasture to flushes, river banks, and seasonal or permanent wetlands. It can occur away from water in areas of high rainfall (British and Irish mountains), or on heavy soils as well as in humid greenhouses.

Biology. This species is able to survive floods that drown other slugs and its eggs can hatch under water. It may deliberately enter the water and survive for days submerged (Welter-Schultes, 2012). It is annual but can mature in as little as one month, and breed at any time of year in suitable conditions. Many populations and lineages are aphallic (i.e. lack a penis) and reproduce purely by self-fertilisation (Quick, 1960; Barker, 1999; Wiktor, 2000; Jordaens *et al.*, 2006).

Some Irish populations, and greenhouse populations, are substantially genetically divergent from the widespread British and Irish *D. laeve* (Rowson *et al.*, 2014). All are aphallic, so it is not clear whether they should be considered part of a single species.

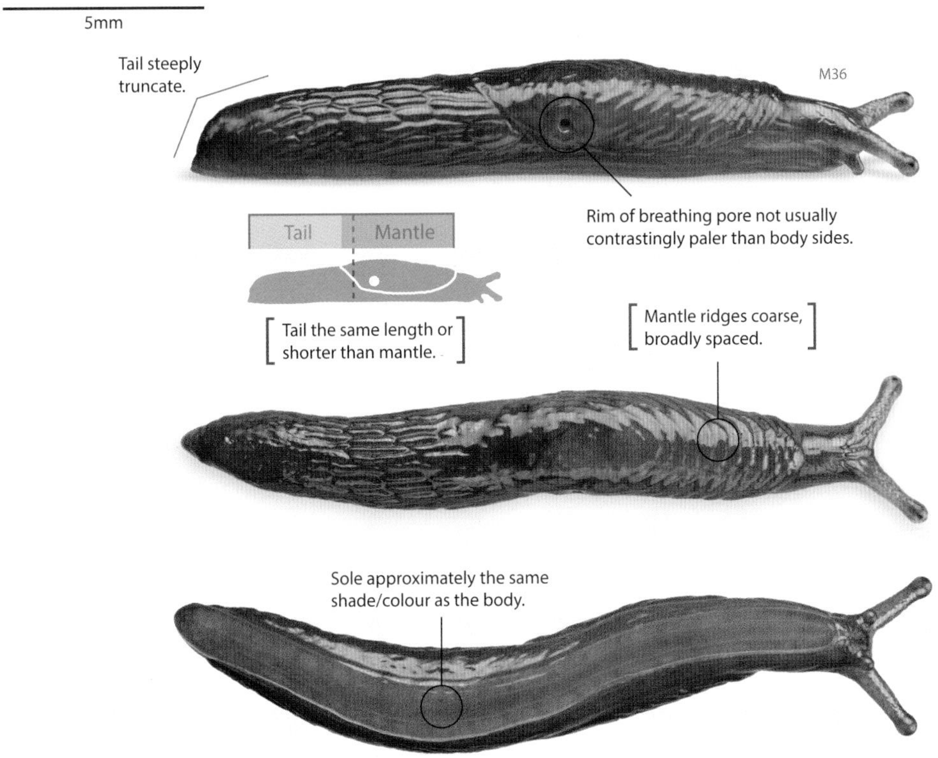

5mm

Tail steeply truncate.

M36

Rim of breathing pore not usually contrastingly paler than body sides.

Tail | Mantle

[Tail the same length or shorter than mantle.]

[Mantle ridges coarse, broadly spaced.]

Sole approximately the same shade/colour as the body.

Variation

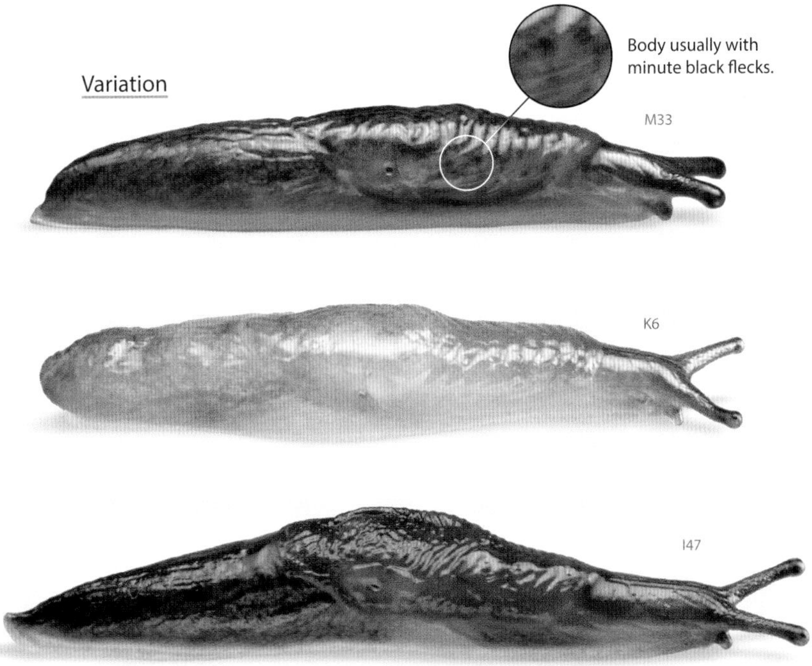

Body usually with minute black flecks.

M33

K6

I47

Additional features

Mucus

Body colour

Adult size

Tandonia budapestensis (Hazay, 1880)

Budapest Keeled Slug (Budapest Slug)

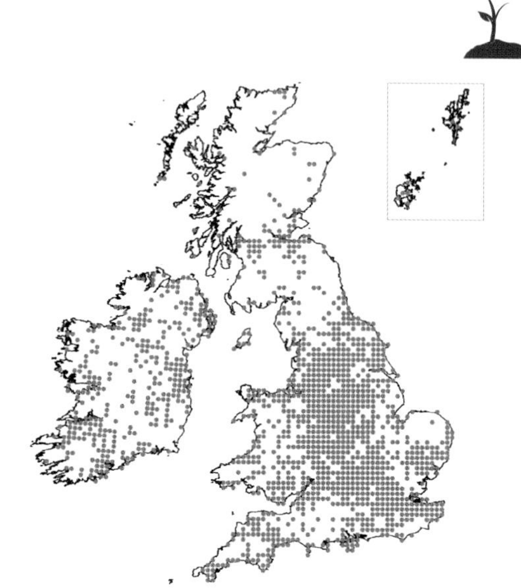

Identification. Up to 50-70 mm extended. A medium-sized slug with a long, distinct keel. The body is round to oval in cross-section and slender and elongate when extended. When contracted, it forms an elongate hump, often characteristically bent into a C-shape or U-shape. The body is elephant-grey to dark grey-brown, occasionally reddish or yellowish, the mantle often slightly browner. The body is densely spattered all over with minute black spots. These sometimes accumulate in grooves on the mantle or both on and between the tubercles. The keel is usually lighter than the body, often a dirty yellow-orange. Characteristically, the sole has pale sides with a darkly pigmented central strip. The mucus is colourless. Juveniles resemble adults.

Similar species. *Tandonia cristata* may have been mistaken for this species in the past. It lacks the dark central strip on the sole, is smaller and less elongate, is less likely to form a U-shape, and has a different distribution of dark pigment on the back. Internally the two species are very similar (see Wiktor, 1987; Rowson *et al.*, 2014).

Likewise, *T. sowerbyi* and *Milax gagates* are also less elongate, form hump shapes when contracted, and lack the dark central strip on the sole. In addition *T. sowerbyi* is triangular in cross-section, while *M. gagates* is generally smoother and is unmarked, with a darker keel.

Dissection not required.

Pest status. A serious pest at and below the soil surface, especially of potatoes, root crops and bulbs. In ploughed fields it can occur well away from the margins.

Range. Widespread and common throughout Britain and Ireland except in the highlands, but probably still spreading.

Originally native to the southern Alps and northern Balkans but established in northern and central Europe since at least the 1880s, and Britain and Ireland since at least the 1920s. Also established in New Zealand and in the eastern US (Philips & Watson, 1930; Wiktor, 1987; Kerney, 1999; Barker, 1999; Reise *et al.*, 2006). Old records of *Milax gagates* and other milacid species may refer to *T. budapestensis*.

Habitat. Disturbed lowland habitats, on all kinds of soil. Sometimes common in woodlands, but usually near margins, along paths, or near ruins. Apparently less common in open semi-natural habitats such as grasslands and wetlands.

Biology. This species is largely subterranean, and able to burrow or at least squeeze through narrow soil cracks. It often occurs in large numbers and in fields and gardens may be one of the commonest slugs (South, 1992). This can make it a difficult species to control. However it may be attracted to food on the surface at night (Phillips & Watson, 1930) including slug pellets (South, 1992).

In southern Britain and Ireland *T. budapestensis* is active almost year-round. It generally lives for two years, reproducing more than once (Hunter, 1968; Wiktor, 1987). In winter adults are often found almost motionless, mating. Mating lasts many hours and involves the production of elaborate spermatophores. Self-fertilisation is rare (Foltz *et al.*, 1984). The oval eggs have been described as yellowish and leathery (Quick, 1960) but when fresh are colourless and transparent. Each adult lays around 30 eggs (Hunter, 1968).

When eaten *Tandonia budapestensis* is toxic to carabid ground beetles that regularly feed on other slugs (Symondson, 1997).

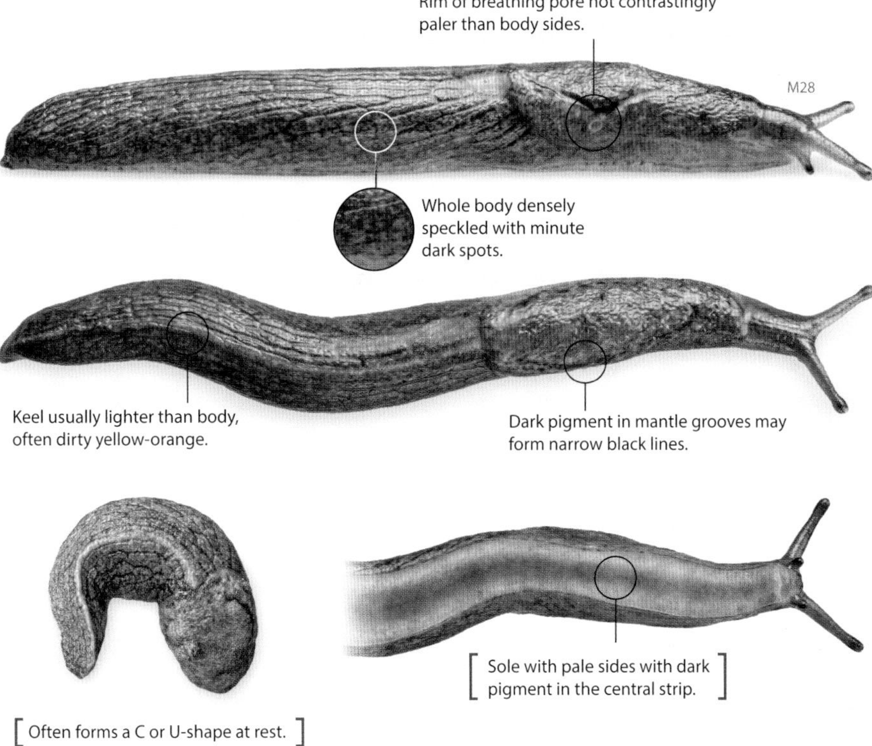

Variation

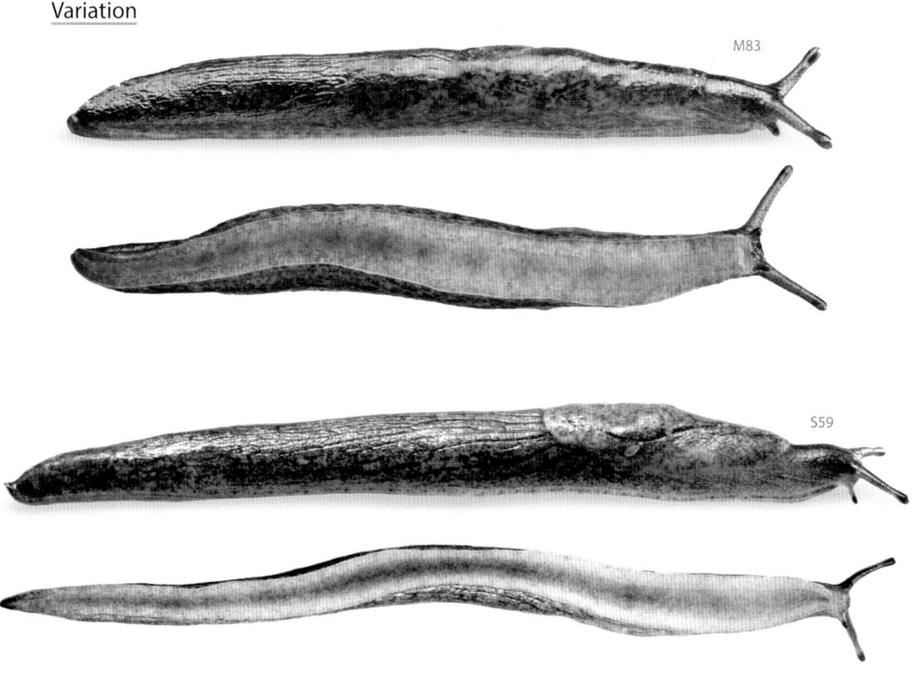

Additional features

Mucus | Contracted shape | Body colour | Adult size

Tandonia cf. *cristata* (Kaleniczenko, 1851)

Crimean Keeled Slug

Identification. Up to 25-35 mm extended. A small slug with a long, distinct keel. The body is round to oval in cross-section and slender and elongate when extended. When contracted, it forms an elongate hump, sometimes bent into a C-shape. The body is light yellow-grey to brown or blue-grey. It usually has a neat reticulate pattern caused by the accumulation of dark pigment (minute dark speckles) between the tubercles. The keel is usually lighter than the body. The sole lacks a dark central pigment strip (beware dark gut contents showing through). The mucus is colourless. Juveniles resemble adults.

Similar species. *Tandonia* cf. *cristata* has evidently been mistaken for other milacid species in the past, including *T. budapestensis*, *Milax gagates* and *T. sowerbyi*. Compared to *T. budapestensis* it lacks the dark central strip on the sole, is smaller and less elongate, is less likely to form a U-shape, and has a different distribution of dark pigment on the back. *M. gagates* is generally smoother and is unmarked with a darker keel. It is a smaller and daintier slug than *T. sowerbyi* but could be mistaken for juveniles, which are nevertheless triangular in cross-section. The distribution of dark pigment on the back also differs.

Dissection not required. Genitailia are similar to *T. budapestensis* and *T. sowerbyi*, though this species matures at a smaller size.

Pest status. Unknown. Potentially a pest of plants at or near the soil surface, including root crops, which it will attack in captivity. It has been found on damaged potatoes lifted from allotments in South Wales.

Range. Scattered localities in Britain and Ireland, but very under-recorded. Some records of *Milax gagates* or other milacids may refer instead to *T.* cf. *cristata*.

First confirmed in Britain and Ireland in 2012 by DNA analysis (Rowson *et al.*, 2014), but with hindsight could have been distinguished earlier. *Tandonia* cf. *cristata* is probably more widespread than is currently known, especially on disturbed land and in urban areas. A specimen in the National Museum of Wales, collected from the Isle of Wight in 1978 had been misidentified as a young *T. sowerbyi*. That said, no specimens of *T.* cf. *cristata* were found among the Milacidae in the Natural History Museum, London in 2013.

This introduced species was described from the Crimea in Ukraine (Kaleniczenko, 1851). It is widespread around the Black Sea (Ukraine, Bulgaria, Romania, northern Turkey) and in Chios, Greece (Wiktor, 1987; 2001; Sysoev & Schileyko, 2009; Welter-Schultes, 2012). Some of these populations, including the Ukrainian ones, are probable introductions (Wiktor, 1987). There are a number of similar species in southeast Europe.

Habitat. In Britain and Ireland found in soil in disturbed lowland habitats, including gardens, allotments, churchyards and waste ground. Also inside the margins of adjacent woodland in South Wales. Around the Black Sea it thrives in woodlands as well as open areas and shows a clear preference for heavy clay soils (Wiktor, 1987).

Biology. Apparently generally similar to *T. budapestensis* and *T. sowerbyi* with which it co-occurs, at least in South Wales.

This is one of several Black Sea slugs now well-established in Britain and/or Ireland. None was recorded by Taylor (1902-7) so it is likely they have spread during the 20th and 21st centuries (see also *Boettgerilla pallens*, *Limacus maculatus* and *Selenochlamys ysbryda*).

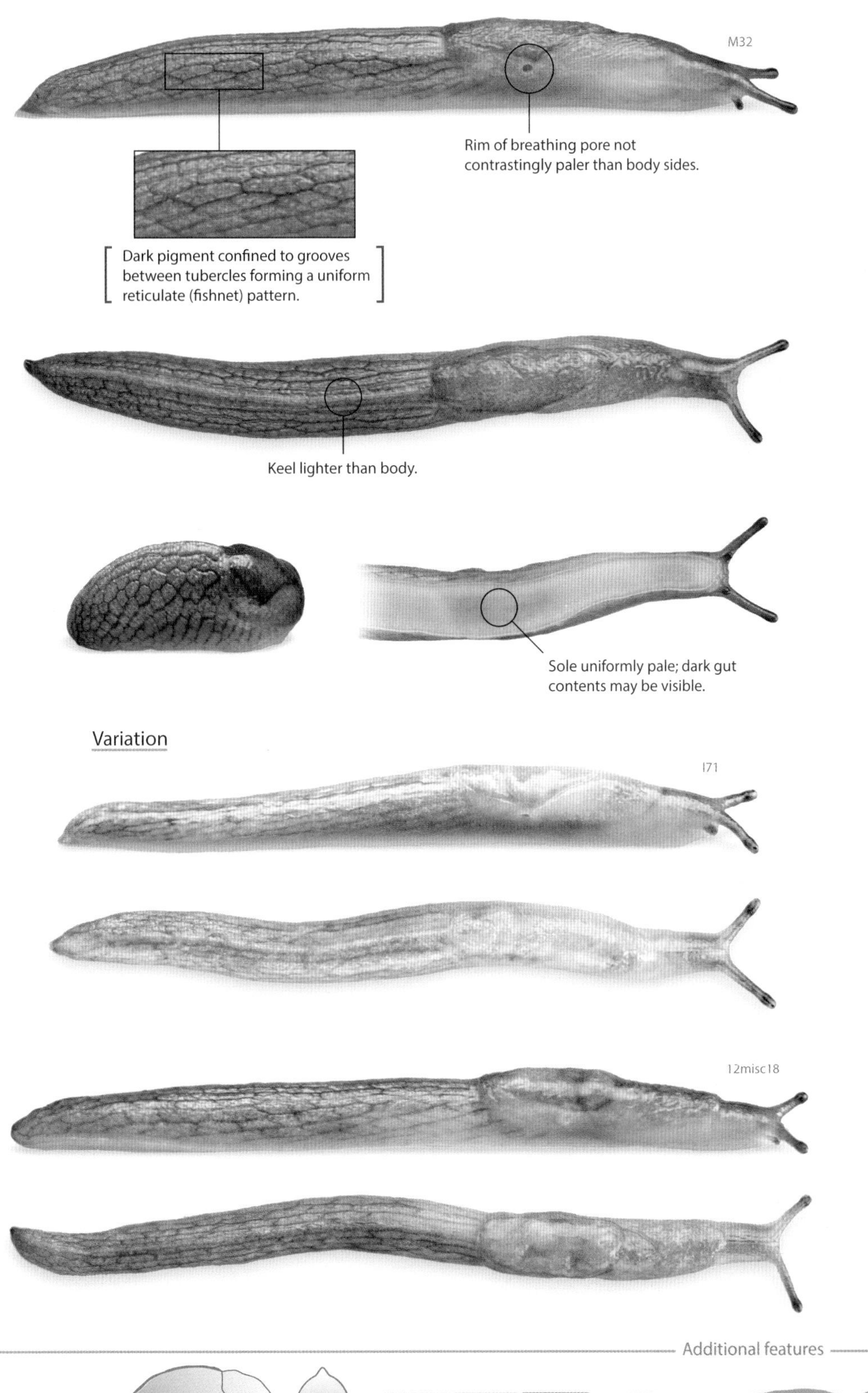
10mm
M32
Rim of breathing pore not contrastingly paler than body sides.
Dark pigment confined to grooves between tubercles forming a uniform reticulate (fishnet) pattern.
Keel lighter than body.
Sole uniformly pale; dark gut contents may be visible.
Variation
I71
12misc18
Additional features
Mucus
Contracted shape
Body colour
Adult size

Tandonia sowerbyi (A. Férussac, 1823)

Sowerby's Keeled Slug (Sowerby's Slug, Keeled Slug)

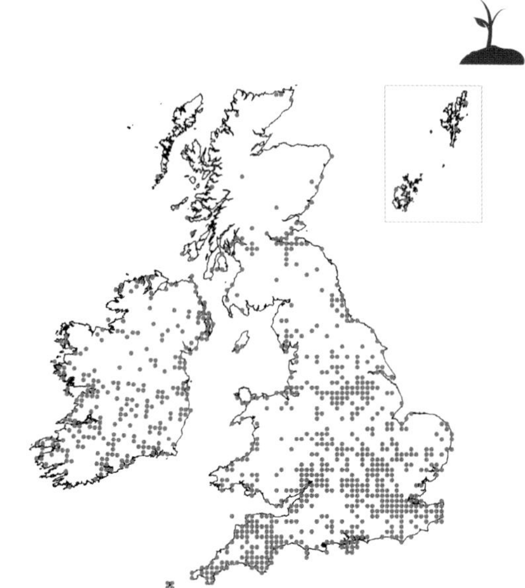

Identification. Up to 60-75 mm extended. A medium-sized slug with a very distinct long keel. The body is tall and triangular in cross-section. It contracts to a hump with the keel standing out and wrinkled, Cornish pasty-style. The brownish body is densely peppered all over with minute black spots. The mantle often has dark grooves and occasionally a third dark line in the centre. The keel is usually lighter or brighter than the body, often an apricot or dirty orange. The sole lacks a dark central strip. The rim of the breathing pore is usually paler than the body sides. The mucus is sticky and yellowish. Juveniles resemble adults.

Similar species. The body shape, keel and colouration of this species readily distinguish it from *T. budapestensis* or *T.* cf. *cristata*. Yellow or pinkish variants can resemble *T. rustica* but have much smaller and denser speckles and are triangular in cross-section. Dissection not required.

Pest status. A pest at and below the soil surface, especially in gardens or at the margins of arable fields (e.g. Godan, 1983; South, 1992).

Range. Widespread and common throughout Britain and Ireland except in the uplands and the far north.

The native range is uncertain. It occurs in the Mediterranean and along the Atlantic coast of Europe. Possibly it is an ancient introduction (see also *T. rustica*). It has been spread by man elsewhere including to South America and New Zealand (Wiktor, 1987).

Habitat. Lowland habitats of all kinds, including disturbed areas, woodland margins and semi-natural grassland, including sea cliffs and maritime grassland especially in the south (Kerney, 1999).

Biology. Generally similar to *T. budapestensis*; probably lives for more than one year, reproducing more than once.

Tandonia rustica (Millet, 1843)

Spotted Keeled Slug (Rustic Slug)

Identification. Up to 50-70 mm extended. A medium-sized slug with a long and very distinct pale keel. The body is warm yellow-brown to pale pinkish brown, characteristically speckled with discrete black spots. The mantle has prominent short lateral bands. The keel is whitish, lighter than the body. The sole lacks a dark central strip. The rim of the breathing pore is usually paler than the body sides. The mucus is sticky and colourless. Juveniles resemble adults.

Similar species. See *T. sowerbyi*.

Pest status. Not considered a pest (Welter-Schultes, 2012).

Range, Habitat and Biology. A central European woodland species associated with limestone rubble and known from this type of habitat in Kent (since 1987) and Co. Cork (since before 1911). It appears genuinely rare. Kerney (1999) considered *T. rustica* potentially native, which could make it a conservation priority. Its absence from apparently suitable habitat (including that in other northwest European countries; Wiktor, 1987) makes recent introduction hard to rule out. However, malicid shells are known from subfossil deposits of 8600 BP (Mesolithic) in Kent (Preece & Bridgland, 1999; Preece, pers. comm.). *Tandonia rustica* can live up to three years, reproducing several times (Wiktor, 1987).

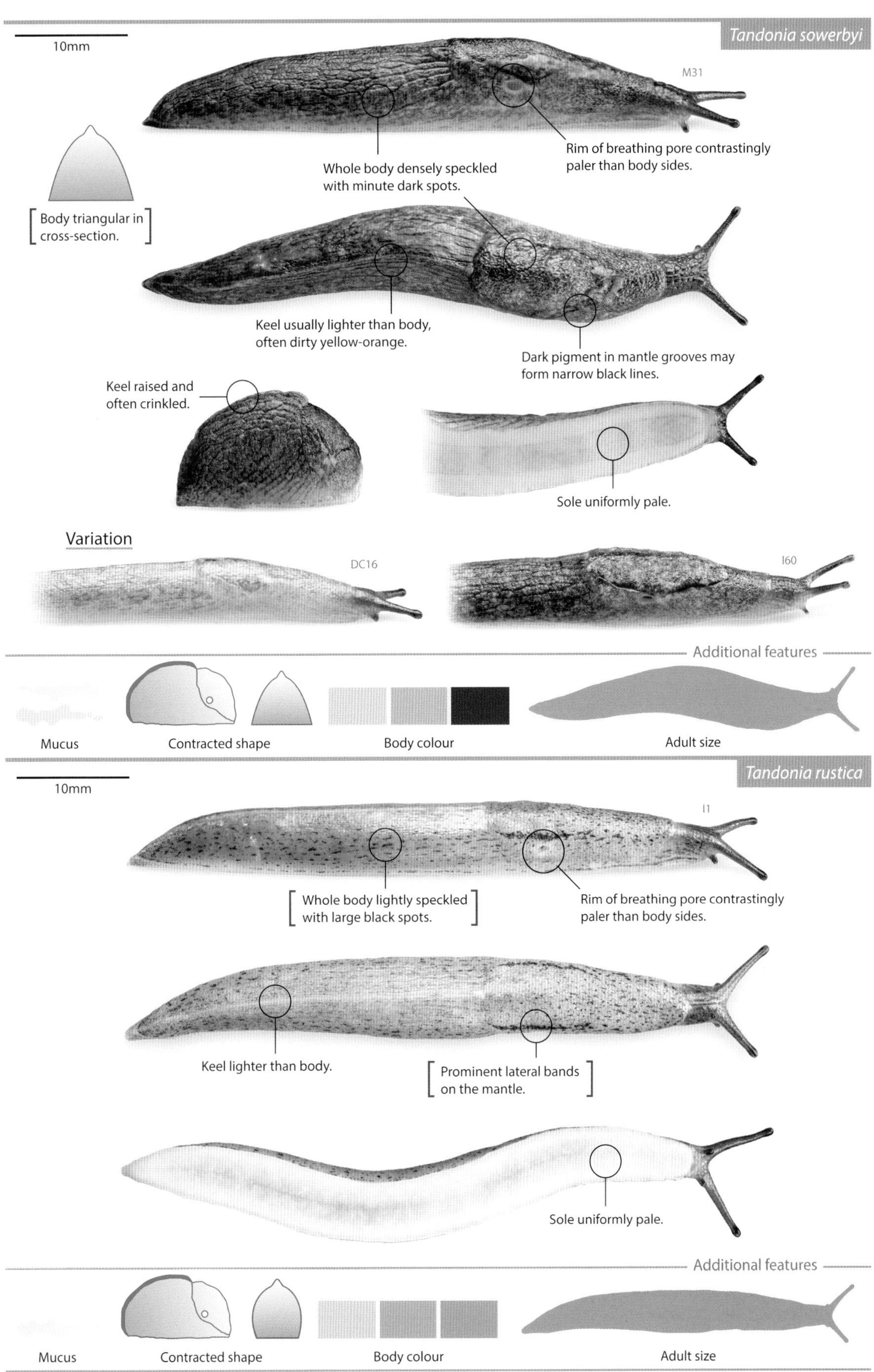
Tandonia sowerbyi
10mm
M31
Whole body densely speckled with minute dark spots.
Rim of breathing pore contrastingly paler than body sides.
Body triangular in cross-section.
Keel usually lighter than body, often dirty yellow-orange.
Dark pigment in mantle grooves may form narrow black lines.
Keel raised and often crinkled.
Sole uniformly pale.
Variation
DC16
I60
Additional features
Mucus
Contracted shape
Body colour
Adult size
Tandonia rustica
10mm
I1
Whole body lightly speckled with large black spots.
Rim of breathing pore contrastingly paler than body sides.
Keel lighter than body.
Prominent lateral bands on the mantle.
Sole uniformly pale.
Additional features
Mucus
Contracted shape
Body colour
Adult size

Milax gagates (Drapanaud, 1801)

Smooth Jet Slug (Jet Slug, Greenhouse Slug, Black Keeled Slug, Small Black Slug)

Identification. Up to 45-55 mm extended. A small to medium-sized slug with a long, distinct keel. The body is round to oval in cross-section. When contracted, it forms a hump with the keel slightly raised. The body is unmarked elephant-grey, blue-grey, brown or black, occasionally reddish-brown. The keel is often slightly darker than the body (sometimes also the rim of the breathing pore). The body sides are pale, sometimes contrastingly so. The sole is uniformly pale. The tubercles appear relatively smooth. The mucus is colourless. Juveniles may have short, dark mantle bands (at least in Spanish populations).

Similar species. *Milax gagates* can be distinguished from the *Tandonia* species by the absence of markings, the darker keel, and the relatively smoother tubercles. It never has the dark central sole strip of *T. budapestensis*, or the pale breathing pore rim of *T. sowerbyi*.

A closely related species, *Milax nigricans* (Philippi, 1836) was reported from near Bexhill, Sussex in 1948 (Quick, 1960). There are no other records and Anderson (2008) considered that there was no evidence this species was established in Britain or Ireland, so it is not included in this guide. It is generally larger, rougher and blacker than *M. gagates*, with a black rather than pale sole (Quick, 1960). This distinction can be resolved by dissection (Quick, 1960).

Pest status. Quick (1960) noted *M. gagates* could be a pest of root crops in Devon and it can cause damage in greenhouses. In other countries, it has been implicated as a pest of many crops including carrots, potatoes, fruit, rapeseed, cereals, as well as garden plants (Godan, 1983; Wiktor, 1987; South, 1992; Herbert, 2010; etc.).

Range. Widespread but very local in lowland and coastal Britain and Ireland; absent from uplands.

The distribution and status of this species are somewhat enigmatic. Kerney (1999) recognised that pre-1930 records were unreliable (not shown on this map). Many of the remainder are also old and may, in some cases, be based on misidentifications of *Tandonia* species. Recent reports of *M. gagates* are concentrated in western Ireland, in Devon and Cornwall, and along western coasts generally, although the species can be hard to find in these regions too.

It is said to be frost-sensitive (e.g. Killeen, 1992; Grimm *et al.*, 2010) which could partly explain the distribution. It is also possible that it has undergone some decline, although Scharff (1891) noted its rarity in Ireland over a century ago.

Milax gagates occurs in the western Mediterranean and the Atlantic coast from Morocco north to Shetland. Opinions differ on whether it is native (e.g. Kerney, 1999) or introduced (e.g. Wiktor, 1987; Turk *et al.*, 2001) to Britain and/or Ireland. It is the most widely introduced milacid species, being established on all continents except Antarctica, including in tropical areas (e.g. see Herbert, 2010).

Habitat. Subterranean (but less so than *Tandonia* species). In Britain and Ireland, in gardens, waste ground, and cliffs and rough pasture near the sea. Also recorded in woods in Cornwall (Turk *et al.*, 2001).

Biology. *Milax gagates* has an annual, or even 6-9 month life-cycle, laying eggs in spring or autumn (Wiktor, 1987). However self-fertilisation and longer lifespans are possible (Barker, 1999; Welter-Schultes, 2012). It seems to be of varying abundance in gardens.

Its taxonomy needs more study. Many authors have questioned whether *M. gagates* and *M. nigricans* are part of a single species. There is also some variability in *M. gagates*: brightly coloured specimens have been reported from the Western Isles and Wiktor (1987) mentioned dark lateral sole strips which do not seem to occur in British or Irish specimens.

10mm

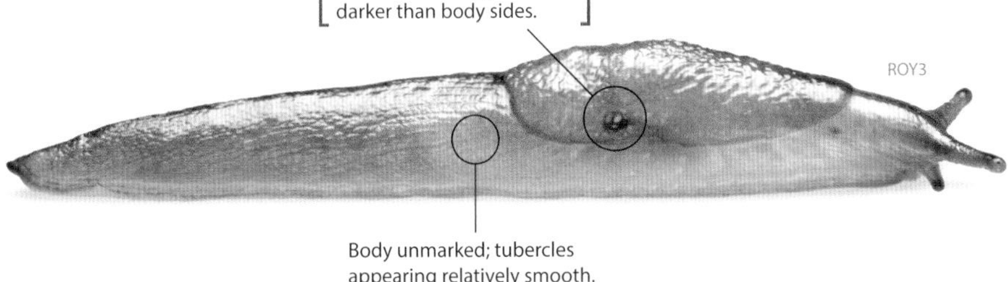

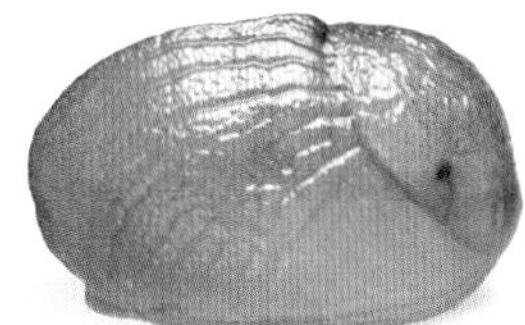

Hump-shaped with keel raised when contracted.

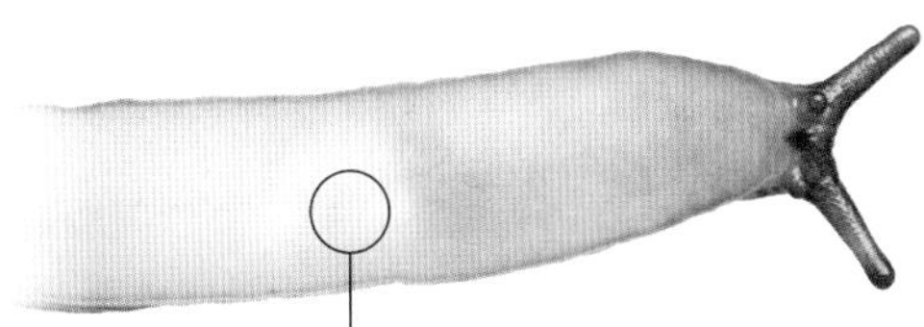

Sole uniformly pale; dark gut contents may be visible.

Variation

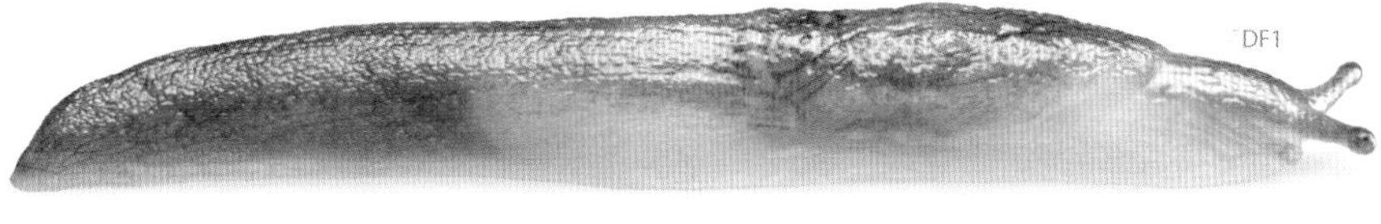

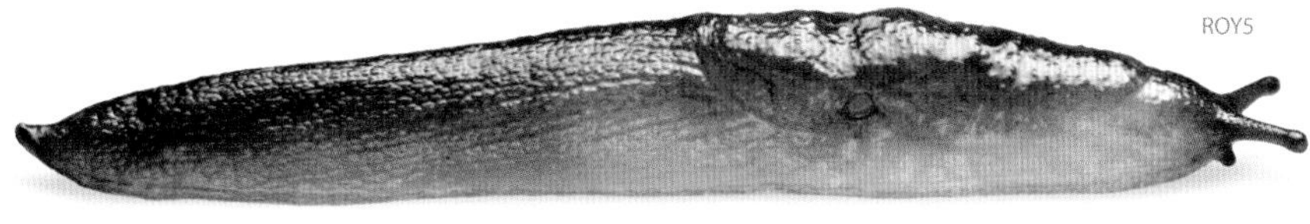

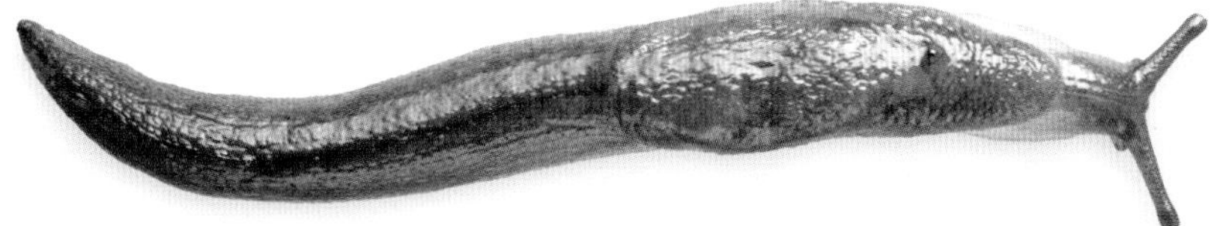

Additional features

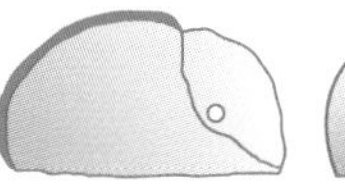

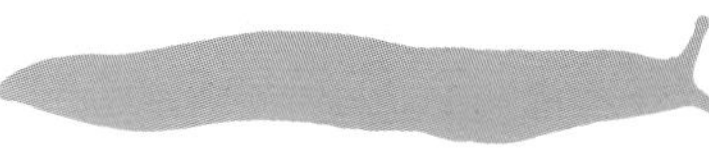

Mucus | Contracted shape | Body colour | Adult size

Boettgerilla pallens (Simroth, 1912)

Worm Slug (Wormslug)

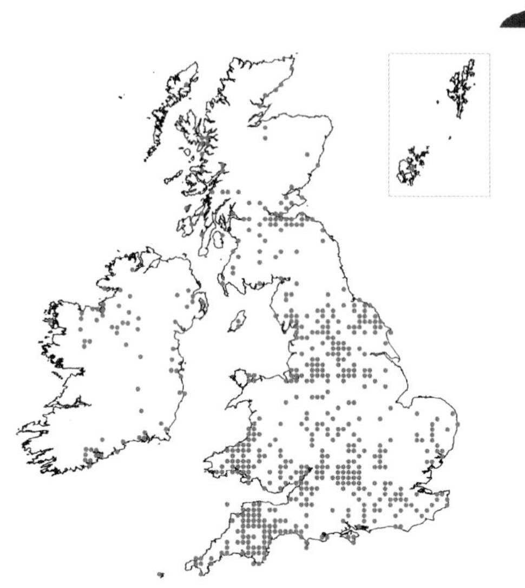

Identification. Up to 35-55 mm extended. A small to medium-sized (but slender) slug with a distinct keel running from the rear of the mantle to the tail. The body is round in cross-section and extremely slender and worm-like when crawling. When at rest it forms a cylindrical or elongate hump. The rear edge of the mantle is characteristically pointed rather than rounded as in other long-keeled slugs. The body is unmarked yellow-white to lavender-grey, pale blue-grey, or lilac-grey. It is paler, and sometimes translucent, at the sides. The tentacles, keel and tip of the tail are usually darker than the body. The sole is uniformly pale. The mucus is colourless and the body may appear smooth. Juveniles tend to be paler than adults and are usually white.

Similar species. Usually unmistakable. The only equally slender and worm-like slug is *Selenochlamys ysbryda*, which pale *Boettgerilla* may resemble. However *S. ysbryda* differs in being a brighter white, in the mantle position at the rear, in the method of contraction, and in lacking black eye spots. Pale *Milax gagates* and other Milacidae are less wormlike when fully extended, and have a rounded rather than pointed rear edge of the mantle.

Dissection not required.

Pest status. Probably only minor, though reported as a pest of chrysanthemums and of delicate plants in greenhouses (Godan, 1983). *B. pallens* prefers roots to shoots, but causes limited damage. It appears unable to bite through the skin of carrots, for example. It is mainly a detritivore feeding on earthworm faeces, dead slugs and other carrion, decaying plants and fungi (Gunn, 1992). It can also feed on the eggs of *Arion* and *Deroceras* slugs (Barker & Efford, 2004).

Range. Widespread in most of Britain and Ireland, especially the south and west; still apparently uncommon in Northern Ireland and some rural regions.

Boettgerilla pallens is a good example of how an introduced invertebrate species can spread over wide areas before being detected. It was described from specimens collected in 1907 in mountain forests in the Caucasus at the far eastern edge of Europe. It was recorded from Poland in 1956 and then throughout central and northern Europe. Museum collections have shown it was present in western Germany in 1949, but it is uncertain how long it occurred in central Europe before that. It was not mentioned by Taylor (1902-7) or Quick (1960) and was first recorded in Britain and Ireland in 1972 and 1973 respectively. It was then widely reported and is now known from most regions. It is clear that both long-distance accidental transport and, on a more local scale, active dispersal, have been involved. The spread of *B. pallens* has been discussed by Reise *et al.* (2000) who reported the species from Vancouver Island, Canada. It has also been found in montane Colombia in South America (Hausdorf, 2002).

Habitat. Generally subterranean in soil cracks and earthworm burrows in disturbed habitats of all kinds, including agricultural land, and on most soil types. Also present in woodland, particularly in the west of Britain and in southern Ireland.

Biology. Insights into the diet and behaviour of *B. pallens* were gained with an underground viewing chamber in North Wales (Gunn, 1992). It lives in the top 2-20 cm of soil and can penetrate as deeply as 60 cm, rarely appearing on the surface. Mating takes place underground in autumn. Several clutches of 1-6 eggs are laid, and hatch a few weeks later. The species is probably annual.

The genus *Boettgerilla* (there are two species) is now classified in its own family, the Boettgerillidae, somewhat distantly related to the Milacidae.

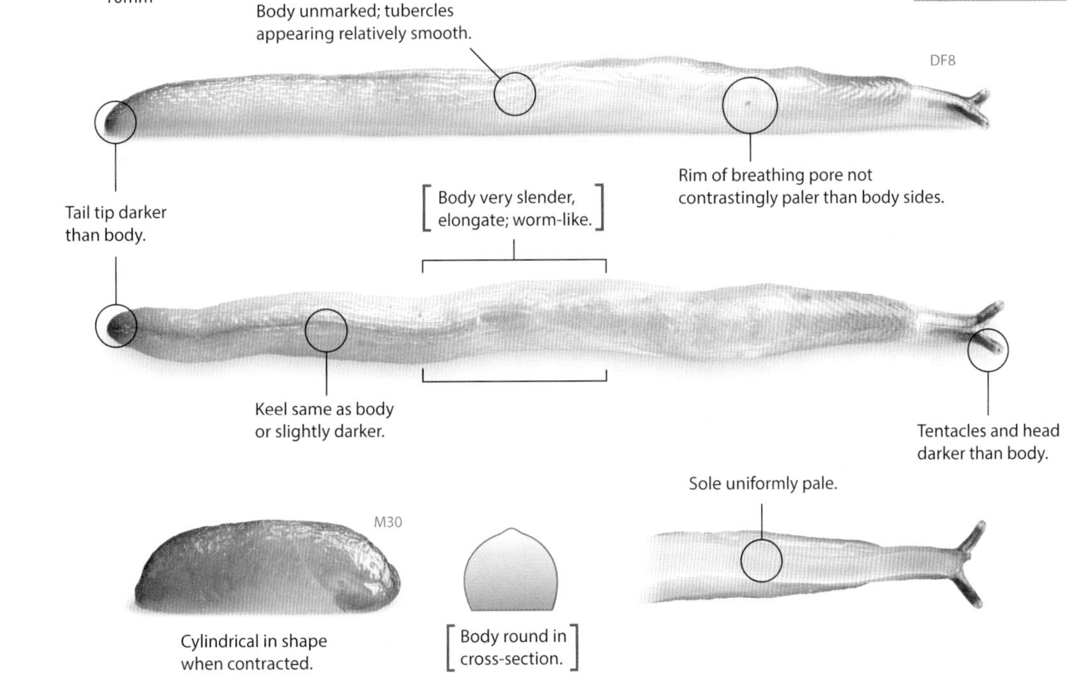

10mm

Body unmarked; tubercles appearing relatively smooth.

DF8

Tail tip darker than body.

Body very slender, elongate; worm-like.

Rim of breathing pore not contrastingly paler than body sides.

Keel same as body or slightly darker.

Tentacles and head darker than body.

Sole uniformly pale.

M30

Cylindrical in shape when contracted.

Body round in cross-section.

Variation

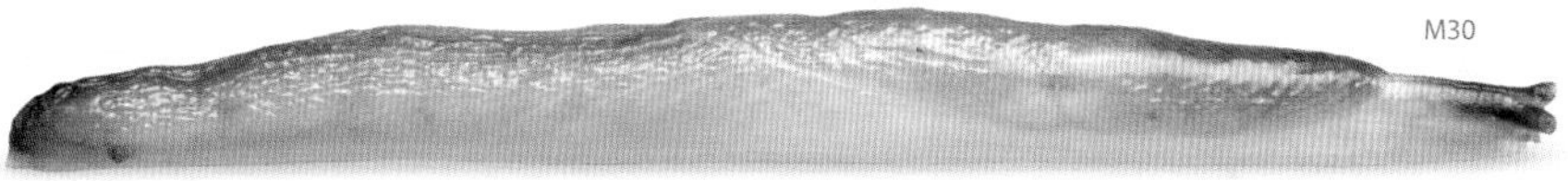

M30

Additional features

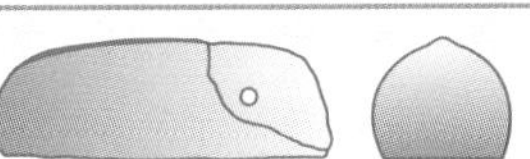

Mucus

Contracted shape

Body colour

Adult size

Testacella (*Testacella*) *maugei* A. Férussac, 1819

Atlantic Shelled Slug (Maugé's Shelled Slug, Maugé's Slug, Dead Man's Fingers)

Identification. Up to 60-100 mm extended. A thick-skinned slug, slow-moving and rather dry to the touch, with a characteristically large, oblong shell. The hind body is less flattened than in other *Testacella*. The two dorsal grooves are very widely separated where they meet the shell and mantle. The body is greyish pink or grey-brown. It is usually heavily speckled with dark brown while the sole and foot fringe are a bright salmon-pink or orange. Green, reddish and black variants have been recorded. Juveniles resemble adults.

Similar species. None (unmistakeable from the shell and body colour).

Pest status. Not considered a pest (feeds on earthworms).

Range. This species has a strongly south-westerly distribution, perhaps more so than any other British terrestrial mollusc. In Ireland it is recorded from near the south coast and around Dublin.

Empty shells of *T. maugei* are robust and can readily be found on soil where the species is (or was) present. They are unlikely to have been overlooked by snail recorders, so the known distribution is probably reasonably accurate. The south-westerly bias may reflect a susceptibility to low winter temperatures or frost.

Quick (1960) and others considered *T. maugei* native to south-western Britain, citing Holocene subfossils, but Kerney (1999) considered it probably introduced. The species was described from specimens from Tenerife (collected as early as 1796) and gardens and a nursery in Bristol (collected circa 1812) (Taylor, 1902-7). It also occurs on Madeira, the Azores, and along the Atlantic coast from Morocco to Dieppe, and on the Mediterranean coast of Spain (and France, as a fossil). It has been accidentally introduced to South Africa, the USA (greenhouses in Philadelphia) and (disputedly) New Zealand (Taylor, 1902-7; Castillejo, 1998; Barker, 1999; Herbert, 2010).

Habitat. Subterranean, in cracks and burrows up to at least 30 cm below the soil surface, rarely surfacing except in wet, mild weather. Live animals are usually difficult to find but may rest under deeply-embedded slabs, debris or deep litter. They can be dug up in soil including patches not dug over for several years.

British and Irish records are mainly from rich, friable loams in long-established gardens, allotments and parks. On south-western coasts *T. maugei* has also been reported from coastal rocks and sea cliffs. Subfossils are known from prehistorically-inhabited caves in Portugal (Rinaldi, 2003).

Biology. This species appears to hunt and feed like other *Testacella*. It feeds largely, if not exclusively, on live earthworms. The evidence for slugs and other animals as prey of *Testacella* species is limited, although they have been found attacking dying slugs killed by pellets (South, 1992). In captivity, within soil, it remains inactive by day. Animals have not been observed to dig, but rather slip through existing cracks and worm burrows, widening them in the process.

When disturbed, crawling *T. maugei* may expel air from the breathing pore with a short audible hiss as they retract. This may also produce a persistent froth of bubbles. Welter-Schultes (2012) also mentions a strong smell. The function of this behaviour, if any, is not known. An adult *T. maugei* is known to have been regurgitated by an adder in south Wales.

The lack of recent records from the eastern and northern parts of its range suggest a decline. This could be attributed to the effect of chemical fertilizer and pesticide use and the disappearance of kitchen gardens (Kerney, 1999). In the south-west (Cardiff) the species remains frequent in allotments, hedgerows and flowerbeds in city parks.

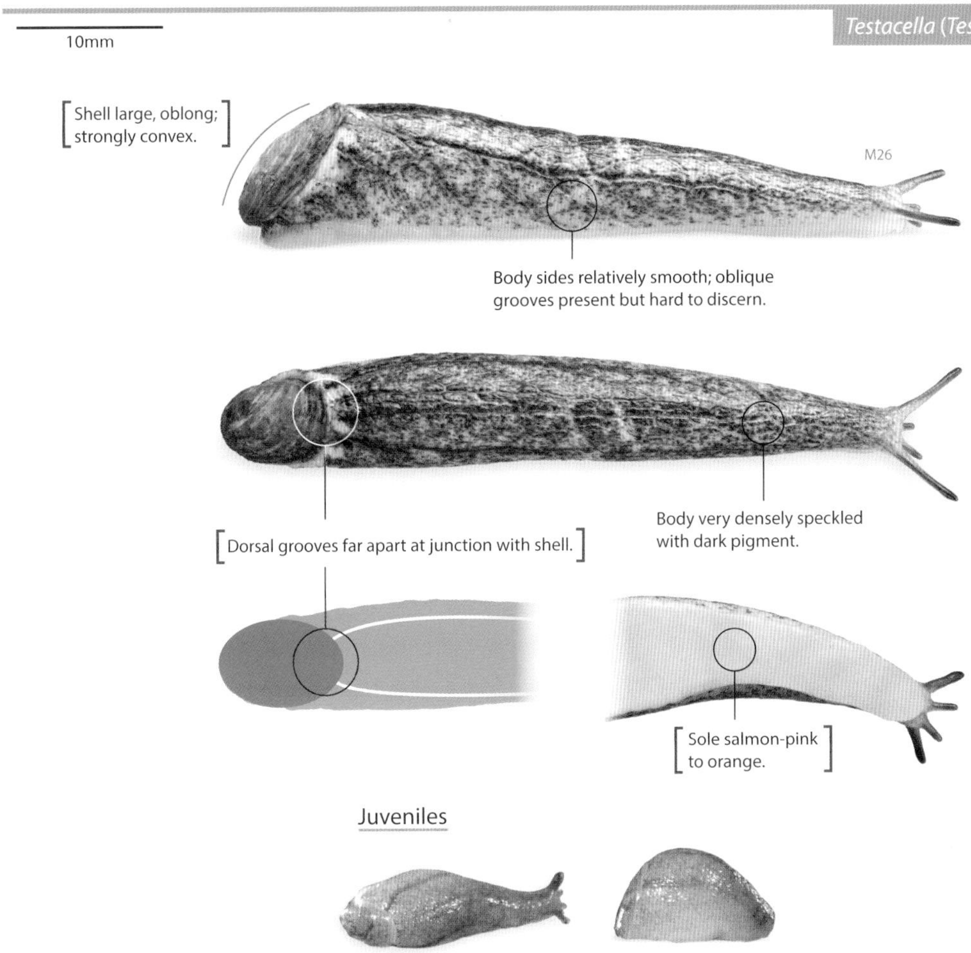

10mm

[Shell large, oblong; strongly convex.]

M26

Body sides relatively smooth; oblique grooves present but hard to discern.

[Dorsal grooves far apart at junction with shell.]

Body very densely speckled with dark pigment.

[Sole salmon-pink to orange.]

Juveniles

Additional features

Body colour

Adult size

Testacella (*Testacella*) *scutulum* Sowerby, 1821

Orange Shelled Slug (Golden Shelled Slug, Shield Slug)

Identification. Up to 70-100 mm extended. A thick-skinned, flattened slug, slow-moving and dry to the touch, with a small, flattened, red-brown shell near the tail. The body is relatively flattened. The two dorsal grooves contact one another at an acute angle or V-shape where they meet the shell and underlying mantle. The body is golden-yellow and heavily speckled. The sole and foot fringe are bright golden yellow or orange. Juveniles resemble adults.

Similar species. This species is very similar to *T.* sp. "*tenuipenis*", a lighter-coloured species in which the dorsal grooves meet at a less acute, more rounded angle or U-shape. The shells do not seem reliably distinguishable but dissection clearly distinguishes the two (p. 120).

Pest status. Not considered a pest (feeds on earthworms).

Range and habitat. Uncertain – populations have been verified from large cemetery in Kensal Green, London and garden in Beverley, Yorkshire. Sowerby described the species from a garden in Lambeth, London. Many other old records may relate to *T.* sp. "*tenuipenis*". Both are probably introduced, originally Mediterranean, species (e.g. see Castillejo, 1998; Beckmann, 2007b; Liberto

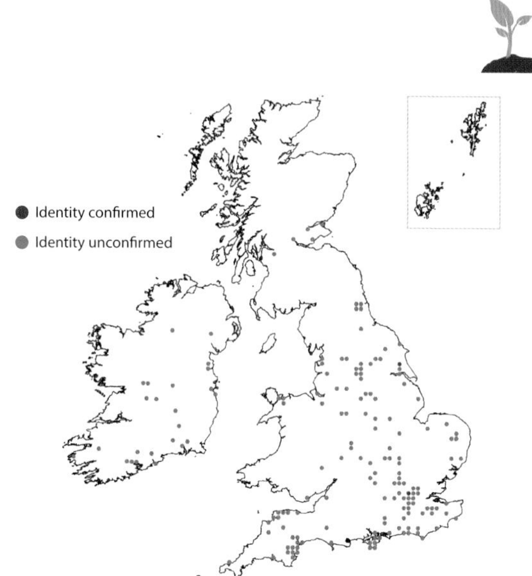

et al., 2011). They appear to have spread less widely than *T. maugei* and *T. haliotidea* although there is an unconfirmed report from Canada (Grimm *et al.*, 2010).

Biology. Generally as for other *Testacella*. The populations studied by Barnes & Stokes (1951) and Stokes (1958) may have belonged to this species or to *T.* sp. "*tenuipenis*". They were occasionally found surviving without a shell.

Testacella (*Testacella*) *sp. "tenuipenis"*

Shelled Slug

Identification. Similar to *T. scutulum* in most respects. Paler and less heavily speckled than *T. scutulum*, with the dorsal grooves meeting at a less acute, more rounded angle or U-shape. The two can be distinguished by dissection.

Pest status. Not considered a pest (feeds on earthworms).

Range and habitat. Uncertain – apparently more common and widespread than true *T. scutulum*. Many of the records for *T. scutulum* may in fact refer to *T.* sp. "*tenuipenis*" Most populations are from gardens and allotments, but in southern Ireland and southern England it can occur in woodlands and on cliffs near the coast.

Biology. Generally as for other *Testacella*. This species was detected during genetic analyses which showed that it and the true *T. scutulum* were genetically deeply divergent from one another. They may originate from different parts of the Mediterranean.

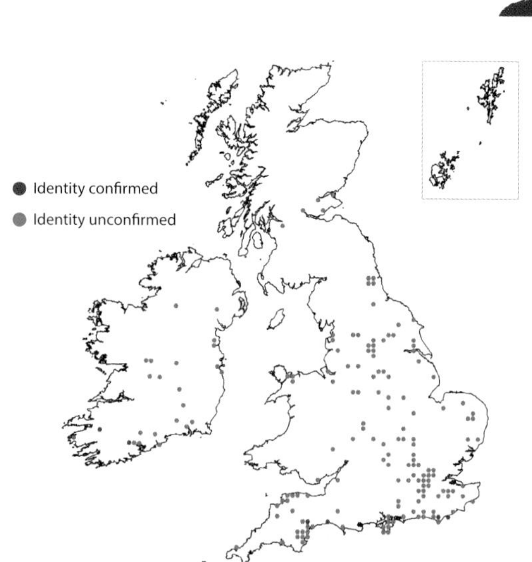

This species has shown the hissing reflex seen in *T. maugei* (although without producing bubbles) and has attempted to bite fingers on at least one occasion.

10mm

Testacella (Testacella) scutulum

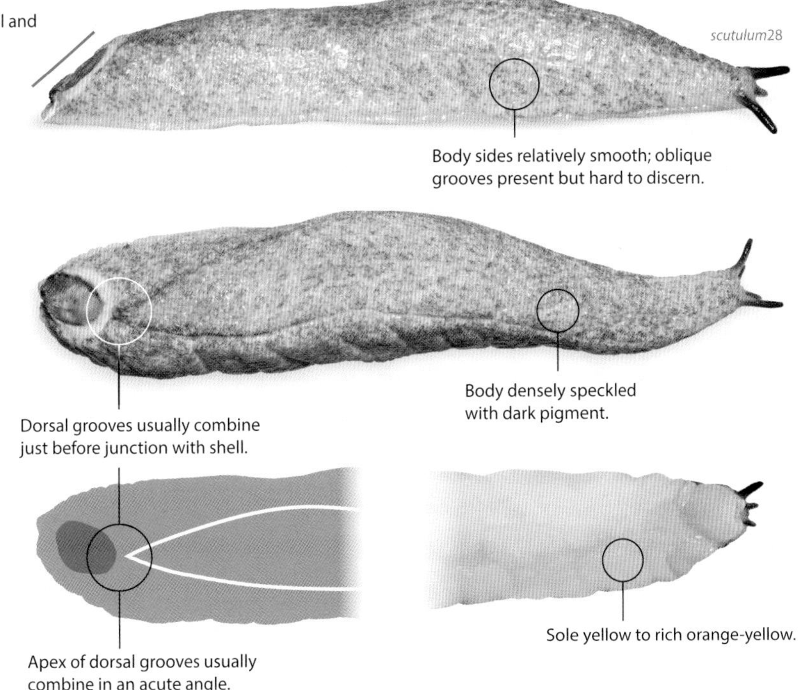

Testacella (Testacella) sp. "tenuipenis"

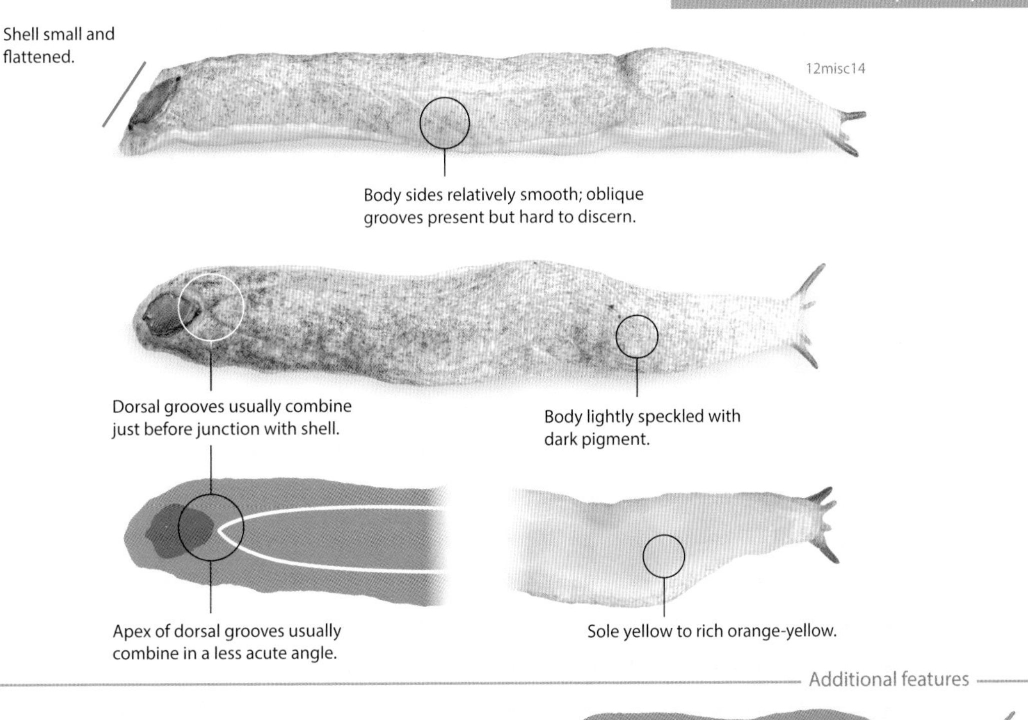

Body colour

Adult size

Testacella* (*Testacella*) *haliotidea Draparnaud, 1801

Ear Shelled Slug (Common Shelled Slug, Shelled Slug, Earshell Slug, Carnivorous Slug)

Identification. Up to 70-100 mm extended. A thick-skinned slug, slow-moving and rather dry to the touch, with a small, slightly convex, ear-shaped shell near the tail. The hind body is less flattened than in other *Testacella* species. The two dorsal grooves are close together but are still separate (by about 2 mm) where they meet the shell and underlying mantle. Parallel oblique grooves are often visible on the body sides, somewhat like a fish steak. The body is pale, grey-white or creamy-white to yellow, the centre of the back often a little darker brown. The animal is unmarked or only lightly speckled with brown. The sole and foot fringe are whitish, like the body. Juveniles resemble adults.

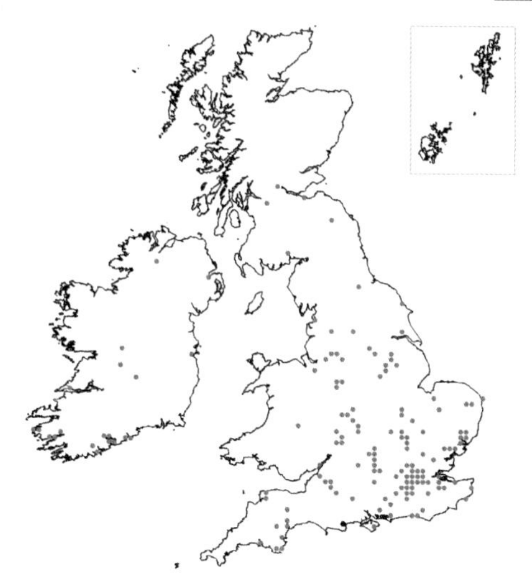

Similar species. This species has frequently been confused with *T. scutulum* and *T.* sp. "*tenuipenis*". It has even been suggested that they belong to the same species (Kerney, 1999) but there is no doubt that *T. haliotidea* is distinct. The separation of the dorsal grooves has fallen in and out of favour as a diagnostic feature. In combination with the colour and shell features, however, it appears to be stable and reliable.

Dissection clearly distinguishes this species (p. 120).

Pest status. Not considered a pest (feeds on earthworms).

Range. Widespread but very local across the lowlands of southern Britain and Ireland. Perhaps most common in the Home Counties and neighbouring parts of England (Surrey, Berks., Bucks., Cambs., etc.). At least half of the records shown are more than 50 years old. Kerney (1999) noted that in recent years *T. haliotidea* had been more rarely reported than other *Testacella* species, a trend which seems to continue. This may reflect a decline or the probability that some old records, especially in the west, were actually of *T. scutulum* or *T.* sp. "*tenuipenis*" (e.g. Turk *et al.*, 2001).

There are scattered records from cultivated lowlands in northern continental Europe but most are probably introductions. *Testacella haliotidea* occurs in more natural habitats in southern France, Iberia, the Balkans and North Africa. It has been reported from eastern and western North America, Cuba, New Zealand and Australia (Barker, 1999; Rinaldi, 2003; Stanisic *et al.*, 2010).

Habitat. As for *T. maugei*. Like that species, nearly all records are from rich soils in allotments and gardens, including the kitchen gardens of country houses. The exceptions are a few from south-western sea coasts in Devon and Co. Cork.

Biology. *Testacella haliotidea* behaves generally like other *Testacella* species. Barnes & Stokes (1951) studied a mixed population of around 300 *T. haliotidea* and *T. scutulum* in a garden. They found that surface activity and the size of individuals peaked in May, with hatchling numbers peaking in November. In captivity, Stokes (1958) found *T. haliotidea* to eat earthworms at a faster rate than *T. scutulum*. It laid fewer and larger eggs than that species, which took longer to hatch, although Quick (1960) noted that the opposite had also been observed. Mating has been recorded as lasting 4 to 5 hours (Barker, 1999) but Stokes showed self-fertilisation is also possible. She also found that *T. haliotidea* could survive freezing of the soil in which it was kept. It can also aestivate in soil within a covering of mucus. In this condition there are reports of the mantle being stretched over the hind half of the animal (e.g. Taylor, 1902-7). According to Taylor (1902-7) individuals may live for 5 or 6 years.

10mm

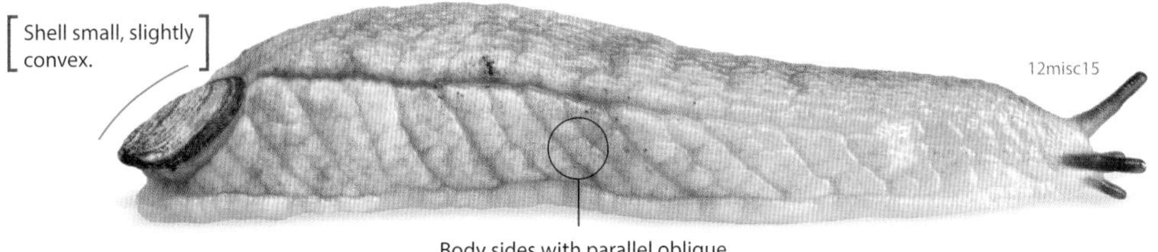

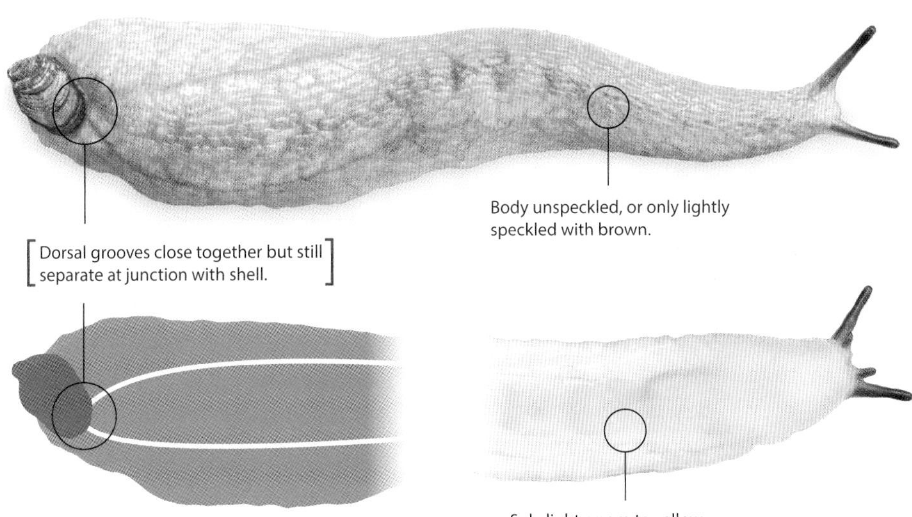

Variation

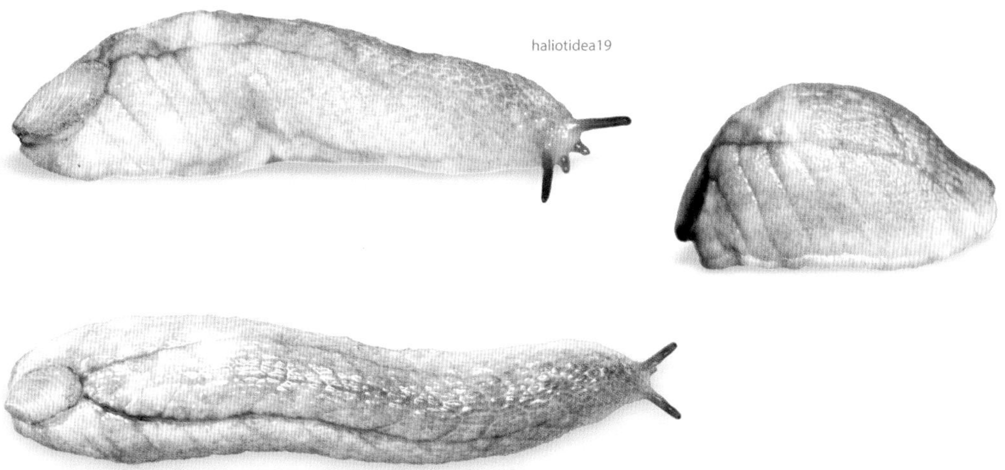

Additional features

Body colour

Adult size

Selenochlamys ysbryda Rowson & Symondson, 2008
Ghost Slug

Identification. Up to 50-75 mm or even longer extended. A medium-sized to large, near-unmistakeable slug with the tiny, disc-shaped mantle and breathing pore at the rear of the body. Behind the mantle is a very short keel or crest on the tail. The body is extremely long, slender and wormlike when extended. When contracted, it is cylindrical with the head characteristically sucked "inside-out" like the finger of a glove. The animal is bright, paper-white to milk-white with the pink-purple internal organs sometimes showing through the translucent skin. Four dorsal grooves run the length of the body. The body is covered in microscopic brown speckles. The eye spots at the tips of the tentacles are small, colourless and barely visible. The sole is very narrow and the same colour as the body. Juveniles resemble adults.

Similar species. Though characteristic, this species has been confused with other pale slugs in the past. *Boettgerilla pallens* is similarly elongate and retracts to a cylindrical shape, but has black eye spots and a large mantle at the front of the body. Pale *Deroceras* populations or rare albinos of other species can also cause initial confusion.

Testacella species also have a small mantle at the rear of the body, and in very rare cases have been recorded surviving without a shell. However the skin of *S. ysbryda* is thinner, softer and moister, and the animal is much more active and extensible. The sole of *Testacella* species forms the widest part of the body, while in *S. ysbryda* the sole is narrower than the body.

Dissection not required.

Pest status. Not considered a pest (feeds on earthworms). The species has not been established in Britain as long as *Testacella* species, but seems to have comparably limited effects on earthworm populations. It appears to occur in lower densities than non-carnivorous slugs, but this is difficult to verify because individuals are seldom seen.

Range. Widespread but local in South Wales and in Bristol; also confirmed (2013) from Wallingford, Oxfordshire. The area of suitable habitat seems large and the species may spread further.

Probably introduced to Britain in the last 10-50 years (it was not reported by Quick, 1960 for example). The earliest record is from Brecon in 2004 (Reise & Hutchinson, 2009); it was later found in Cardiff (Rowson & Symondson, 2008). Almost all other records are from specimens or photographs submitted by members of the public – the species is difficult to find even in gardens where it is known to be present. The Trigonochlamydidae are native to the Caucasus and surrounding areas. It appears that the Crimea, Ukraine is the source of the British species, rather than the Caucasus where the similar *S. pallida* (Simroth) occurs (Balashov, 2012).

Habitat. Subterranean, up to a metre deep, and rarely surfacing. Records are from urban and rural gardens, allotments, and adjacent disturbed habitats. In the Crimea and Caucasus *Selenochlamys* also occurs in woodlands.

Biology. As far as is known, *S. ysbryda* feeds only on live earthworms in a manner like *Testacella*. Juveniles have been reared on enchytraeid worms at first. In captivity the species can survive for over 6 months without food or water by remaining inactive in soil. Many populations have also survived the relatively cold winters of the last four years.

The evolutionary relationships of the Trigonochlamydidae are not fully understood, but they appear unrelated to the Testacellidae. Their similarities are a striking example of convergent evolution.

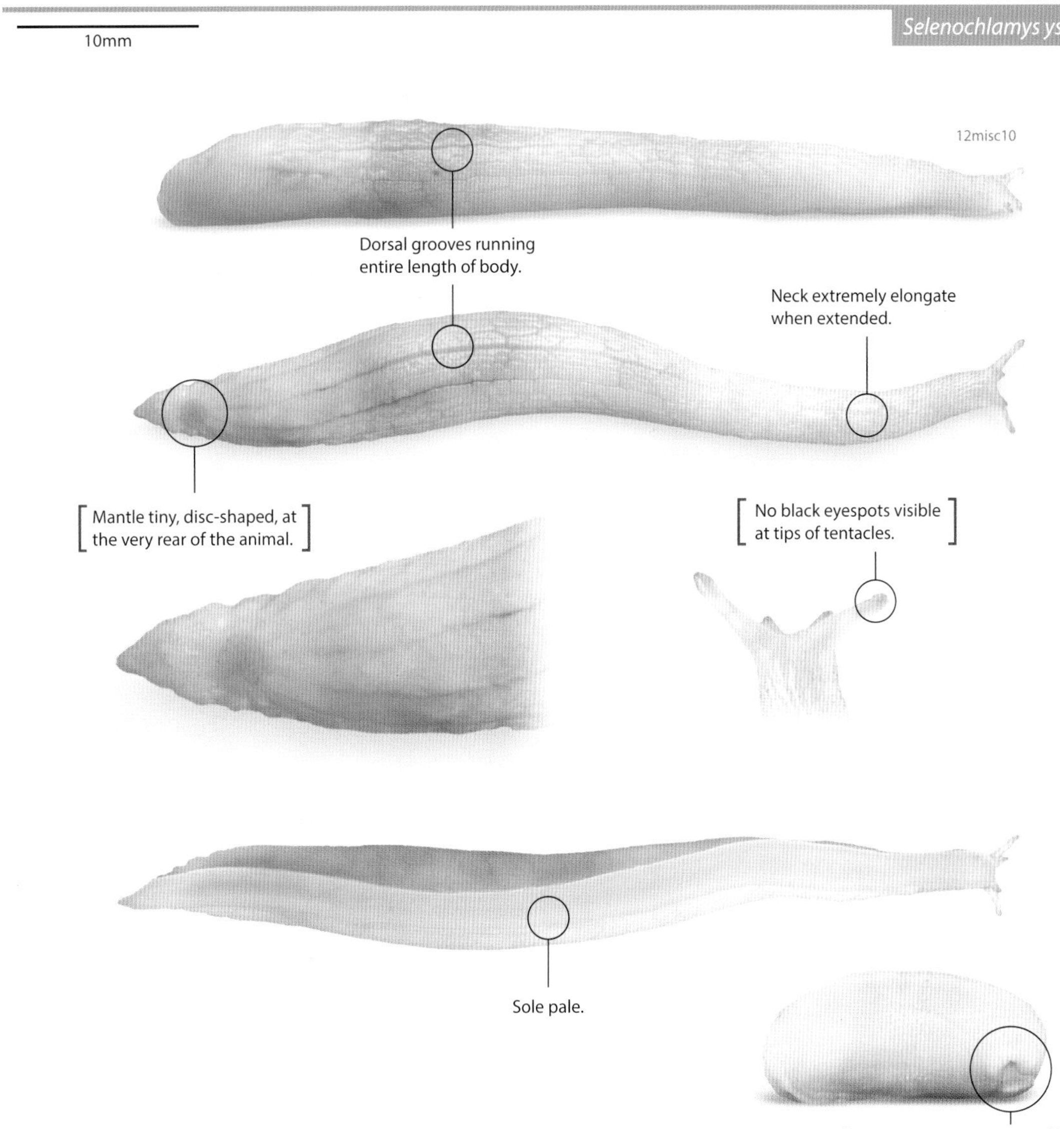

10mm

12misc10

Dorsal grooves running entire length of body.

Neck extremely elongate when extended.

[Mantle tiny, disc-shaped, at the very rear of the animal.]

[No black eyespots visible at tips of tentacles.]

Sole pale.

[Head pulled 'inside-out' when contracted.]

Juveniles

1mm

Additional features

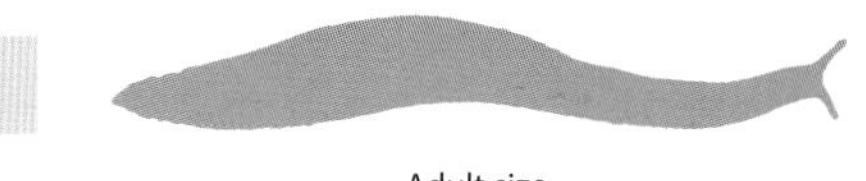

Body colour

Adult size

Vitrina pellucida (O. F. Müller, 1774)

Winter Semi-slug (Pellucid Glass Snail, Western Glass-Snail)

Identification. Up to 10 mm extended (shell diameter 4.5-6.0 mm). The mantle lobe barely extends onto the shell. The mantle is pale grey. The shell is smaller and less flattened than in *Phenacolimax major*. The pale grey, snail-like animal is able to withdraw almost completely into the shell.

Pest status. Not considered a pest.

Range, habitat and biology. Widespread throughout Britain and Ireland. Native throughout Europe, into the Arctic Circle. Also native to western North America (Kerney, 1999; Grimm *et al.*, 2010). Almost all habitats, including mountain summits. Shells or animals tend to be found in large numbers only on calcareous soils and in sand dunes. Live adults are found mainly in winter (Cameron, 2008). Seasonality may vary geographically however (Welter-Schultes, 2012).

Phenacolimax major (A. Férussac, 1807)

Greater Semi-slug (Greater Pellucid Glass Snail)

Identification. Up to 16 mm extended (shell diameter 5-6 mm). The mantle lobe extends well onto the shell and nearly reaches the shell apex. The mantle is mottled with black. The shell is larger and more flattened than in *Vitrina pellucida*. The mid-grey animal is not able to withdraw completely into the shell when adult.

Pest status. Not considered a pest.

Range, habitat and biology. Rare in southern England and South Wales. Not known in Ireland. Occurs from lowland France to western Germany (Kerney, 1999). Restricted to litter in ancient woodland and its remnants in wet places like stream valleys, on both calcareous and non-calcareous soils. Live adults are found mainly in spring and early summer, seldom into June (Cameron, 2008; R. Boyce, pers. comm.). Seasonality may vary geographically however (Welter-Schultes, 2012).

Semilimax pyrenaicus (A. Férussac, 1821)

Pyrenean Semi-slug (Pyrenean Glass Snail)

Identification. Up to 16 mm extended (shell diameter 5-6 mm). The mantle lobe covers the shell apex. The mantle is broad, and grey with dark markings. The shell is much more flattened and ear-like than in *Vitrina pellucida*. The animal is very active and fast-moving, and light grey to dark grey. It is much too large to withdraw completely into the shell.

Pest status. Not considered a pest.

Range, habitat and biology. Local but apparently spreading in Ireland (Anderson, 1991). Not in Britain but present in the Pyrenees and perhaps elsewhere in France (Kerney, 1999; NMNI, 2010; Welter-Schultes, 2012). Found in damp litter in woodland, alder and willow carr and wet grassland. May be abundant, but susceptible to drought so generally confined to wetter woodlands, glens and ravines. Live adults have been found in all months of the year, breeding in spring and perhaps autumn. Mating and egg laying have not been observed.

Vitrina pellucida

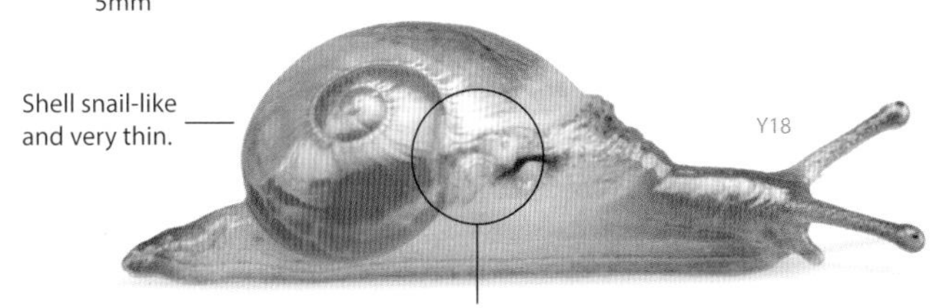

Adult size

Phenacolimax major

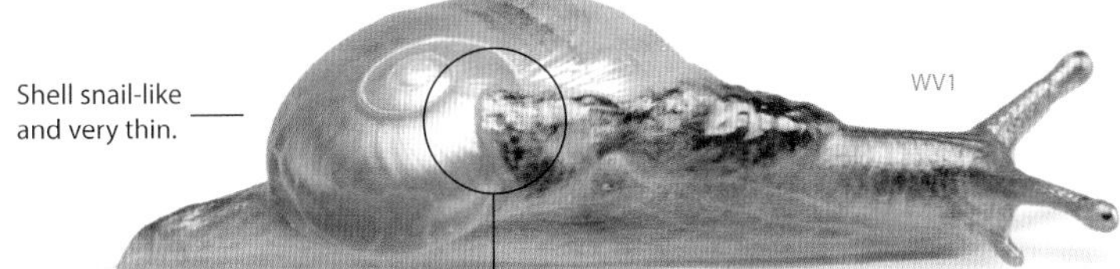

Adult size

Semilimax pyrenaicus

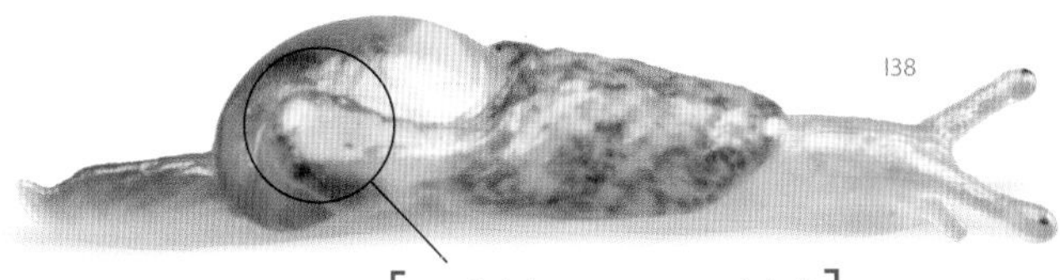

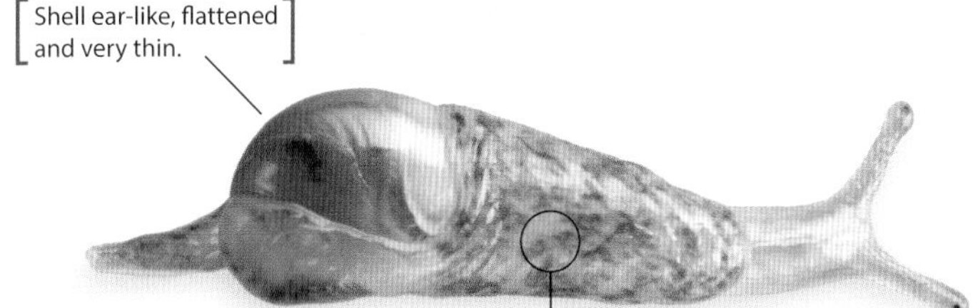

Adult size

Why dissect slugs?

The genitalia of many invertebrates are a reliable guide to their identity. As indicated elsewhere, some slug species can only be distinguished by examining their adult genitalia. This guide covers only those cases where this is useful or necessary.

The genitalia lie inside the body except when parts are everted (pushed inside-out like the finger of a glove) during courtship and mating. Fortunately, revealing them is easy and takes only a few minutes. A slug is essentially a muscular tube inside which the organs lie loosely coiled. They are exposed simply by opening the tube lengthways. There are no hard parts to get in the way, the genitalia are generally robust and easy to locate, and every individual has both male and female organs at once. This can lead them to appear complex but only a few key features need to be examined.

Killing and preservation

Unless killed by beer traps or other collecting methods, slugs need to be killed before dissection. This can be done by drowning overnight in tapwater or (slightly quicker) carbonated or recently boiled and cooled water. The jar should have a tight fitting flexible cap which can be snapped shut so that no air bubbles remain inside when closed. Quicker methods are plunging into boiling water, or by freezing for at least a few hours. Killing by immersion in strong alcohol should be avoided as it will cause the animal to contract strongly, which may distort the internal organs,.

If necessary slugs and dissections can be preserved in individual containers, either frozen or pickled in strong (75-80%) ethanol, methylated spirits or isopropanol. The preservative can be replaced once or twice until it stays clear of suspended matter. Provided they do not dry out such specimens will last for years. Formalin (formaldehyde) should be avoided. For research studies where the DNA of slugs (or their parasites, etc.) is to be extracted, killing and storage by freezing is recommended. Drowning will degrade DNA, so tissue samples should be removed before drowning if this method is used.

To be of future value all containers should be labelled with standard recording data (locality, date, species name etc.). Labels should be written on durable paper in pencil or permanent pen (use pencil if in doubt) and kept inside the container so that they cannot rub off.

A stepwise guide to dissection

The simplest method requires a scalpel or small scissors, some pins, and one or two fine forceps (tweezers) or bent needles to manipulate the organs. Good light is required and a microscope, loupe or lens is useful for the smaller species. Also needed is a flat-bottomed dish or jar lid with sides at least 10 mm high, its base covered by a 5 mm depth of cork, plastazote, dark paraffin wax, or the wax from a cheese covering. This will grip the pins (plasticine tends to be too soft). The dish allows the organs to be located under water or alcohol, preventing them adhering to one another and reducing distracting reflections.

Dead slugs can first be wiped to remove excess slime. Frozen slugs should of course be defrosted. The steps are as follows:

1. Cut along left edge of sole. Holding the slug in the fingers, cut along the entire edge of the sole on the left-hand side (the side away from the genitalia). The cut should only be deep enough to go through the body wall, but it is still easy to accidentally pierce the crop or gut. This may release a cloud of their contents which can be flushed away under a tap.

2. Cut across back of head. Make a second cut across the back of the head, in front of the mantle, all the way to the edge of the sole on the other side. This allows the sides and back of the body to be peeled away from the sole and organs. The skin here is very thin so care should be taken not to penetrate too deeply. It is so thin it can often simply be torn. If necessary, a third cut across the back or tail can be made.

3. Open and pin down. Peel the slug open. The attachments of a few ribbon-like muscles and ducts may impede the opening process. These should be snipped through as close to the body wall as possible. To hold the body open, push one or more pins through the sole and through the peeled-back body wall, and through the head if necessary. If the slug will not stay open, the whole sole can be removed and the body pinned open upside-down (it is equally easy to find the organs).

4. Fill with water and identify organs. Fill the dish with water, or 75% alcohol, rinsing any clouds of mucus or gut contents away under a tap. Try to identify the important organs as detailed below. A good starting point is to locate the eye tentacles running back from the head, and the buccal mass between them. The buccal mass is a muscular ball containing the radula, and jaw if present (in *Testacella* and *Selenochlamys*, the elongated buccal mass runs the length of the body). The buccal mass and eye tentacles each have ribbon-like retractor muscles attaching them to the body wall. The genitalia begin to the right of the buccal mass and run either side of the right eye tentacle retractor. They run back through the slug, winding around the crop as far as the digestive gland. The gut runs through this large, soft, liver-like organ. The hind part of the gut or rectum bends forward and runs up to the diaphragm to the anus near the breathing pore. An appendix-like rectal caecum branches off in some species. The broccoli-like gonad or ovotestis is often visible between the lobes of the digestive gland.

(*N.B. The accompanying photographs have been partly coloured in order to pinpoint the position of particular organs.*)

5. Remove genitalia (optional). With experience, some identifications can be made without further dissection. For beginners, however, it is worth trying to recognise and tease out the front parts of the genitalia. These can be stretched out and held in place with pins. They can be separated from the rest of the body by cutting out a small piece of the body wall that includes the genital pore on the right-hand side near the head. For some species, it is necessary to look inside the genitalia for identification.

During dissection, the genitalia and other organs will still be loosely bound together by thin, gooey connective tissue and thin nerves. These are much finer than the important organs and can be safely picked away as they are found.

After dissection, the pins can be removed and the slug folded shut. The genitalia can be photographed or drawn and they and/or the body preserved if necessary.

A variant of this method, where the whole head is first cut off with scissors, is even simpler. It works well for Arionidae and can also be used to kill slugs quickly, but risks damaging the genitalia in other families.

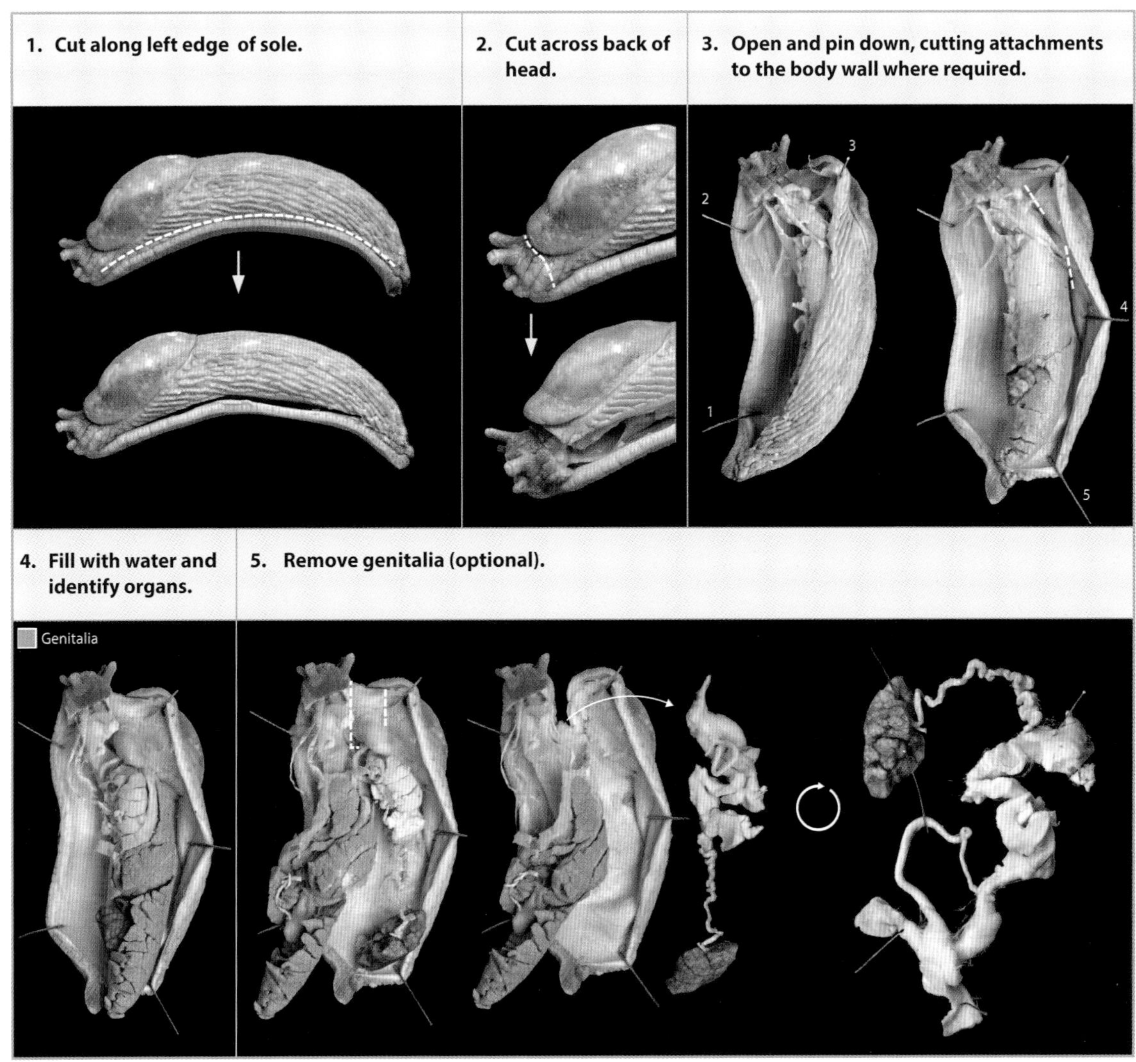

What to look for in the genitalia

Genitalia vary within slug species just as external features do, and in some species no two individuals' genitalia look the same. The identification features used here are therefore simple, consistent, differences in shape. Colour is usually irrelevant and measurements are not needed. The illustrations are based on removed and pinned genitalia, laid out to show the features as clearly as possible. The features generally apply only to adults, although some may also be visible in older juveniles. In young juveniles, the genitalia exist only as very thin ribbons or cannot be found at all.

The parts normally used in identification are the ones directly involved in mating. These form a set of ducts (tubes) that meet to form a short atrium near the genital pore. In the Arionidae, the atrium itself is muscular, is everted during mating, and may contain the diagnostic features of a ligula, shaped something like a set of lips or a tongue, or a small epiphallus process. The atrium needs to be slit open to see these. In the Milacidae, the atrium may have mucus glands attached by thin tubes and contain a tongue-like muscular stimulator.

The three main ducts running away from the atrium are:

I. The ***penis*** is the most muscular and robust duct. It is everted during mating to deliver sperm and is withdrawn by a retractor muscle at its tip. The penis often has one or more additional features (a gland, lobe, flagellum or stimulator) that can be diagnostic. Two groups of slugs lack a penis. In the Arionidae the sperm are delivered instead by an ***epiphallus*** that is not everted. In certain Agriolimacidae some individuals lack a penis and are termed aphallic.

II. The ***oviduct*** is the next most robust duct and is sometimes partly everted. It may be attached to the body wall by short muscles. In some species, the ligula or mucus glands are associated with the oviduct rather than the atrium. The oviduct leads back to the non-muscular egg-producing organs including the albumen gland. This is tiny in juvenile slugs but swells for egg production in adults.

   The penis or epiphallus and the oviduct are connected to each other by a thin duct, the vas deferens. This delivers sperm to the penis or epiphallus ready for mating.

   Both sperm and egg cells are produced by the dark, broccoli-like gonad or ovotestis. This is embedded between the lobes of the digestive gland, and is used to distinguish some species in Arionidae. The gonad is connected to the oviduct by a thin, squiggly hermaphroditic duct.

III. The ***bursa*** or ***bursa copulatrix*** is a thin-walled bag connected to the atrium by the shortest and most delicate duct. The bursa is easily split open but is usually loosely bound to the oviduct so is difficult to lose completely. It receives sperm during mating and digests it afterwards. In the Milacidae and Arionidae it may contain one or more spermatophores. These are stiff, chitinised, sperm-holding capsules received from previous mates. In the Milacidae they are thorny and elaborate.

For identification, it is usually important to locate the atrium and at least the front parts of the three ducts.

It does not usually matter if the vas deferens is broken, or if the rear parts of the oviduct, albumen gland and gonad break off.

Internal features of slugs

Genitalia
Cut edge of sole
Salivary glands
Brain
(ganglia)
Buccal mass
(contains radula and jaw)
Crop
Tail tip
Gut
Top of head
Digestive gland
Oviduct
Gonad
Penis
Eye tentacles
(right tentacle is looped around penis)
Rectal caecum
Rectum
Gut
(looped over aorta)
Underside of mantle
Diaphragm
(obscuring heart, kidney, lung and shell)
Cut edge of body wall

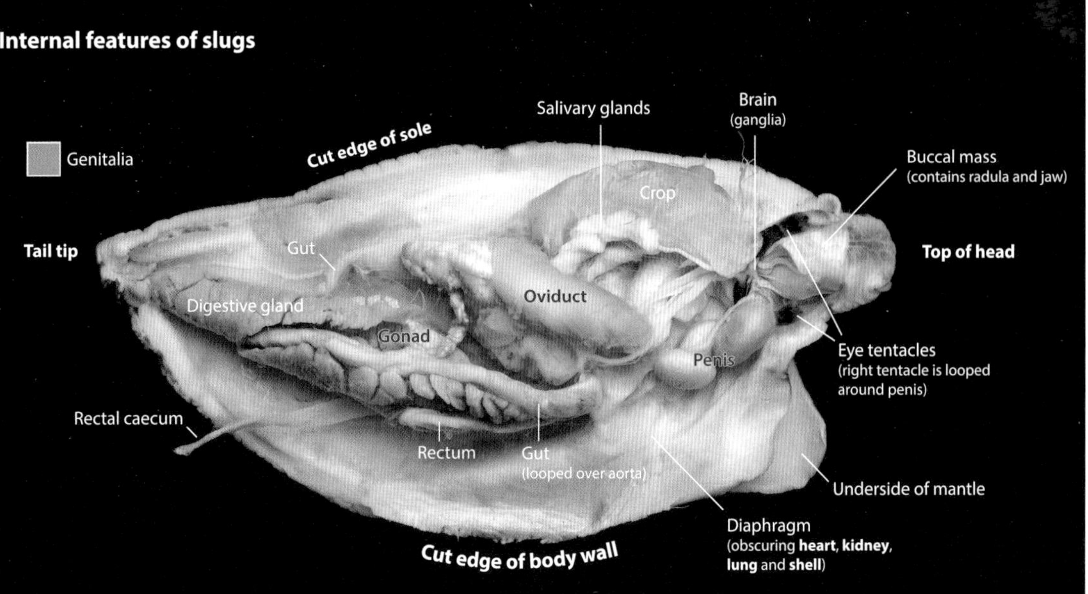

Internal anatomy as seen from above in an adult *Limacus maculatus*, dissected as far as Stage 4. The organs have been slightly teased apart. Below are the extracted genitalia of two species positioned in the standard orientation used for identification purposes.

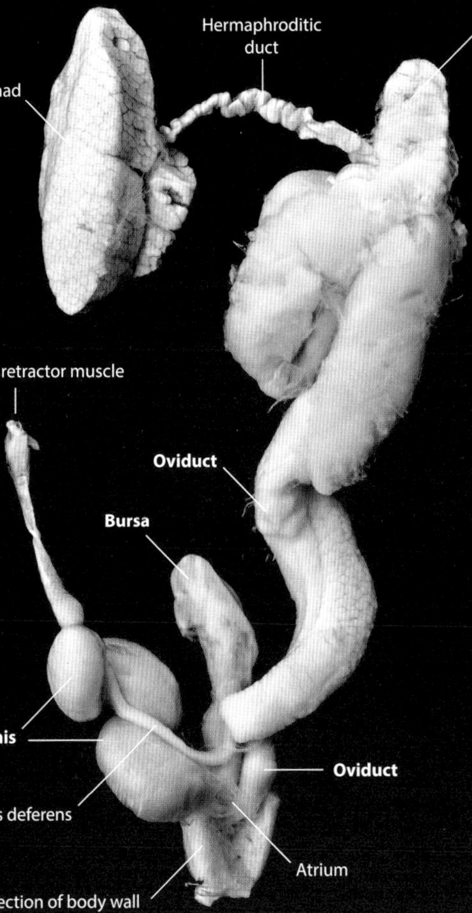

Hermaphroditic
duct
Albumen gland
Gonad
Penial retractor muscle
Oviduct
Bursa
Penis
Oviduct
Vas deferens
Atrium
Section of body wall

Limacus maculatus

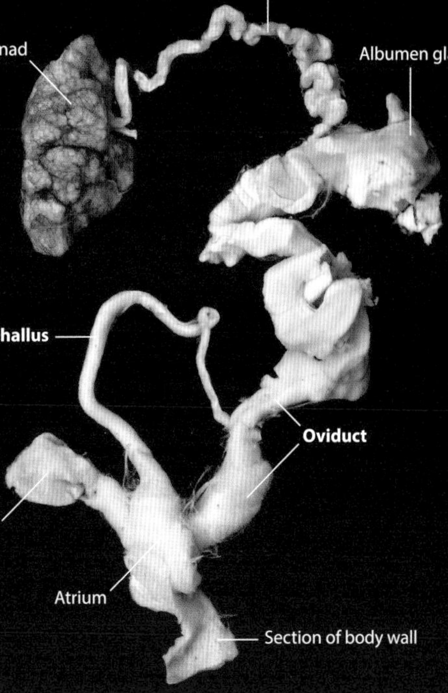

Hermaphroditic
duct
Gonad
Albumen gland
Epiphallus
Oviduct
Bursa
Atrium
Section of body wall

Arion (Arion) flagellus

Arionidae: *Arion* (*Arion*). In this group the atrium or oviduct needs to be cut open to see the ligula. There are two sets of species, those with the ligula in the upper atrium and those with the ligula in the oviduct.

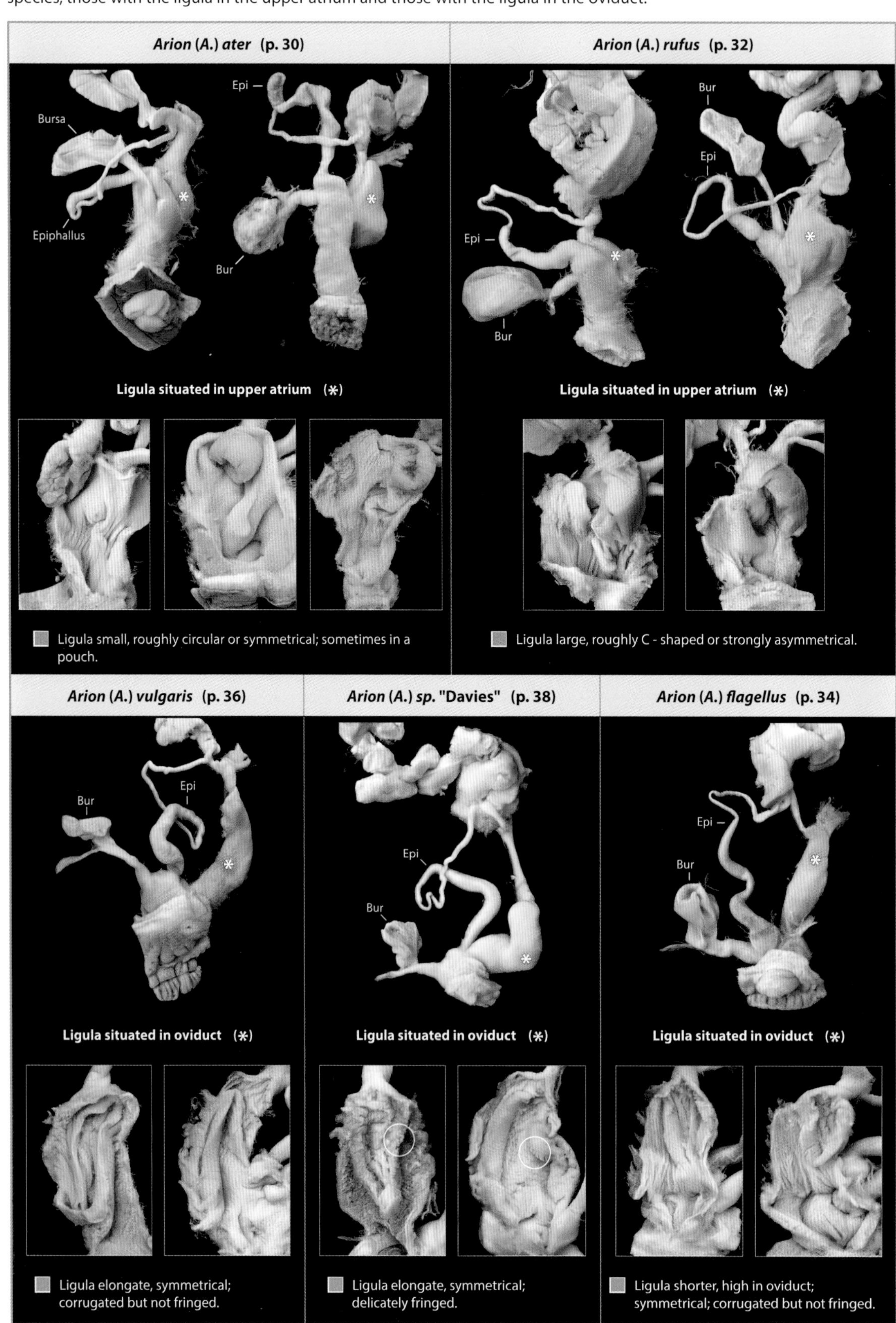

Arionidae: *Arion* (*Mesarion*)

In continental Europe, *A.* (*M.*) *fuscus* and *A.* (*M.*) *subfuscus* are distinguished by the form of the gonad, although this appears to be less reliable in Britain and Ireland. *Arion* (*M.*) cf. *iratii* has a gonad like *A.* (*M.*) *subfuscus*.

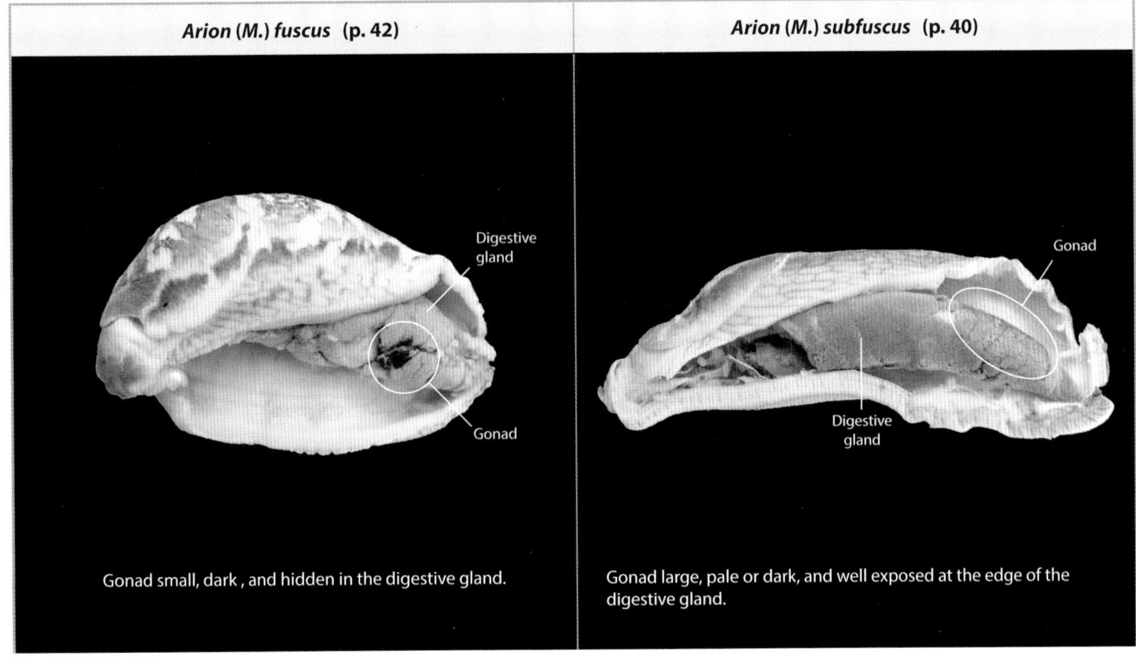

***Arion* (*M.*) *fuscus* (p. 42)**	***Arion* (*M.*) *subfuscus* (p. 40)**
Gonad small, dark , and hidden in the digestive gland.	Gonad large, pale or dark, and well exposed at the edge of the digestive gland.

Arionidae: *Arion* (*Carinarion*). As with the external features of these species, doubts have been raised about the reliability of these internal differences, which are relative rather than absolute.

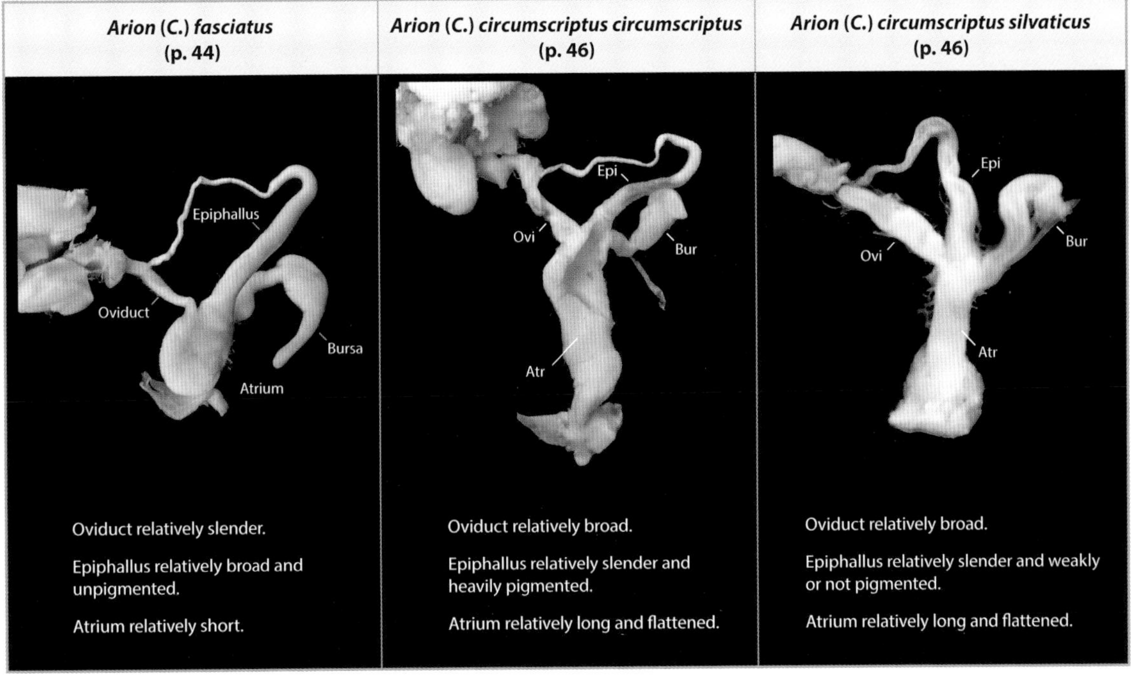

***Arion* (*C.*) *fasciatus* (p. 44)**	***Arion* (*C.*) *circumscriptus circumscriptus* (p. 46)**	***Arion* (*C.*) *circumscriptus silvaticus* (p. 46)**
Oviduct relatively slender. Epiphallus relatively broad and unpigmented. Atrium relatively short.	Oviduct relatively broad. Epiphallus relatively slender and heavily pigmented. Atrium relatively long and flattened.	Oviduct relatively broad. Epiphallus relatively slender and weakly or not pigmented. Atrium relatively long and flattened.

Arionidae: ***Arion*** **(*Kobeltia*).** In this group the atrium needs to be cut open. In three of the species there is a distinctively shaped process where the epiphallus enters the atrium. It is absent in the other two, which are easier to distinguish externally.

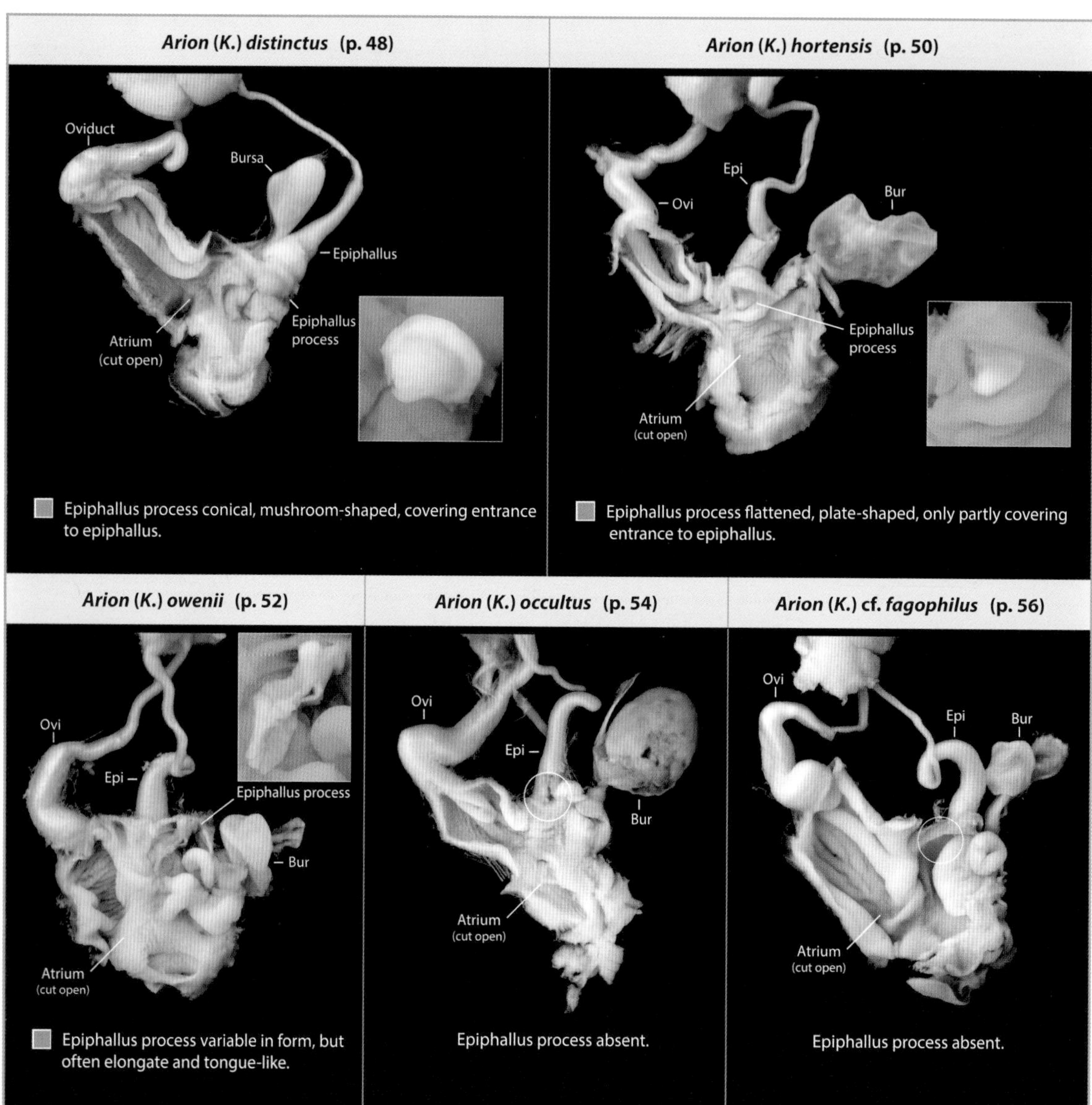

Arion **(*K.*)** ***distinctus*** **(p. 48)**

Epiphallus process conical, mushroom-shaped, covering entrance to epiphallus.

Arion **(*K.*)** ***hortensis*** **(p. 50)**

Epiphallus process flattened, plate-shaped, only partly covering entrance to epiphallus.

Arion **(*K.*)** ***owenii*** **(p. 52)**

Epiphallus process variable in form, but often elongate and tongue-like.

Arion **(*K.*)** ***occultus*** **(p. 54)**

Epiphallus process absent.

Arion **(*K.*) cf.** ***fagophilus*** **(p. 56)**

Epiphallus process absent.

Limacidae: *Limacus*. The attachment of the bursa duct is the important feature.

Limacus flavus **(p. 68)**	***Limacus maculatus*** **(p. 70)**

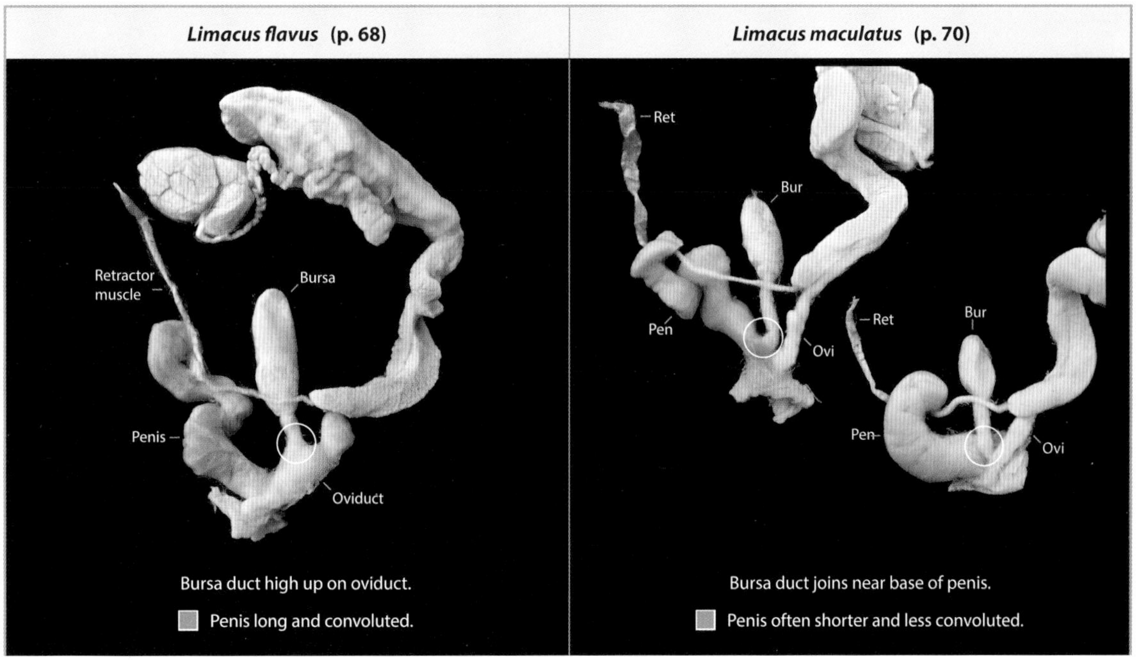

Bursa duct high up on oviduct.	Bursa duct joins near base of penis.
■ Penis long and convoluted.	■ Penis often shorter and less convoluted.

Limacidae: *Limax*. The species differ in the form of the penis.

Limax maximus **(p. 62)**	***Limax cinereoniger*** **(p. 64)**	***Limax*** **cf.** ***dacampi*** **(p. 66)**
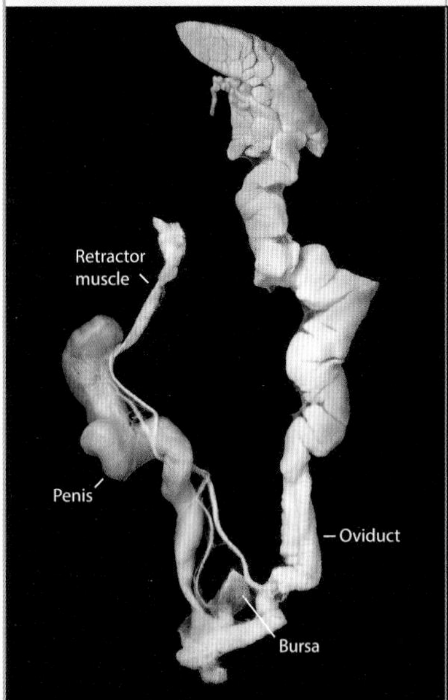 Retractor muscle; Penis; Oviduct; Bursa	Ret; Pen; Bur; Ovi	Ret; Bur; Ovi; Pen
■ Penis relatively short, broadening towards the tip.	■ Penis relatively short, evenly narrow throughout its length.	■ Penis extremely long, evenly narrow throughout its length.

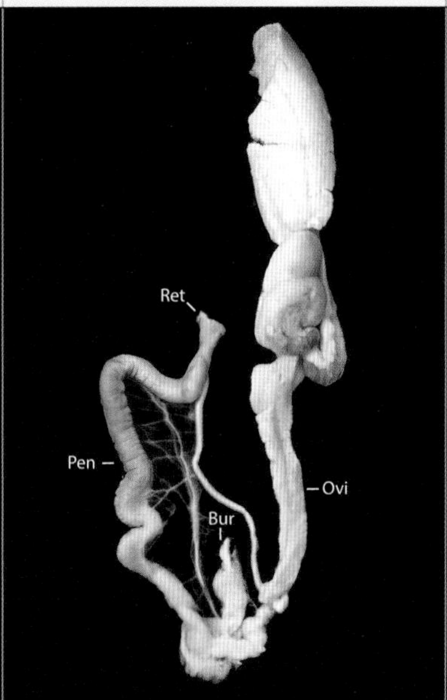

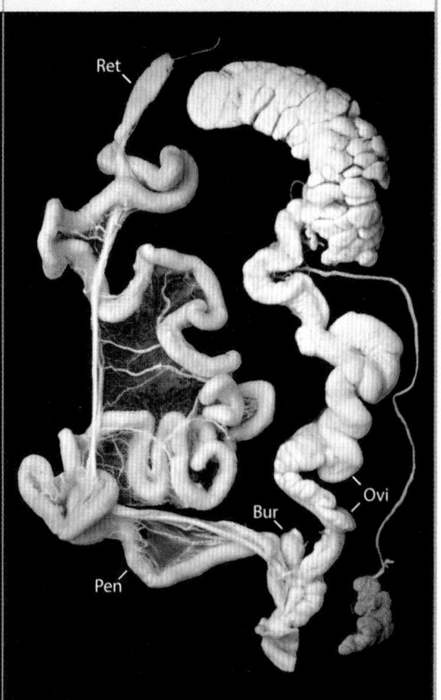

Limacidae: *Lehmannia & Ambigolimax*. Species differ in the presence and form of an appendage on the penis.

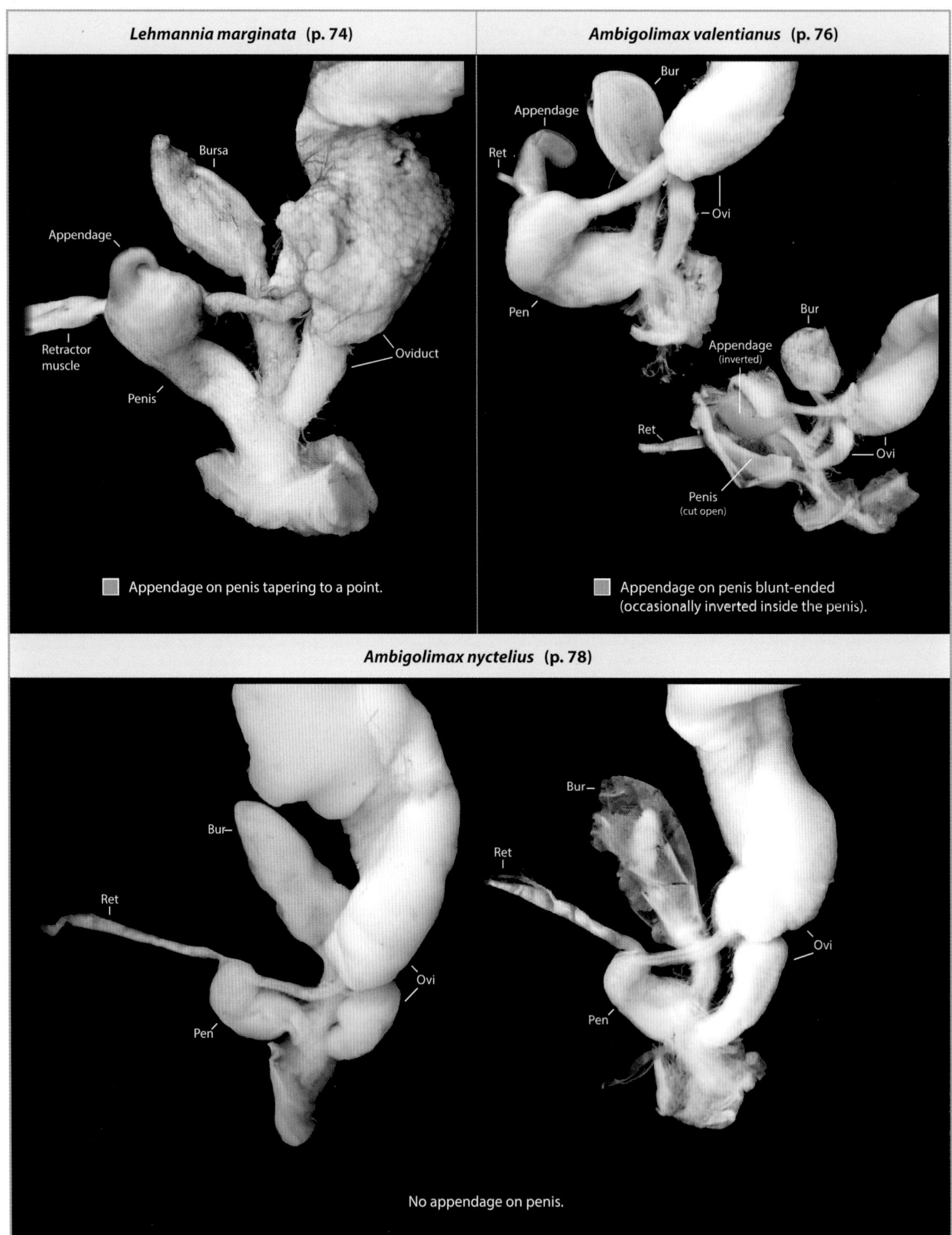

Agriolimacidae: *Deroceras*. Species differ in the form of the penis, penial gland and appendages.

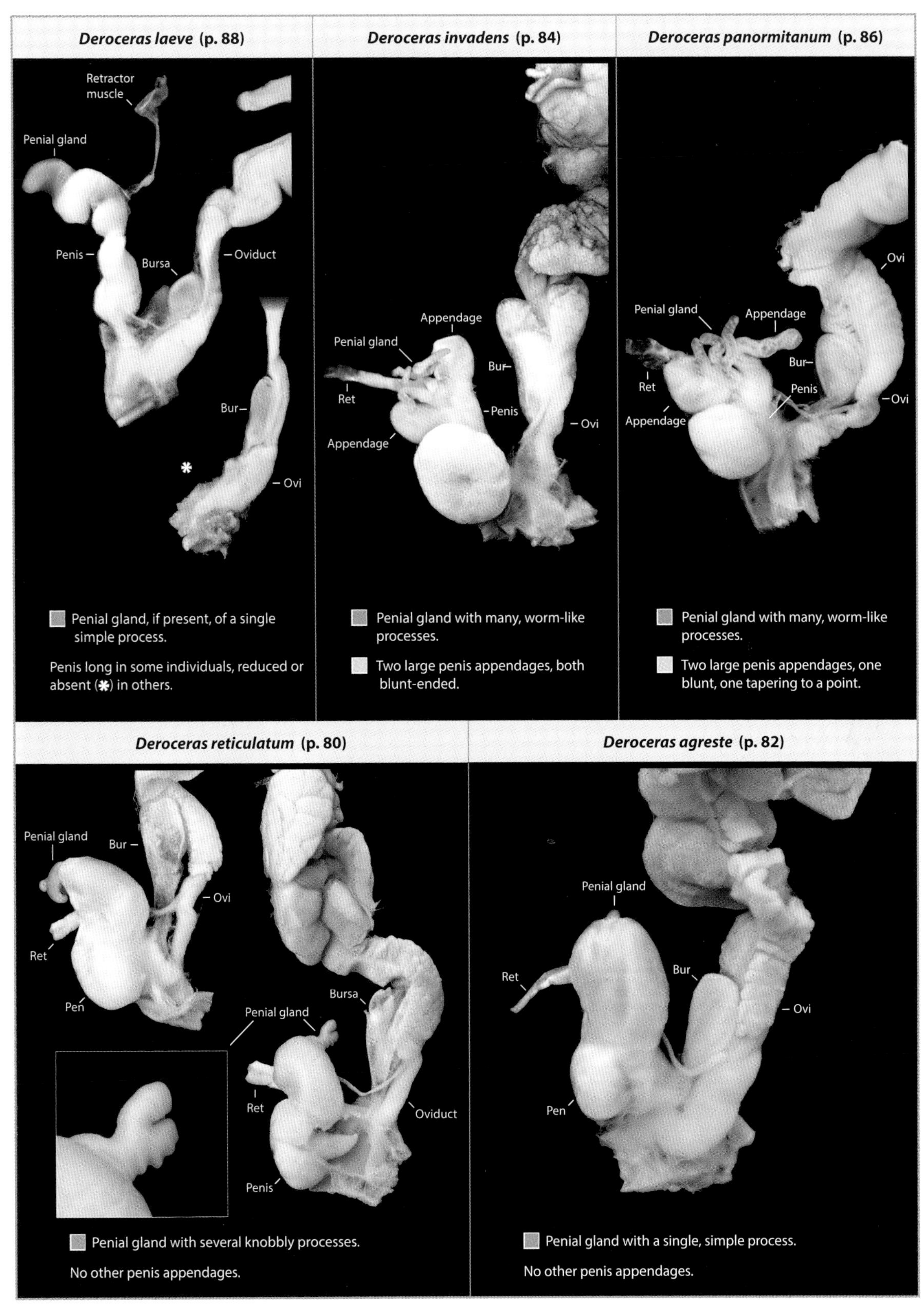

Testacellidae: *Testacella*. Species differ in the form of the penis.

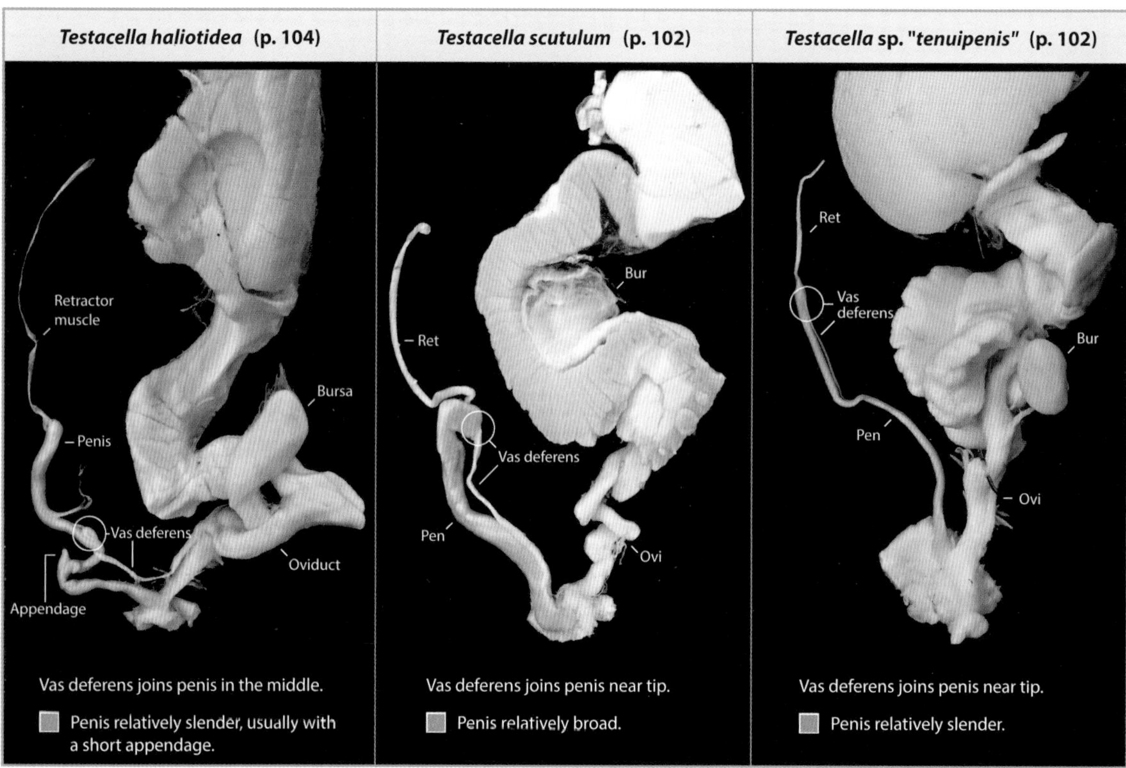

***Testacella haliotidea* (p. 104)**

Vas deferens joins penis in the middle.

- Penis relatively slender, usually with a short appendage.

***Testacella scutulum* (p. 102)**

Vas deferens joins penis near tip.

- Penis relatively broad.

***Testacella* sp. "*tenuipenis*" (p. 102)**

Vas deferens joins penis near tip.

- Penis relatively slender.

Vitrinidae. Species differ in various aspects.

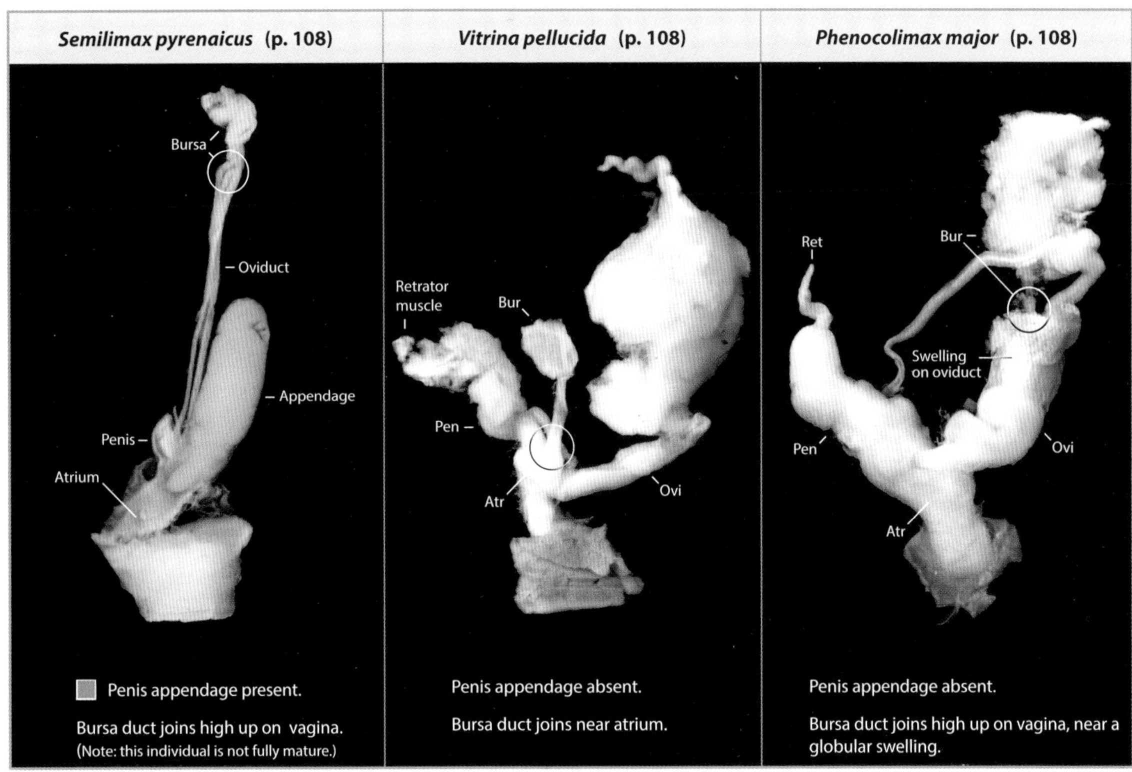

Slug eggs

All our slugs lay eggs (in contrast, a few of our snails have live young). Slug eggs are frequently encountered, especially in autumn and winter, in damp soil leaf litter or under debris. They are usually laid in clutches of up to several dozen. Each egg contains a single embryo that hatches after a few weeks into a miniature version of an adult. Destroying the eggs laid under slabs or refuge traps may help control garden slug populations. The accidental transport of eggs in plant pots, soil and unsterilized compost is almost certainly one of the main ways in which slug species have spread around the world.

Not all slug eggs can be distinguished from those of snails common in the same area. Others are **characteristic of the family, group of species, or even species** to which they belong. Some species' eggs have an opaque, calcareous eggshell. Others are translucent or transparent, but calcium carbonate shell crystals may be visible under magnification. In most species egg shape varies a little within and between clutches. Size data here are from Taylor (1902-7), Quick (1960) and Davies (1987). All slug eggs tend to darken in colour after being laid, from white or colourless through yellow to amber.

Arionidae: *Geomalacus maculosus*: Eggs elongate-ovoid, thinly-shelled, translucent, very large (around 8 x 4 mm).

Arionidae: *Arion* (*Arion*): Eggs ovoid, opaquely shelled, large (around 5 x 4 mm in *A.* (*A.*) *ater* and *A.* (*A.*) *rufus*). Those of *A.* (*A.*) *vulgaris* tend to be smaller (up to 4 mm) and those of *A.* (*A.*) *flagellus* smaller still (up to 3 mm).

Arionidae: *Arion* (*Mesarion*) & *Arion* (*Carinarion*): Eggs ovoid, flexibly-shelled and leathery, opaque to translucent, medium-sized (up to 3.25 x 2.25 mm). Clutches stick tightly together in *A.* (*Mesarion*), less so in *A.* (*Carinarion*).

Arionidae: *Arion* (*Kobeltia*): Eggs ovoid, very thinly shelled, or unshelled, usually translucent, very small (around 2.5 x 2 mm). Clutches may stick loosely together. Taylor (1902-7) disputed the common nineteenth-century statement that they were phosphorescent for 15 days after being laid.

Limacidae: *Limax*: Eggs almost spherical, unshelled, transparent, large (around 5.5 x 5 mm).

Limacidae: *Limacus*: Eggs rugby-ball or lemon-shaped, unshelled, transparent, very large (up to 6 x 4 mm).

Limacidae: *Lehmannia*, *Ambigolimax* & *Malacolimax*: Eggs-elongate ovoid, unshelled, very transparent, large to small (up to 4.5 x 3.5 mm in *L. marginata*). Those of *Ambigolimax* spp. and *M. tenellus* are similar but smaller (around 3.5 x 3 mm, or as little as 2.25 x 1.5 mm in some *Ambigolimax*).

Agriolimacidae: Eggs ovoid, unshelled, translucent to transparent, small to very small (from 3 x 2.5 mm in *Deroceras reticulatum*, to 1.75 x 1.5 mm in *D. invadens*). *D. laeve* lays relatively larger eggs (2 x 1.5 mm), often singly.

Milacidae: Eggs elongate-ovoid, unshelled, translucent to transparent, medium-sized to small (up to 4 x 3.5 mm in *Tandonia* spp., 2 x 1.5 mm in *Milax gagates*).

Boettgerillidae: Eggs ovoid, unshelled, transparent, small (2.5 x 1.5 mm in diameter). In clutches of 1-6 (Gunn, 1992) but sometimes more.

Trigonochlamydidae: Eggs spherical, unshelled, transparent, small (2 mm in diameter).

Testacellidae: Eggs large (up to 7 mm), shelled, elongate-ovoid to rugby-ball-shaped, laid deep in the soil. It has been said that the eggs of *Testacella* explode upon contact with a warm hand (Taylor, 1902-7). This was confirmed for freshly-laid eggs of *T. scutulum* by Barnes & Stokes (1951).

The eggs of *T. haliotidea* are white, rugby-balled shaped and very large (around 7 x 4 mm). Those of *T. maugei* are white, ovoid and medium-sized (around 5 x 4 mm). Those of *T. scutulum* and *T.* sp. "*tenuipenis*" are ovoid, brown and relatively small (around 4 x 3 mm), closely resembling the cocoons of young earthworms.

Slug eggs (Approximately actual size)

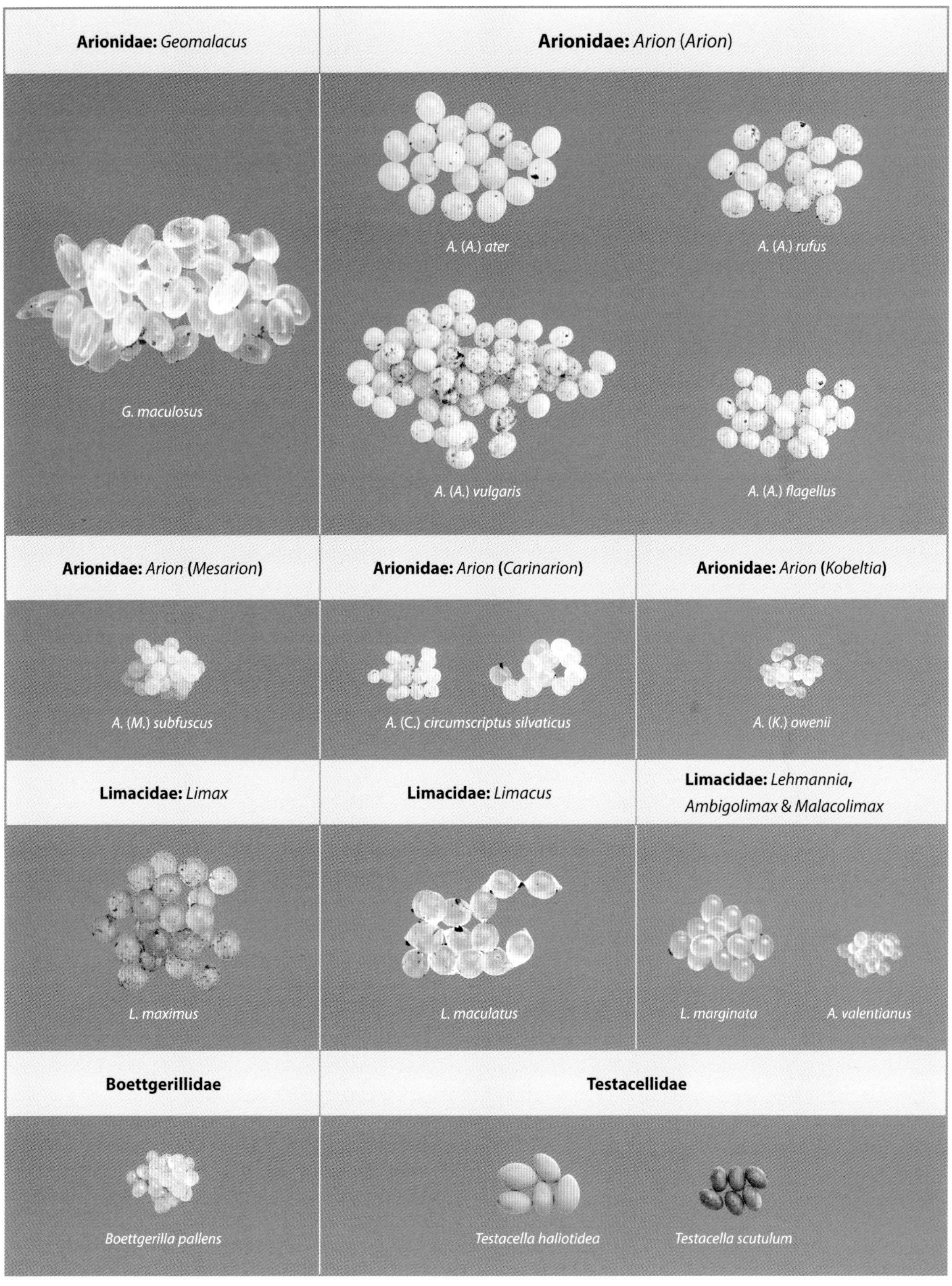

Slug shells

With the exception of *Testacella* and *Arion* species, the reduced shell of most slugs remains as a small, whitish plate under the rear skin of the mantle. These "slug plates" can be **characteristic of the family or group of species** to which a slug belongs. However within most species they vary greatly in shape, and change with growth, so are rarely diagnostic of particular species. Slug plates can be common in calcareous soil and in archaeological deposits, potentially providing information about past habitats. When found as Holocene (or possibly earlier) fossils, they can also indicate which groups of species are native to Britain or Ireland.

The extremely reduced shells of the very extensible species in Boettgerillidae and Trigonochlamydidae (both of which are introduced) are not included here. The AIDGAP key by Cameron (2008) gives more details on the shells of the vitrinid semi-slugs.

Arionidae: *Geomalacus maculosus*: Shell a nearly symmetrical, roughly oval plate up to 5 x 3 mm.

Arionidae: *Arion* (all subgenera): Shell reduced to a whitish paste of minute calcium carbonate crystals, each far less than a millimetre in length. These vary in quantity and resemble grains of salt or tiny grains of rice. The crystals may coagulate in life or in the soil, especially in calcareous areas, to form a crust or irregular granules up to a few millimetres in diameter. It seems the subgenera and species cannot be distinguished from the form of the crystals or granules. Furthermore in some archaeological studies, slug granules have probably been confused with the calcareous granules secreted by earthworms (e.g. Preece & Bridgland, 1999; Canti & Piearce, 2003). Taylor (1902-7) records the shell paste from arionids being used as a medicine in the past.

Limacidae: Shell a rectangular to oval plate up to 13 x 7 mm in *Limax maximus*. Limacid shells are characteristically strongly asymmetrical, with the centre of the growth rings displaced to the left side of the animal. The opposite (right) edge of the shell is often slightly concave. The amount of calcium carbonate in the shell varies greatly, even within species, with some shells consisting only of a flexible membrane of protein. This membrane also fringes the edges of the plate in fresh specimens. Larger shells (longer than about 7 mm) probably belong to *Limax* or *Limacus*. Shape differences between the plates of *Limax maximus* and *L. cinereoniger* suggested by past authors (Taylor, 1902-7; Quick, 1960) do not appear to be reliable. The shells of *Lehmannia marginata* are often relatively less elongate than the other native British species, although Taylor (1902-7) considered the shell of this species particularly variable.

Agriolimacidae: Shell strongly asymmetrical and similar to that of Limacidae, although often containing more calcium carbonate and more robust as a result. Despite this, agriolimacid shells are not always distinguishable from those of limacids (Wiktor, 2000). They reach around 5 x 3 mm long in *Deroceras reticulatum*. The shells of *D. laeve* are relatively less elongate than other *Deroceras* species (Quick, 1960) but it is doubtful that other distinctions can be made.

Milacidae: Shell a nearly symmetrical, thick, convex, oval plate up to 5 x 3 mm. The shell is smaller in relation to the animal than in Limacidae or Agriolimacidae. The shell of *Tandonia sowerbyi* is relatively less elongate than that of *Milax gagates* (Quick, 1960). Fossil milacid shells have appeared in British soils since at least 8600 years ago (Preece & Bridgland, 1999).

Testacellidae: Shell strong, external. Two of the species can readily be distinguished (see also species accounts). The shell of *Testacella maugei* is large, oblong and very convex (12-16 x 6-7 mm). That of *T. haliotidea* is smaller, more flattened, and ear-like (7-8 x 5-6 mm). The brownish skin (periostracum) covering the shell is readily abraded away. The shells of *T. scutulum* and *T.* sp. "*tenuipenis*" are very flattened, sometimes even concave (6-7 x 4 mm). They have a reddish-brown periostracum. The shells of the last two species do not appear to be reliably distinguishable.

Slug shells (not to scale)

Adams, L. E. 1910. Observations on the pairing of *Arion ater* (L.). *Journal of Conchology* 13: 116-119.

Allan, E., & Crawley, M. J. 2011. Contrasting effects of insect and molluscan herbivores on plant diversity in a long-term field experiment. *Ecology Letters* 14: 1246-1253.

Alexander, K. N. 2010. *Malacolimax tenellus* (Müller 1774) (Pulmonata: Limacidae) in the north midlands of England. *Journal of Conchology* 40: 355-357.

Altena, C. O. van Regteren. 1963. Notes sur les limaces. 8. Sur l'état de deux espèces nominales du genre *Arion*. *Basteria* 27: 1-6.

Anderson, R. 1991. Evidence of recent spread in *Semilimax pyrenaicus* (Férussac) and *Arion owenii* Davies (Mollusca: Gastropoda). *Irish Naturalists' Journal* 23: 510.

Anderson, R. 2004. *Arion occultus* sp. nov., a new slug in *Arion* Subgenus *Kobeltia*, from Ireland. *Journal of Conchology* 38: 13-26.

Anderson, R. 2006. A first record of *Deroceras agreste* (L.) (Agriolimacidae) in Ireland. *Journal of Conchology* 39: 106.

Anderson, R. 2008. *Annotated list of the non-marine Mollusca of Britain & Ireland.* Available from: www.conchsoc.org/node/540

Backeljau, T., & de Bruyn, L. 1990. On the infrageneric systematics of the genus *Arion* Férussac, 1819 (Mollusca, Pulmonata). *Bulletin de l'Institut Royal des Sciences Naturelles de Belgique, Biologie* 60: 35-68.

Backeljau, T., & Van Beeck, M. 1986. Epiphallus anatomy in the *Arion hortensis* species aggregate (Mollusca, Pulmonata). *Zoologica Scripta* 15: 61-68.

Balashov, I. 2012. *Selenochlamys ysbryda* in the Crimean Mountains, Ukraine: first record from its native range? *Journal of Conchology* 41: 141-144.

Bank, R. A., Falkner, G., & Von Proschwitz, T. 2007. A revised checklist of the non-marine Mollusca of Britain and Ireland. *Heldia* 5: 41-72.

Barker, G. M. 1999. *Naturalised terrestrial Stylommatophora* (Mollusca: Gastropoda). Fauna of New Zealand 38. Manaaki, Whenua Press, Lincoln, New Zealand.

Barker, G. M. (ed.) 2002. *Molluscs as crop pests.* CABI Publishing, Wallingford, UK.

Barker, G. M. (ed.) 2004. *Natural enemies of terrestrial molluscs.* CABI Publishing, Wallingford, UK.

Barker, G. M., & Efford, M. G. 2004. Predatory Gastropods as Natural Enemies of Terrestrial Gastropods and Other Invertebrates. In: Barker, G. M. (ed.) *Natural Enemies of Terrestrial Molluscs.* CABI Publishing, Wallingford, UK.

Barnes, H. F., & Stokes, B. M. 1951. Marking and breeding *Testacella* slugs. *Annals of Applied Biology* 38: 540-545.

Barr, R. A. 1927. Some notes on the mucous and skin glands of *Arion ater. Quarterly Journal of Microscopical Science* 71: 503-525.

Barr, N. B., Cook, A., Elder, P., Molongoski, J., Prasher, D., & Robinson, D. G. 2009. Application of a DNA barcode using the 16S rRNA gene to diagnose pest *Arion* species in the USA. *Journal of Molluscan Studies* 75: 187-191.

Beckmann, K.-H. 2007a. *Arion* (*Kobeltia*) *occultus* R. Anderson 2004 und weitere Nacktschnecken auf den Aran-Inseln (Irland). *Heldia* 5 (3): 99-100.

Beckmann, K.-H. 2007b. *Die Land- und Süsswassermollusken der Balearischen Inseln.* ConchBooks, Hackenheim, Germany.

Bourguignat, J. R. 1861. Des limaces algériennes. *Revue et Magasin de Zoologie pure et appliqué* (2) 13: 299-306.

Boycott, A. E. 1934. The habitats of land Mollusca in Britain. *Journal of Ecology* 22: 1-38.

Boycott, A. E. 1936. The relation of slugs and snails to man in Britain. *Proceedings of the Cotteswold Naturalists' Field Club* 26: 73-82.

Boycott, A.E., & Oldham, C. 1930. The food of *Geomalacus maculosus*. *Journal of Conchology* 19: 36.

Bratton, J. H. (ed.) 1991. *British Red Data Books: 3. Invertebrates other than insects.* Joint Nature Conservation Committee, Peterborough, UK.

Briner, T., & Frank, T. 1998. The egg-laying activity of the slug *Arion lusitanicus* (Mabille). *Journal of Conchology* 36: 9-15.

Bruelheide, H. & Scheidel, U. 1999. Slug herbivory as a limiting factor for the geographical range of Arnica montana. *Journal of Ecology* 87: 839-848.

Burnet, B. 1972. Enzyme protein polymorphism in the slug *Arion ater. Genetical Research* 20: 161-173.

Byrne, A., Moorkens, E. A., Anderson, R., Killeen, I. J., & Regan, E. C. 2009. *Ireland Red List no. 2: non-marine molluscs.* National Parks and Wildlife Service, Department of the Environment, Heritage and Local Government, Dublin, Ireland.

Cain, A. J. & Williamson, M. H. 1958. Variation and specific limits in the *Arion ater* aggregate. *Proceedings of the Malacological Society of London* 33: 72-86.

Canti, M. G., & Piearce, T. G. 2003. Morphology and dynamics of calcium carbonate granules produced by different earthworm species. *Pedobiologia* 47: 511-521.

Cameron, R. A. D., Jackson, N., & Eversham, B. 1983. A field key to the slugs of the British Isles. *Field Studies Journal* 5: 807-824.

Cameron, R. A. D. 2008 (1st edn. 2003). *Keys for the identification of land snails in the British Isles.* FSC Publications, Preston Montford, UK.

Castillejo, J. 1992. The anatomy of *Arion flagellus* Collinge, 1893, present in the Iberian peninsula. *The Veliger* 35: 146-156.

Castillejo, J. 1998. *Guia de las babosas Ibericas.* Real Academia Galega de Ciencias, Santiago, Spain.

Chatfield, J. 1976. *Limax grossui* Lupu, 1970, a slug new to the British Isles. *Journal of Conchology* 29: 1-4.

Chevallier, H. 1981. Taxonomie des "Limaces rouges" (genre *Arion*, sous-genre *Arion* s.s., Mollusca, Pulmonata). *Haliotis* 11: 87-99.

Chichester, L. F., & Getz, L. L. 1973. The terrestrial slugs of northeastern North America. *Sterkiana* 51: 11-42.

Choi, Y. H., Bohana, D. A., Potting, R. P. J., Semenov, M. A., & Glen, D. M. 2006. Individual based model of slug population and spatial dynamics. *Ecological Modelling* 190: 336-350.

Connolly, M. 1939. A monographic survey of South African non-marine Mollusca. *Annals of the South African Museum* 33: 1-660.

Cook, A., & Radford, D. J. 1988. The comparative ecology of four sympatric limacid slug species in Northern Ireland. *Malacologia* 28: 131-146.

Dance, S. P. 1969. Vertical range of molluscs on Ben Lawers, Scotland. *Journal of Conchology* 27: 509-515.

Davies, S. M. 1977. The *Arion hortensis* complex with notes on *A. intermedius* Normand (Pulmonata: Arionidae). *Journal of Conchology* 29: 173-187.

Davies, S. M. 1979. Seggregates of the *Arion* hortensis complex (Pulmonata: Arionidae) with description of a new species, *Arion* owenii. *Journal of Conchology* 30: 123-128.

Davies, S. M. 1987. *Arion flagellus* Collinge and *A.* lusitanicus Mabille in the British Isles. A morphological, biological and taxonomic investigation. *Journal of Conchology* 32: 339-354.

Dreijers, E., Reise, H., & Hutchinson, J. M. C. 2013. Mating of the slugs *Arion lusitanicus* auct. non Mabille and *A. rufus* (L.); different genitalia and mating behaviours are incomplete barriers to interspecific sperm exchange. *Journal of Molluscan Studies* 79: 51–63.

Ellis, A. E. 1941. The Mollusca of a Norfolk Broad. *Journal of Conchology* 21: 224-243.

Ellis, A. E. 1969 (1st edn. 1926). *British snails: the non-marine Gastropoda of Great Britain and Ireland.* Clarendon Press, Oxford, UK.

Evans, J. G. 1972. *Land snails in Archaeology.* Seminar Press, London, UK.

Evans, N. J. 1978a. *Limax pseudoflavus* sp. n. a new species of slug for Ireland. *Irish Naturalists' Journal* 19: 173.

Evans, N. J. 1978b. *Limax pseudoflavus* Evans. A critical description and comparison with related species. *Irish Naturalists' Journal* 19: 231-236.

Evans, N. J. 1983. Notes on self-fertilization and variation in body colour in *Limax flavus* L. and *L. pseudoflavus* Evans. *Irish Naturalists' Journal* 21: 37-40.

Evans, N. J. 1986. An investigation of the status of the terrestrial slugs *Arion ater ater* (L.) and *Arion ater rufus* (L.) (Mollusca, Gastropoda, Pulmonata) in Britain. *Zoologica Scripta* 15: 313-322.

Falkner, G., Ripken, T. E. J., & Falkner, M. 2002 *Mollusques continentaux de France, liste de référence annotée et bibliographie.* Muséum National d'Histoire Naturelle, Paris, France.

Foltz, D. W., Ochman, H., Jones, J. S., Evangelisti, S. M., & Selander, R. K. 1982. Genetic population structure and breeding systems in arionid slugs (Mollusca: Pulmonata). *Biological Journal of the Linnean Society* 17: 225-241.

Foltz, D. W., Ochman, H., & Selander, R. K. 1984. Genetic diversity and breeding systems in terrestrial slugs of the families Limacidae and Arionidae. *Malacologia* 25: 593–605.

Frank, T. 1998. Slug damage and numbers of slugs in oilseed rape bordering on grass strips. *Journal of Molluscan Studies* 64: 461-466.

Gargominy, O., Prie, V., Bichain, J.-M., Cucherat, X., & Fontaine, B. 2011. Liste de reference annotée des mollusques continentaux de France. *Malaco* 7: 307-382.

Garrido, C., Castillejo, J., & Iglesias, J. 1995. The *Arion* subfuscus complex in the eastern part of the Iberian Peninsula, with redescription of *Arion subfuscus* (Draparnaud, 1805) (Gastropoda: Pulmonata: Arionidae). *Archiv für Molluskenkunde* 124: 103–118.

Geenen, S., Jordaens, K., & Backeljau, T. 2006. Molecular systematics of the *Carinarion* complex (Mollusca: Gastropoda: Pulmonata) : a taxonomic riddle caused by a mixed breeding system. *Biological Journal of the Linnean Society* 89 (4): 589-604.

Godan, D. 1983 (English translation). *Pest slugs and snails: biology and control.* Springer-Verlag, New York, USA.

Glen, D. M., & Moens, R. 2002. *Agriolimacidae, Arionidae and Milacidae as pests in West European cereals.* In: Barker, G. M. (ed.) 2002. *Molluscs as crop pests.* CABI Publishing, Wallingford, UK.

Griffiths, O. L., & Florens, V. F. B. 2006. *A field guide to the non-marine molluscs of the Mascarene Islands (Mauritius, Rodrigues and Réunion) and the Northern Dependencies of Mauritius.* Bioculture Press, Mauritius.

Grimm, F. W., Forsyth, R. G., Schueler, F. W., & Karstad, A. 2010. *Identifying land snails and slugs in Canada: introduced species and native genera.* Canadian Food Inspection Agency, Quebec, Canada.

Grindon, A., & Davidson, A. 2013. Irish *Cepaea nemoralis* land snails have a cryptic Franco-Iberian origin that is most easily explained by the movements of Mesolithic humans. *PLoS ONE* 8(6): e65792. doi:10.1371/journal.pone.0065792.

Gunn, A. 1992. The ecology of the introduced slug *Boettgerilla pallens* (Simroth) in North Wales. *Journal of Molluscan Studies* 58: 449-453.

Hagnell, J., von Proschwitz, T., & Schander, C. 2006. Two notes on the invasive Iberian slug, *Arion lusitanicus* Mabille, 1868. *Journal of Conchology* 39: 108-110.

Haro, R. J., Gillis, R., & Cooper, S. T. 2004. First report of a terrestrial slug (*Arion fasciatus*) living in an aquatic habitat. *Malacologia* 45: 451-452.

Hatteland, B. A., Grutle, K., Mong C. E., Skartveit, J., Symondson, W. O. C., & Solhøy, T. 2010. Predation by beetles (Carabidae, Staphylinidae) on eggs and juveniles of the Iberian slug *Arion lusitanicus* in the laboratory. *Bulletin of Entomological Research* 100: 559-567.

Hausdorf, B. 2002. Introduced land snails and slugs in Colombia. *Journal of Molluscan Studies* 68: 127-131.

Hayward, J. F. 1954. *Agriolimax carunae* Pollonera as a Holocene fossil. *Journal of Conchology* 23: 403-404.

Herbert, D. G. 2010. *The introduced terrestrial Mollusca of South Africa.* SANBI Biodiversity Series 15. South African National Biodiversity Institute, Pretoria, South Africa.

Herbert, D., & Kilburn, D. 2004. *Field guide to the land snails and slugs of eastern South Africa.* Natal Museum, Pietermaritzburg, South Africa.

Holyoak, D. T., & Seddon, M. B. 1983. Land Mollusca from Norway, Finland and Sweden. *Journal of Conchology* 31: 190.

Horrill, J. C., & Richards, A. J. 1986. Differential grazing by the mollusc *Arion hortensis* Fér. on cyanogenic and acyanogenic seedlings of the white clover, *Trifolium repens* L. *Heredity* 56: 277-281.

Hunter, P. J. 1968. Studies on slugs of arable ground: II. Life cycles. *Malacologia* 6: 379-389.

Jordaens, K., Van Riel, P., Geenen, S., Verhagen, R., & Backeljau, T. 2001. Food-induced body pigmentation questions the taxonomic value of colour in the self-fertilizing slug *Carinarion* spp. *Journal of Molluscan Studies* 67: 161-167.

Jordaens, K., Van Dongen, S., Van Riel, P., Geenen, S., Verhagen, R., & Backeljau, T. 2002. Multivariate morphometrics of soft body parts in terrestrial slugs: comparison between two datasets, error assessment and taxonomic implications. *Biological Journal of the Linnean Society* 75: 533-542.

Jordaens, K., Pinceel, J., & Backeljau, T. 2006. Life-history variation in selfing multilocus genotypes of the land slug *Deroceras laeve* (Pulmonata: Agriolimacidae). *Journal of Molluscan Studies* 72: 229-233.

Jordaens K., Pinceel J., Van Houtte N., Breugelmans K., & Backeljau, T. (2010) *Arion transsylvanus* (Mollusca, Pulmonata, Arionidae): rediscovery of a cryptic species. *Zoologica Scripta* 39: 343-362.

Kaleniczenko, J. 1851. Description d'un nouveau genre de limaces de la Russie Méridionale. *Bulletin de la Société Impériale des Naturalistes due Moscou* 25: 215-228.

Kearney, J. 2010. Kerry slug recorded at Lettercraffroe, County Galway. *Irish Naturalists' Journal* 31: 68-69.

Kerney, M. 1999. *Atlas of the Land and Freshwater Molluscs of Britain and Ireland.* Harley Books, Colchester, UK.

Kerney M. P., & Cameron, R. A. D. 1979. *A field guide to the land snails of Britain and North-west Europe.* Collins, London, UK.

Kew, H. W. 1902. On the mucous-threads of land-slugs. *Journal of Conchology* 10: 153-165.

Killeen, I. J. 1992. *The land and freshwater molluscs of Suffolk.* Suffolk Naturalists' Society, Ipswich, UK.

Kozłowksi, J. 2007. The distribution, biology, population dynamics and harmfulness of *Arion lusitanicus* Mabille, 1868 (Gastropoda: Pulmonata: Arionidae) in Poland. *Journal of Plant Protection Research* 47: 219-230.

Landler, L. & Nuñez, J. L. 2012. European invaders in South America: terrestrial snails and slugs in southern Chile. *Journal of Conchology* 41: 263-265.

Liberto, F., Renda, W., Colomba, M. S., Giglio, S., & Sparacio, I. 2011. New records of *Testacella scutulum* Sowerby, 1821 (Gastropoda, Pulmonata, Testacellidae) from Southern Italy and Sicily. *Biodiversity Journal* 2: 27-34.

Mair, J. , & Port, G. R. 2002. The influence of mucus production by the slug, *Deroceras reticulatum*, on predation by *Pterostichus madidus* and *Nebria brevicollis* (Coleoptera: Carabidae). *Biocontrol Science and Technology* 12: 325-335.

Marren, P. & Mabey, R. 2010. *Bugs Brittanica.* Chatto & Windus, London, UK.

McCracken, G. F. & Selander, R. K. 1980. Self-fertilization and monogenic strains in natural populations of terrestrial slugs. *Proceedings of the National Academy of Sciences* USA 77: 684-688.

McDonnell R.J., Paine T.D., & Gormally M.J. (2009) *Slugs: a guide to the invasive and native fauna of California.* University of California publication no. 8336. http://anrcatalog.ucdavis.edu/Items/8336.aspx

Van Mol, J.-J., Sheridan, R., & Bouillon, J. 1970. Contribution a l'étude de la glande caudale des pulmonés stylommatophores I. *Arion rufus* (L): morphologie, histology, histochimie. *Annales de la Société Royale Zoologique de Belgique* 100: 61-83.

Moquin-Tandon, A. 1855. *Histoire naturelle des mollusques terrestres et fluviatiles de France.* Tome 2. Paris. Baillière, Paris, France.

Morgan, E. & Shaw, S. 2010. *Angiostrongylus vasorum* infection in dogs: continuing spread and developments in diagnosis and treatment. *Journal of Small Animal Practice* 51: 616-621.

National Museums of Northern Ireland. 2010. *MolluscIreland.* http://www.habitas.org.uk/molluscireland/index.htm

Nitz, B., Falkner, G., & Haszprunar, G. 2010. Inferring Multiple Corsican *Limax* (Pulmonata: Limacidae) radiations: a combined approach using morphology and molecules. In: Glaubrecht, M. (Ed.) 2010: *Evolution in Action - Case studies in Adaptive Radiation, Speciation and the Origin of Biodiversity.* Springer Verlag, Berlin, Germany.

Nitz, B., Heim, R., Schneppat, U. E., Hyman, I., & Haszprunar, G. 2009. Towards a new standard in slug species descriptions: the case of *Limax sarnensis* Heim & Nitz n. sp. (Pulmonata: Limacidae) from the western central Alps. *Journal of Molluscan Studies* 75: 279-224.

Noble, L. R., & Jones, C. S. 1996. *A molecular and ecological investigation of the large arionid slugs of North-West Europe: the potential for new pests.* pp 93-131 in: Symondson, W. O. C., & Liddell, J. E. (eds.) 1996. *The Ecology of Agricultural Pests: Biochemical Approaches.* Systematics Association Special Volume Series 53, Chapman & Hall, London, UK.

Oldham, C. 1942. Notes on *Geomalacus maculosus. Proceedings of the Malacological Society of London* 25: 10-11.

Pinceel, J., Jordaens, K., Backeljau, T. 2005a. Extreme mtDNA divergences in a terrestrial slug (Gastropoda, Pulmonata, Arionidae): accelerated evolution, allopatric divergence and secondary contact. *Journal of Evolutionary Biology* 18: 1264-1280.

Pinceel, J., Jordaens, K., Van Houtte, N., Bernon, G., & Backeljau, T. 2005b. Population genetics and identity of an introduced terrestrial slug: *Arion subfuscus* s.l. in the north-east USA (Gastropoda, Pulmonata, Arionidae). *Genetica* 125: 155-171.

Pintér, L., & Suara, R. 2004. *Magyarországi puhatestűek katalógsa. Hazai malakológusok gyűjtései alapján.* Magyar Természettudományi Múzeum, Budapest, Hungary.

Phillips, R. A., & Watson, H. 1930. *Milax gracilis* (Leydig) in the British Isles. *Journal of Conchology* 19: 65-93.

Platts, E. A., & Speight, M. C. D. 1988. The taxonomy and distribution of the Kerry Slug *Geomalacus maculosus* Allman, 1843 (Mollusca: Arionidae) with a discussion of its status as a threatened species. *Irish Naturalists' Journal* 22: 417-460.

Preece, R. C., & Bridgland, D. R. 1999. Holywell Coombe, Folkestone: a 13,000 year history of an English chalkland. *Quaternary Science Reviews* 18: 1075-1125.

von Proschwitz, T. 1997. *Arion lusitanicus* Mabille and *A. rufus* (L.) in Sweden: a comparison of occurrence, spread and naturalization of two alien slug species. *Heldia* 4 (5): 137-138.

Quick, H. E. 1947. *Arion ater* (L.) and *A. rufus* (L.) in Britain and their specific differences. *Journal of Conchology* 22: 178-182.

Quick, H. E. 1952. Rediscovery of *Arion lusitanicus* Mabille in Britain. *Proceedings of the Malacological Society of London* 29: 93-101.

Quick, H. E. 1960. British Slugs (Pulmonata; Testacellidae, *Arion*idae, Limacidae) *Bulletin of the British Museum (Natural History) Zoology* 6: 103-226.

Quinteiro, J., Rodríguez-Castro, J., Castillejo, J., Iglesias-Piñeiro, J., & Rey-Méndez, M. 2005. Phylogeny of slug species of the genus *Arion*: evidence of monophyly of Iberian endemics and of the existence of relict species in Pyrenean refuges. *Journal of Zoological Systematics and Evolutionary Research* 43: 139-148.

Reise, H., Hutchinson, J. M. C., Forsyth, R. G., & Forsyth, T. 2000. The ecology and spread of the terrestrial slug *Boettgerilla pallens* in Europe with reference to its recent discovery in North America. *Veliger* 43: 313-318.

Reise, H., Hutchinson, J. M. C., & Robinson, D. G. 2006. Two introduced pest slugs: *Tandonia budapestensis* new to the Americas, and *Deroceras panormitanum* new to the Eastern USA. *Veliger* 48: 110-115.

Reise, H., & Hutchinson, J. M. C. 2009. An earlier record of the slug *Selenochlamys ysbryda* from Brecon, UK. *Journal of Conchology* 40: 103.

Reise, H., Hutchinson, J. M. C., Schunack, S., & Schlitt, B. 2011. *Deroceras panormitanum* and congeners from Malta and Sicily, with a redescription of the widespread pest slug as *Deroceras invadens* n. sp. *Folia Malacologica* 19: 201-233.

Reise, H., Zimdars, B., Jordaens, K., & Backeljau, T. 2001. First evidence of possible outcrossing in the terrestrial slug *Arion intermedius* (Gastropoda: Pulmonata). *Hereditas* 134: 267-270.

Rinaldi, A. C. 2003. Notes on *Testacella* Cuvier, 1800 (Gastropoda, Pulmonata, Testacellidae). *La Conchiglia* 309: 47-54.

Roebuck, W. D. 1919. A new variety of *Arion ater*. *Journal of Conchology* 16: 9.

Rowson, B., & Symondson, W. O. C. 2008. *Selenochlamys ysbryda* sp. nov. from Wales, UK: a *Testacella*-like slug new to Western Europe (Stylommatophora: Trigonochlamydidae). *Journal of Conchology* 39: 537-552.

Rowson, B., Anderson, R., Turner, J. A., & Symondson, W. O. C. 2014. The slugs of Britain and Ireland: undetected and undescribed species increase a well-studied, economically important fauna by more than 20%. PLOS One (in press).

Scharff, R. F. 1891. The Slugs of Ireland. *Scientific Transactions of the Royal Dublin Society* Series II 4: 4513-563.

Schmid, G. 1970. *Arion lusitanicus* in Deutschland. *Archiv für Molluskenkunde* 100: 95-102.

Simroth, H. 1885. Versuch einer Naturgeschichte der Deutschen Nacktschnecken und ihrer Europaischen Verwandten. *Zeitschrift für Wissenschaftliche Zoologie* 42: 203-366.

Slotsbo, S., Damgaard, C., Hansen, L. M., & Holmstrup, M. 2012. The influence of temperature on life history traits in the Iberian slug, *Arion lusitanicus*. *Annals of Applied Biology* 162: 80-88

Solem, G. A. 1976. *The shell makers: introducing mollusks*. J. Wiley & Sons, New York, USA.

South, A. 1992. *Terrestrial slugs: biology, ecology, and control*. Chapman & Hall, London, UK.

Stanisic, J., Shea, M., Potter, D., & Griffiths, O. 2010. *Australian land snails. Volume 1: a field guide to eastern Australian species*. Bioculture Press, Mauritius.

Stokes, B. M. 1958. The worm-eating slugs *Testacella scutulum* Sowerby and *T. haliotidea* Draparnaud in captivity. *Proceedings of the Malacological Society of London* 33: 11-20.

Svanberg, I. 2006. Black slugs (*Arion ater*) as grease: a case study of technical use of gastropods in pre-industrial Sweden. *Journal of Ethnobiology* 26: 299-309.

Symondson, W. O. C. 1990. Slug control. In: Kenyon, J., & Franklin, B. (eds.) The New Gardeners' World Handbook. BBC Books, London.

Symondson, W. O. C. 1997. Does *Tandonia budapestensis* (Mollusca: Pulmonata) contain toxins? Evidence from feeding trials with the slug predator *Pterostichus melanarius* (Coleoptera: Carabidae). *Journal of Molluscan Studies* 63: 541-545.

Symondson, W. O. C., Glen, D. M., Wiltshire, C. W., Langdon, C. J., & Liddell, J. E. 1996. Effects of cultivation techniques and methods of straw disposal on predation by *Pterostichus melanarius* (Coleoptera: Carabidae) upon slugs (Gastropoda: Pulmonata) in an arable field. *Journal of Applied Ecology* 33: 741-753.

Sysoev, A., & Schileyko, A. 2009. Land snails and slugs of Russia and adjacent countries. Pensoft, Sofia, Bulgaria.

Tattersfield, P. 1990. Terrestrial mollusc faunas from some south Pennine woodlands. *Journal of Conchology* 33: 355-374.

Taylor, J. W. 1902-1907. *Monograph of the land and freshwater Mollusca of the British Isles. 2: Testacellidae, Limacidae, Arionidae.* Taylor Bros., Leeds, UK.

Turk, S. M., Meredith, H. M., & Holyoak, G. A. 2001. *Atlas of the land and freshwater molluscs of Cornwall and the Isles of Scilly with drawings of the species.* Environmental Records Centre for Cornwall and the Isles of Scilly, Truro, UK.

Wade, C. M., Mordan, P. B., and Naggs, F. 2006. Evolutionary relationships among the Pulmonate land snails and slugs (Pulmonata, Stylommatophora). *Biological Journal of the Linnean Society* 87: 593-610.

Waldén, H. W. 1981. Communities and diversity of land molluscs in Scandinavian woodlands. 1. High diversity communities in taluses and boulder slopes in SW Sweden. *Journal of Conchology* 30: 351-372.

Welter-Schultes, F. 2012. *European non-marine molluscs, a guide for species identification*. Planet Poster Editions, Göttingen, Germany.

Wiktor, A. 1983. The slugs of Bulgaria (Arionidae, Milacidae, Limacidae, Agriolimacidae – Gastropoda, Pulmonata). *Annales Zoologici* 37: 71-206.

Wiktor, A. 1987. Milacidae (Gastropoda, Pulmonata) – systematic monograph. *Annales Zoologici* 41: 153-319.

Wiktor, A. 1996. The slugs of the former Yugoslavia (Gastropoda terrestrial nuda - Arionidae, Milacidae, Limacidae, Agriolimacidae). *Annales Zoologici* 46: 1-110.

Wiktor, A. 2000. Agriolimacidae (Gastropoda: Pulmonata) – a systematic monograph. *Annales Zoologici* 49: 347-590.

Wiktor, A. 2001. *The slugs of Greece (Arionidae, Milacidae, Limacidae, Agriolimacidae – Gastropoda, Stylommatophora).* Fauna Graeciae 8. Natural History Museum of Crete, Irakleio, Greece.

Wiktor, A. & Norris, A. 1982. The synonymy of *Limax maculatus* (Kaleniczenko 1851) with notes on its European Distribution. *Journal of Conchology* 31: 75-77.

Wiktor, A., Chen, D.-N., & Wu, M. 2000. Stylommatophoran slugs of China (Gastropoda: Pulmonata) – prodromus. Folia *Malacologia* 8: 3-36.

De Wilde, J. J. A. 1983. Notes on the *Arion hortensis* complex in Belgium (Mollusca, Pulmonata: *Arion*idae). *Annales de la Société Royale Zoologique de Belgique* 113: 87-96.

De Wilde, J. J. A. 1986. Further notes on the species of the *Arion hortensis* complex in Belgium (Mollusca, Pulmonata: Arionidae). *Annales de la Société Royale Zoologique de Belgique* 116: 71-74.

de Winter, A. J. 1984. The *Arion hortensis* complex (Pulmonata: Arionidae): designation of types, descriptions, and distributional patterns, with special reference to The Netherlands. *Zoologische Mededelingen Leiden* 59: 1-17.

de Winter, A. J. 1986. Little known and new south-west European slugs (Pulmonata: Agriolimacidae, Arionidae). *Zoologische Mededelingen Leiden* 60: 135-158.

de Winter, A. J. 1988. Remarks on the non-marine molluscan fauna of the Azores. 1-2. *Basteria* 52: 105-109.

Photographed specimen locality data

***Arion* (*Arion*) *ater* - 12misc2**: Breconshire (VC42), Valley of Blaen Taf Fawr stream, route to Pen y Fan from A470, Brecon Beacons NP, 550-600m, Lat. 51.88, Long. -3.46. **DF6**: Nottinghamshire (VC56), Dyscarr Wood NR (Notts. WT) & Langold Country Park, Langold, N of Worksop, 40m, Lat. 53.37, Long. -1.13. **I13**: North Kerry (H2), Muckross Peninsula, W of Cloghereen, Killarney NP, 30m, Lat. 52.02, Long. -9.51. **I32**: North Kerry (H2), Mangerton Mountain, above Gortagullane, Killarney NP, 150-680m, Lat. 51.98, Long. -9.49. **K3**: East Kent (VC15), Homestall Wood, Blean Woods NNR, E of Rough Common, W of Canterbury, 75m, Lat. 51.29, Long. 1.04. **L1**: Westmorland (VC69), Lane to Low Hall Garth, Moss Rigg Wood, W of Ambleside, Lake District NP, 150m, Lat. 54.42, Long. -3.06. **SN1**: Caernarvonshire (VC49), near Pencraig, NE of Betws-y-Coed, Snowdonia NP, 200m, Lat. 53.11, Long. -3.84. **Y37**: North-east Yorkshire (VC62), Baxton's Wood, N of Carlton, Helmsley, North Yorks Moors NP, 220m, Lat. 54.29, Long. -1.06.

***A.* (*A.*) *rufus* - DF7**: Nottinghamshire (VC56), Dyscarr Wood NR (Notts. WT) & Langold Country Park, Langold, N of Worksop, 40m, Lat. 53.37, Long. -1.13. **L2**: Westmorland (VC69), Baysbrown Farm Woods, Elterwater, W of Ambleside, Lake District NP, 200-300m, Lat. 54.43, Long. -3.05. **M16**: Nottinghamshire (VC56), Burton Joyce, E of Nottingham, 50m, Lat. 52.99, Long. -1.04. **PYC1**: Glamorganshire (VC41), Pontyclun, Rhondda Cynon Taf, W of Cardiff, 55m, Lat. 51.53, Long. -3.39. **SN2**: Merionethshire (VC48), Grounds of Plas Tan-y-Bwlch, N of Maentwrog, Vale of Ffestiniog, Snowdonia NP, 60m, Lat. 52.95, Long. -4.

***A.* (A). *flagellus* - DN1**: Denbighshire (VC50), Glyn Ceiriog, Ceiriog Valley, SE of Llangollen, 230m, Lat. 52.91, Long. -3.2. **I9**: West Cork (H3), Schull and environs, near Ballydehob, c10m, Lat. 51.53, Long. -9.55. **K5**: East Sussex (VC14), Powdermill Reservoir, Brede High Woods (WT), near Cripp's Corner, High Weald AONB, N of Hastings, 25m, Lat. 50.95, Long. 0.56. **PYC2, PYC4**: Glamorganshire (VC41), Pontyclun, Rhondda Cynon Taf, W of Cardiff, 55m, Lat. 51.53, Long. -3.39. **S25**: West Ross & Cromarty (VC105), Rassall Ashwood NNR, near Kishorn River, NE of Lochcarron, 70m, Lat. 57.43, Long. -5.59.

***A.* (*A.*) *vulgaris* -12misc9**: Antrim (H39), Belvoir Park Forest, Lagan Valley Regional Park, S suburbs of Belfast, 35m, Lat. 54.56, Long. -5.93. **DC1**: South Devon (VC3), Exhibition Road, East Town, Crediton, 45m, Lat. 50.79, Long. -3.64. **I93**: Antrim (H39), Belvoir Park Forest, Lagan Valley Regional Park, S suburbs of Belfast, 35m, Lat. 54.56, Long. -5.93. **PGO2**: West Sussex (VC13), Findon Valley, N suburbs of Worthing, 50m, Lat. 50.85, Long. -0.39. **M55, M56, M62**: Surrey (VC17), Allotments between railway lines, South Croydon, 80m, Lat. 51.35, Long. 0.09.

***A.* (*A.*) sp. "Davies" - M3, M4**: Cambridgeshire (VC29), Wicken, SE of Soham, S of Ely, 5m, Lat. 52.31, Long. 0.3. **Y2**: North-east Yorkshire (VC62), Buttercrambe Moor Woods, N of Stamford Bridge, E of York, 15m, Lat. 54, Long. -0.92.

***A.* (*Mesarion*) *subfuscus* - I40**: North Kerry (H2), Mangerton Mountain, above Gortagullane, Killarney NP, 150-680m, Lat. 51.98, Long. -9.49. **I7**: East Cork (H5), Near Rostellan, E coast of Cork Harbour, 35m, Lat. 51.85, Long. -8.18. **M38, M39**: Co. Antrim (H39), Duncrue St., north Belfast, 5m, Lat. 54.62, Long. -5.91. **NF3**: South Wiltshire (VC8), Rufus Stone area, Upper Canterton, NE of Minstead, New Forest NP, 85m, Lat. 50.91, Long. -1.62. **REH2**: Worcestershire (VC37), Abberley Hill, Abberley, Great Witley, SW of Kidderminster, 275m, Lat. 52.3, Long. -2.36.

***A.* (*M.*) *fuscus* - DF9**: Nottinghamshire (VC56), Ash Tree Hill Wood, Clumber Park Country Park (NT), Sherwood Forest area, S of Worksop, 90m, Lat. 53.27, Long. -1.05.

***A.* (*M.*) *iratii* - 12BB1**: Breconshire (VC42), Talybont Forest near Abercynafon, W end of Talybont Reservoir, Brecon Beacons NP, 210m, Lat. 51.84, Long. -3.34. **12BB7**: Breconshire (VC42), A470 layby just S of Garwnant turnoff, Coed Taf Fawr FC, N of Llwyn-on village and reservoir, 260m, Lat. 51.8, Long. -3.44.

***A.* (*Carinarion*) *fasciatus* - DF2**: Nottinghamshire (VC56), Beckingham, Trent floodplain W of Gainsborough, 15m, Lat. 53.4, Long. -0.83. **Y19**: Mid-west Yorkshire (VC64), Grass Wood NR (WT), Grassington, Wharfedale, Yorkshire Dales NP, 250m, Lat. 54.09, Long. -2.02.

***A.* (*C.*) *circumscriptus circumscriptus* - 12misc20**: Glamorganshire (VC41), Miskin, Rhondda Cynon Taf, W of Cardiff, 40m, Lat. 51.53, Long. -3.38.

***A.* (*C.*) *circumscriptus silvaticus* - I99**: Antrim (H39), S face of Cave Hill, overlooking N suburbs of Belfast, 255m, Lat. 54.64, Long. -5.96.

***A.* (*Kobeltia*) *distinctus* - 12misc21**: Glamorganshire (VC41), Miskin, Rhondda Cynon Taf, W of Cardiff, Alt. 40m, Lat. 51.53, Long. -3.38. **M81**: Glamorganshire (VC41), Morganstown allotments, Morganstown, N of Cardiff, Alt. 40m, Lat. 51.53, Long. -3.26. **WF2**: Worcestershire (VC37), Withybed Wood, Wyre Forest NNR, near Callow Hill, W of Kidderminster, Alt. 75m, Lat. 52.39, Long. -2.36.

***A.* (*K.*) *hortensis* - BP1**: Glamorganshire (VC41), Bute Park, Cathays, Cardiff, Alt. <50m, Lat. 51.49, Long. -3.19. **I8**: West Cork (H3), Schull and environs, near Ballydehob, Alt. c10m, Lat. 51.53, Long. -9.55. **PYC7**: Glamorganshire (VC41), Miskin, Rhondda Cynon Taf, W of Cardiff, Alt. 40m, Lat. 51.53, Long. -3.38.

***A.* (*K.*) *owenii* - DC5**: South Devon (VC3), Exhibition Road, East Town, Crediton, Alt. 45m, Lat. 50.79, Long. -3.64. **DN4, DN7**: Denbighshire (VC50), Pontfadog, Ceiriog Valley, SE of Llangollen, Alt. 200m, Lat. 52.93, Long. -3.15. **I52**: West Galway (H16), E end of Rusheen Bay, Knocknacarra, E of Salthill, Galway city, Alt. <10m, Lat. 53.26, Long. -9.11.

***A.* (*K.*) *occultus* - ROY7, ROY9**: Co. Down (H38), Ballywalter, SE of Newtownards, Alt. <50m, Lat. 54.54, Long. -5.49.

***A.* (*K.*) cf. *fagophilus* - 12misc22**: Glamorganshire (VC41), Miskin, Rhondda Cynon Taf, W of Cardiff, Alt. 40m, Lat. 51.53, Long. -3.38. **BP2, BP3**: Glamorganshire (VC41), Bute Park, Cathays, Cardiff, Alt. <50m, Lat. 51.49, Long. -3.19. **PYC8**: Glamorganshire (VC41), Tyle-garw, W of Pontyclun, Rhondda Cynon Taf, W of Cardiff, Alt. 45m, Lat. 51.52, Long. -3.4.

***A.* (*K.*) *intermedius* - I12**: North Kerry (H2), Muckross Peninsula, W of Cloghereen, Killarney NP, Alt. 30m, Lat. 52.02, Long. -9.51. **I100**: Antrim (H39), S face of Cave Hill, overlooking N suburbs of Belfast, Alt. 255m, Lat. 54.64, Long. -5.96. **S10**: West Ross & Cromarty (VC105), Meall Fearna, Beinn Eighe NNR, near Kinlochewe, Alt. 200m, Lat. 57.59, Long. -5.33. **Y17**: South-east Yorkshire (VC61), Braisthwaite Bridge, Howsham Woods, N of Stamford Bridge, E of York, Alt. 20m, Lat. 54.05, Long. -0.89.

***Geomalacus maculosus* - I42**: South Kerry (H1), Glenbeigh Wood, above road bridge to between Glenbeigh & Rossbehy, near Loch Caragh, Alt. 30m, Lat. 52.05, Long. -9.95. **I45, I46:** North Kerry (H2), Derricunihy Woods, NE of Lady's View along road, Killarney NP, Alt. 155m, Lat. 51.98, Long. -9.57.

***Limax maximus* - EA7**: East Norfolk (VC27), Wheatfen Broad/Ted Ellis Trust NR, Norfolk & Suffolk Broads NP, Surlingham, SE of Norwich, Alt. <10m, Lat. 52.6, Long. 1.43. **EA8**: West Suffolk (VC26), Great Grove wood, near Sapiston, N of Ixworth, S of Thetford, Alt. 30m, Lat. 52.35, Long. 0.84. **I89**: Fermanagh (H33), Florence Court Demesne, near Gortnacally, SW of Enniskillen, Alt. 90m, Lat. 54.26, Long. -7.73. **REH1**: Worcestershire (VC37), South Copse, Highbury Park, King's Heath, S Birmingham, Alt. c50m, Lat. 52.44, Long. -1.9. **S28**:West Ross & Cromarty (VC105), Rassall Ashwood NNR, near Kishorn River, NE of Lochcarron, Alt. 70m, Lat. 57.43, Long. -5.59. **SK1, SK2**: Pembrokeshire (VC45), Skomer Island NNR, Pembrokeshire Coast NP, Alt. 60m, Lat. 51.74, Long. -5.29.

***L. cinereoniger* - 12misc11**: Worcestershire (VC37), New Parks Wood, Wyre Forest NNR, near Callow Hill, W of Kidderminster, Alt. 100m, Lat. 52.38, Long. -2.38. **AB3**: Glamorganshire (VC41), Coed Groes-faen (E part), N of Bargoed, Darren Valley, Caerphilly County Borough, Alt. 220m, Lat. 51.7, Long. -3.24. **I37**: North Kerry (H2), Torc Waterfalls, Killarney NP, Alt. 65m, Lat. 52, Long. -9.53. **I64**: West Galway (H16), around Lettercraffoe Lough, SW of Oughterard, W of Lough Corrib, Alt. 220m, Lat. 53.38, Long. -9.39. **I98**: Roscommon (H25), St. John's Wood, W shore of Loch Ree near Lecarrow, N of Athlone, Alt. 45m, Lat. 53.56, Long. -8.01.**K1**: East Kent

(VC15), Grimshill Wood, Blean Woods NNR, E of Blean, NW of Canterbury, Alt. 85m, Lat. 51.31, Long. 1.03. **WF5**: Worcestershire (VC37), New Parks Wood, Wyre Forest NNR, near Callow Hill, W of Kidderminster, Alt. 100m, Lat. 52.38, Long. -2.38.

***L.* cf. *dacampi* - Y39, Y40**: North-east Yorkshire (VC62), Fylingthorpe, Robin Hood's Bay, North York Moors NP, Alt. 135m, Lat. 54.43, Long. -0.56.

***Limacus maculatus* - M60, M61**: Surrey (VC17), Roots & Shoots (horticulture charity), Walnut Tree Walk, Lambeth, C London, Alt. 15m, Lat. 51.49, Long. 0.11. **NL2**: North Lincolnshire (VC54), Market Rasen, NE of Lincoln, Alt. 25m, Lat. 53.38, Long. -0.35. **PGO4**: Glamorgan (VC41), Romilly Road, Canton, Cardiff, Alt. <50m, Lat. 51.48, Long. -3.21. **SW2**: Glamorganshire (VC41), Slade Wood, Southerndown, near Ogmore-by-Sea, Alt. 30m, Lat. 51.45, Long. -3.6.

***L. flavus* - M19**: South Devon (VC3), East Street, Crediton, Alt. 50m, Lat. 50.79, Long. -3.65. **OL1**: Middlesex (VC21), Oliver's Island, R. Thames E of Kew Bridge, Chiswick, central London, Alt. <5m, Lat. 51.48, Long. -0.28. **SW1**: Glamorganshire (VC41), Pontyclun, Rhondda Cynon Taf, W of Cardiff, Alt. 55m, Lat. 51.53, Long. -3.39.

***Malacolimax tenellus* - K2**: East Kent (VC15), Grimshill Wood, Blean Woods NNR, E of Blean, NW of Canterbury, Alt. 85m, Lat. 51.31, Long. 1.03. **S47**: Moray (VC95), near Roches Moutonèes picnic area, Dulnain Bridge, Cairngorms NP, Alt. 210m, Lat. 57.3, Long. -3.66. **WF1**: Worcestershire (VC37), New Parks Wood, Wyre Forest NNR, near Callow Hill, W of Kidderminster, Alt. 100m, Lat. 52.38, Long. -2.38.

***Lehmannia marginata* - 12BB2**: Breconshire (VC42), Llyn y Fan Fawr, foot of Fan Brycheiniog, N of Glyntawe, Black Mountains, Brecon Beacons NP, Alt. 620m, Lat. 51.88, Long. -3.7. **DC4**: West Cornwall (VC1), above Porthmeor Beach, W of St. Ives, Alt. 20m, Lat. 50.22, Long. -5.49. **EA6**: East Norfolk (VC27), Wheatfen Broad/Ted Ellis Trust NR, Norfolk & Suffolk Broads NP, Surlingham, SE of Norwich, Alt. <10m, Lat. 52.6, Long. 1.43. **I11**: North Kerry (H2), Muckross Peninsula, W of Cloghereen, Killarney NP, Alt. 30m, Lat. 52.02, Long. -9.51. **I29**: North Kerry (H2), Mangerton Mountain, above Gortagullane, Killarney NP, Alt. 150-680m, Lat. 51.98, Long. -9.49. **NF5**: South Wiltshire (VC8), Rufus Stone area, Upper Canterton, NE of Minstead, New Forest NP, Alt. 85m, Lat. 50.91, Long. -1.62. **SK3**: Pembrokeshire (VC45), Skomer Island NNR, Pembrokeshire Coast NP, Alt. 60m, Lat. 51.73, Long. -5.31.

***Ambigolimax valentianus* - I35**: Mid Cork (H4), Near Booleypatrick, near Blarney, Alt. 55m, Lat. 51.93, Long. -8.58. **I92**: Antrim (H39), Belvoir Park Forest, Lagan Valley Regional Park, S suburbs of Belfast, Alt. 35m, Lat. 54.56, Long. -5.93. **OL2**: Middlesex (VC21), Oliver's Island, R. Thames E of Kew Bridge, Chiswick, central London, Alt. <5m, Lat. 51.48, Long. -0.28.

***A. nyctelius* - DC2, DC3, M17**: South Devon (VC3), East Street, Crediton, Alt. 50m, Lat. 50.79, Long. -3.65. **GB1**: Lanarkshire (VC77), Glasgow Botanical Gardens, Kelvinside, Glasgow, Alt. 50m, Lat. 51.48, Long. -2.62.

***Deroceras reticulatum* - 12misc1**: Glamorganshire (VC41), Pontyclun, Rhondda Cynon Taf, W of Cardiff, Alt. 55m, Lat. 51.53, Long. -3.39. **I10**: South Kerry (H1), Moll's Gap viewpoint at junction of N71 & R568, Alt. 260m, Lat. 51.94, Long. -9.66. **M27, M29**: Glamorganshire (VC41), Clun Avenue, Pontyclun, Rhondda Cynon Taf, W of Cardiff, Alt. 55m, Lat. 51.52, Long. -3.39.

***D. agreste* - EA4**: East Norfolk (VC27), Wheatfen Broad/Ted Ellis Trust NR, Norfolk & Suffolk Broads NP, Surlingham, SE of Norwich, Alt. <10m, Lat. 52.6, Long. 1.43. **M34**: Breconshire (VC42), Base of Craig y Fro, W of Storey Arms, Brecon Beacons NP, Alt. 400m, Lat. 51.88, Long. -3.49. **S33**: East Inverness-shire (VC96), Roadside of B9154 near Daviot, above River Nairn, SE of Inverness, Alt. 170m, Lat. 57.42, Long. -4.13. **Y13**: Mid-west Yorkshire (VC64), Middle Pasture NT, N of Cray, N of Buckden, Yorkshire Dales NP, Alt. 490m, Lat. 54.22, Long. -2.1.

***D. invadens* - DF5**: Nottinghamshire (VC56), Walkeringham NR (Notts. WT), Walkeringham, Trent floodplain W of Gainsborough, Alt. 15m, Lat. 53.42, Long. -0.86. **DN3, DN6**: Denbighshire (VC50), Pontfadog, Ceiriog Valley, SE of Llangollen, Alt. 200m, Lat. 52.93, Long. -3.15. **ROY6**: Crete, Kavros, Alt. 10m, Lat. 35.35, Long. 24.3.

***D. panormitanum* - M82, NF1**: Glamorganshire (VC41), Garden at rear of Old Library, The Hayes, Cardiff, Alt. 15m, Lat. 51.48, Long. -3.18.

***D. laeve* - I47**: South-east Galway (H15), Coole Lough, near Gort, E edge of the Burren area, Alt. 150m, Lat. 53.09, Long. -8.84. **K6**: East Sussex (VC14), Powdermill Reservoir, Brede High Woods (WT), near Cripp's Corner, High Weald AONB, N of Hastings, Alt. 25m, Lat. 50.95, Long. 0.56. **M33**: West Gloucestershire (VC34), Bristol University Botanical Gardens, Stoke Bishop, Bristol, Alt. 100m, Lat. 51.48, Long. -2.62. **M36**: Co. Antrim (H39), Portmore Lough, E shore of Loch Neagh, W of Glenavy, Alt. 15m, Lat. 54.56, Long. -6.27.

***Tandonia budapestensis* - M28**: Glamorganshire (VC41), Clun Avenue, Pontyclun, Rhondda Cynon Taf, W of Cardiff, Alt. 55m, Lat. 51.52, Long. -3.39. **M83**: Glamorganshire (VC41), Bute Park, Cathays, Cardiff, Alt. <50m, Lat. 51.49, Long. -3.19. **S59**: Mid Perthshire (VC88), Hill above Easter Moncreiffe, N of Bridge of Earn, S of Perth, Alt. 50m, Lat. 56.36, Long. -3.38.

***T. cristata* - 12misc18**: Glamorganshire (VC41), Miskin, Rhondda Cynon Taf, W of Cardiff, Alt. 40m, Lat. 51.53, Long. -3.38. **I71**: West Galway (H16), Spiddal churchyard and surrounding coastal areas, W of Galway city, Alt. <10m, Lat. 53.24, Long. -9.31. **M32**: Glamorganshire (VC41), Both sides of Clun Avenue, Pontyclun, Rhondda Cynon Taf, W of Cardiff, Alt. 55m, Lat. 51.52, Long. -3.39.

***T. sowerbyi* - DC16**: South Devon (VC3), Brunel Woods, near Daccombe, N part of Torquay, Alt. 130m, Lat. 50.49, Long. -3.95. **I60**: South-east Galway (H15), Coole Lough, near Gort, E edge of the Burren area, Alt. 150m, Lat. 53.09, Long. -8.84. **M31**: Glamorganshire (VC41), Clun Avenue, Pontyclun, Rhondda Cynon Taf, W of Cardiff, Alt. 55m, Lat. 51.52, Long. -3.39.

***T. rustica* - I1**: Mid Cork (H4), Near Booleypatrick, near Blarney, Alt. 55m, Lat. 51.93, Long. -8.58

***Milax gagates* - DF1**: Cambridgeshire (VC29), Wicken, SE of Soham, S of Ely, Alt. 5m, Lat. 52.31, Long. 0.3. **ROY3**: Waterford (H6), Lismore, 30km E of Mallow, Alt. c30mm, Lat. 52.14, Long. -7.93. **ROY5**: West Mayo (H27), Mullet Peninsula, Alt. <90m, Lat. 54.2, Long. -10.06.

***Boettgerilla pallens* - DF8**: South-west Yorkshire (VC63), near Anston Stones Wood, South Anston, E of Worksop, Alt. 90m, Lat. 53.35, Long. -1.22. **M30**: Glamorganshire (VC41), Both sides of Clun Avenue, Pontyclun, Rhondda Cynon Taf, W of Cardiff, Alt. 55m, Lat. 51.52, Long. -3.39.

***Testacella maugei* - M26**: Glamorganshire (VC41), W side of Roath Park, Roath, Cardiff, Alt. 50m, Lat. 51.51, Long. -3.18.

***T. scutulum* - scutulum28**: Middlesex (VC21), Kensall Green Cemetery, Kensall Green, WC London, Alt. 50m, Lat. 51.53, Long. -0.23.

T. sp. "*tenuipenis*" - 12misc14: South Devon (VC3), Uplyme, NW of Lyme Regis, Alt. 50-100m, Lat. 50.73, Long. -2.96.

***T. haliotidea* - 12misc15**: Berkshire (VC22), Woodley, central Reading, Alt. 45m, Lat. 51.45, Long. -0.93. **haliotidea19**: Surrey (VC17), Godalming, S of Guildford, Alt. 100m, Lat. 51.19, Long. -0.62.

***Selenochlamys ysbryda* - 12misc10**: Breconshire (VC42), Talgarth, NE of Brecon, Alt. 120m, Lat. 52, Long. -3.23.

***Vitrina pellucida* - Y18**: Mid-west Yorkshire (VC64), Tor Dike, N of Kettlewell, Wharfedale, Yorkshire Dales NP, Alt. 500m, Lat. 54.18, Long. -2.02.

***Phenacolimax major* - WV1**: West Gloucestershire (VC34), The Slaughter, E of Lady Park Wood NNR, S/E bank of R. Wye, S of Symonds Yat, Wye Valley AONB, Alt. 60m, Lat. 51.82, Long. -2.65.

***Semilimax pyreniacus* - I38**: North Kerry (H2), Torc Waterfalls, Killarney NP, Alt. 65m, Lat. 52, Long. -9.53.

Arion (A.) ater, p. 30

Arion (A.) rufus, p. 32

Arion (A.) vulgaris, p. 36

Arion (A.) flagellus, p. 34

Arion (A.) sp. "Davies", p. 38

Arion (M.) subfuscus, p. 40

Arion (C.) fasciatus, p. 44

Arion (C.) circumscriptus circumscriptus, p. 46

Arion (C.) circumscriptus silvaticus, p. 46

Arion (M.) fuscus, p. 42

Arion (K.) distinctus, p. 48

Arion (M.) cf. iratii, p. 42

Arion (K.) hortensis, p. 50

Arion (K.) owenii, p. 52

Arion (K.) occultus, p. 54

Geomalacus maculosus, p. 60

Arion (K.) intermedius, p. 58

Arion (K.) cf. fagophilus, p. 56

Limax maximus, p. 62

Limax cinereoniger, p. 64

Limax cf. *dacampi*, p. 66
Limacus flavus, p. 68
Limacus maculatus, p. 70
Malacolimax tenellus, p. 72
Ambigolimax valentianus, p. 76
Lehmannia marginata, p. 74
Ambigolimax nyctelius, p. 78
Deroceras reticulatum, p. 80
Deroceras agreste, p. 82
Tandonia budapestensis, p. 90
Deroceras invadens, p. 84
Deroceras laeve, p. 88
Tandonia cf. *cristata*, p. 92
Deroceras panormitanum, p. 86
Tandonia rustica , p. 94
Boettgerilla pallens, p. 98
Tandonia sowerbyi, p. 94
Milax gagates , p. 96
Testacella (T.) maugei, p. 100
Testacella (T.) haliotidea, p. 104
Testacella (T.) scutulum, p. 102
Selenochlamys ysbryda, p. 106
Vitrina pellucida, p. 108
Phenacolimax major, p. 108
Testacella (T.) sp. "*teniupenis*" , p. 102
Semilimax pyrenaicus, p. 108